OUR DAILY BREAD

The Essential Norman Borlaug

NOEL VIETMEYER

Memorial Edition

There is a saying in Gita that, from time to time, God appears on earth in disguise. When the world was in a serious food crisis one of the godly forms who appeared was Norman Borlaug.

M.S. Swaminathan
Member of Parliament, India

He made the world a better place — a much better place. Though others helped, the driving force was his.

Ed Runge
Department of Soil and Crop Sciences
Texas A&M University

Norman Borlaug spent his youth on a small farm in Iowa, dreaming of becoming a high school science teacher and athletics coach. In the end, he spent his life working to keep food production ahead of population growth. His last spoken words on the day of his death were "take it to the farmer." This was his credo for 65 years, and his research added hundreds of millions of tons of grain to world harvests.

Christopher Dowswell
CIMMYT, Mexico

He worked tirelessly, and the result was a high-yield, dwarf-wheat variety with more kernels and a stalk strong enough to support the extra weight. Still unsatisfied, he continued developing those even further, keeping his hand in the Mexican dirt while traveling the world to urge prime ministers and presidents to help their farmers grow more food.

Ronald Phillips
Regents Professor of Agronomy and Plant Genetics
University of Minnesota

During his university days Borlaug was a Gopher wrestler. For years afterwards he often visited the wrestling room. He liked the sweat, the discipline, the dedication, the hard work. Those were things he could relate to — they were the cornerstones of his life.

J Robinson
Head Wrestling Coach
University of Minnesota

The message of Norman Borlaug's life is that we write our own destiny, and that one person, bending over seedlings under the Mexican sun, can change the world.

Pioneer Press
Twin Cities, Minnesota

Once I asked him: "What is your biggest achievement? What you would like to be remembered for?" I thought he would say his contribution to plant sciences and fighting global hunger. But he replied: "As someone who introduced baseball in Mexico." When I burst out laughing, he gave me a detailed account of the hours he spent playing and promoting baseball.

Devinder Sharma
Pantnagar University, Uttarakhand, India

Greatest Human Being, R.I.P.

Obituary headline in the New York Times

In South Asia, and elsewhere, conditions were right for Norman Borlaug to solve a problem for humanity, and he did so with spectacular success. We need more like him.

Avik Sengupta, McGill University
Montreal, Canada

I never met Dr. Norman Borlaug, the Nobel Prize-winning plant scientist who did more than anyone in history to fight hunger, but I've admired him for years. When I started learning about agricultural development, his name came up so often that I felt as if he were my teacher.

Bill Gates

Norman Borlaug was driven to eliminate hunger from the world. It was in his soul that no one should die from hunger. And he was incredibly successful. It is now up to new Borlaugs to be the taskmasters of the future. No one wants to look into the eyes of a starving person.

John Carver
Decorah, Iowa

Norman Borlaug's commitment to impact meant that as the potential of the Mexican wheats was revealed by testing around the world he became a powerful, courageous and generally effective advocate for radical policy change in the face of opposition. He pushed for importing thousands of tons of improved seed from across the world, boosting of fertilizer supplies, creating floor prices for grain, and promoting agriculture as the way forward instead of heavy industry.

Tony Fischer
Canberra, Australia

To witness the warmth of the welcome Norm would receive from crowds of small farmers and officials alike in the Punjab of India and of Pakistan was as exhilarating as it was undeniable proof of his impact.

Tony Fischer
Canberra, Australia

Norman Borlaug remains one of the University's most distinguished alumni — a scientist, educator, humanitarian, and Nobel laureate whose work made him a hero around the world. From his early wheat research in Mexico to his ongoing advocacy for modern farming practices and policy, he saw the human face of hunger in the world and never strayed from his principles.

Robert Bruininks, President
University of Minnesota

Even in recent years, Dr. Borlaug continued to push the University — and me personally — to a greater understanding of the world's food needs in the face of growing environmental concerns. Without a doubt, he was still the tough-minded grappler from Iowa who first came to the University more than 75 years ago.

Robert Bruininks, President
University of Minnesota

Dr. Borlaug is the giant we in the seed industry look up to.

Andy LaVigne,
Alexandria, Virginia

There is a song that says, "Let there be peace on earth, and let it begin with me," I think this was the essence of Norman Borlaug's motivation as well as the basis of his Nobel Peace Prize.

Ronald Phillips
Regents Professor of Agronomy and Plant Genetics
University of Minnesota

Dr. Borlaug proved that agricultural experts can change the course of history for the betterment of humanity.

Dr Zafar Altaf, Chairman
Pakistan Agricultural Research Council

Just think of the despots and warmongers who have gone down in history as "the Great": Alexander the Great, Catherine the Great, Charles the Great (Charlemagne), Frederick the Great, Peter the Great. Wouldn't it be nice to see humanity's benefactors designated as "the Great"? Let us therefore start with the benefactor of the world's poorest people: Borlaug the Great!

David Boaz
Cato Institute, Washington, DC

Once I heard Dr. Borlaug give a lecture to undergrads and was struck by how accessible and down-to-earth he was. Given his many honors and accomplishments, this seemed beyond belief.

Nadilia Gomez
Department of Entomology, University of Minnesota

So many of us go into grad school hoping we'll help the world, but not Norman Borlaug. He began with an interest in plants, and then by being in the moment and by following his interest he got to help the world.

Nadilia Gomez
Department of Entomology, University of Minnesota

Borlaug was a plant breeder of a rare type who did everything in his power to share his seed and his knowledge with those who most needed them. By fostering the free flow of improved crop varieties he had a global impact.

Phil Pardey
Department of Applied Economics, University of Minnesota

Norm spent his life helping hungry nations, but by 1990 in California, a pretty big wheat state, every wheat variety came directly or indirectly from him. The financial windfall just from the higher yields in the U.S. is at least $13.6 billion per year.

Phil Pardey
Department of Applied Economics, University of Minnesota

Sonora, Mexico — On the walls of some farmhouses in Ciudad Obregon, a photo of a onetime Iowa farm boy hangs along with a portrait of the pope. The American long ago wrought a kind of miracle in the wheat fields of the Yaqui Valley, one that today's world hungers for anew.

Julie Watson, ASSOCIATED PRESS

Some critics say the world's efforts to improve poor people's lives are doomed. But Dr. Borlaug is proof that large-scale progress is possible. He is a genuine hero, and his story should make us optimistic about the future.

Bill Gates

BOOKS BY NOEL VIETMEYER

BORLAUG SERIES

Borlaug: Right off the Farm. 1914 – 1944*

Borlaug: Wheat Whisperer. 1944 – 1959*

Borlaug: Bread Winner. 1960 – 1969*

Our Daily Bread; the Essential Norman Borlaug*

MODERNITY'S MOTIVATORS SERIES

Emergence from Darkness; 1750 - 1799

The Grand Awakening; 1800 – 1829 [in preparation]

Dawning of Technology; 1830 – 1839 [in preparation]

Sense Comes to Life; 1840 – 1849 [in preparation]

For National Academy of Sciences

Lost Crops of Africa: Volume 1 – Grains*

Lost Crops of Africa: Volume 2 – Vegetables

Lost Crops of Africa: Volume 3 - Fruits

Lost Crops of the Incas

Underexploited Tropical Plants

Tropical Legumes

Amaranth: Modern Prospects for an Ancient Crop*

Jojoba: A New Crop for Arid Lands*

Quality-Protein Maize*

Triticale: A Promising Addition to the World's Cereal Grains*

Vetiver: A Thin Green Line Against Erosion*

Neem: A Tree for Solving Global Problems

Leucaena: Promising Forage and Tree Crop for the Tropics

Mangium and Other Fast-Growing Acacias*

Calliandra: A Versatile Tree for the Humid Tropics*

Casuarinas: Nitrogen-Fixing Trees for Adverse Sites*

Firewood Crops: Shrub and Tree Species for Energy*

Water Buffalo: New Prospects for an Underutilized Animal*

Butterfly Farming *

Crocodiles as a Resource for the Tropics*

Little-Known Asian Animals with Promising Economic Futures*

Microlivestock*

More Water for Arid Lands*

Sowing Forests from the Air*

Producer Gas: Another Fuel for Motor Transport*

* Available (while supplies last) from **BracingBooks.com**

OUR DAILY BREAD

The Essential Norman Borlaug

NOEL VIETMEYER

Memorial Edition

BRACING BOOKS
LORTON, VIRGINIA

Index provided by Paul Vasold.

First Edition, Version 1.1: September 2012.
Memorial Edition: June, 2013

Library of Congress Cataloguing-in-Publication Data

Vietmeyer, Noel Duncan, 1940-

ISBN 978-0-578-09555-4

Biography & Autobiography/Science & Technology

BRACING BOOKS
5921 River Drive
Lorton, VA 22079-4128
USA

Printed in the United States of America

Signature Book Printing, www.sbpbooks.com

CONTENTS

PROLOGUE

Norman Borlaug grew up hungry; he grew up poor; he only wanted to be a forester. After creating super-productive food crop varieties he donated their seeds to the world and saved hundreds of millions from starvation. He is our age's humanitarian hero.

As a professional at the National Academy of Sciences I often worked with Norm. His own words, which form this book's backbone, were recorded during discussions over more than twenty years.

Before he died on September 12, 2009 he saw and approved these quotes – some with a detail or two of correction.

Noel Vietmeyer
Lorton, Virginia

PART I

The Home Side
[USA]

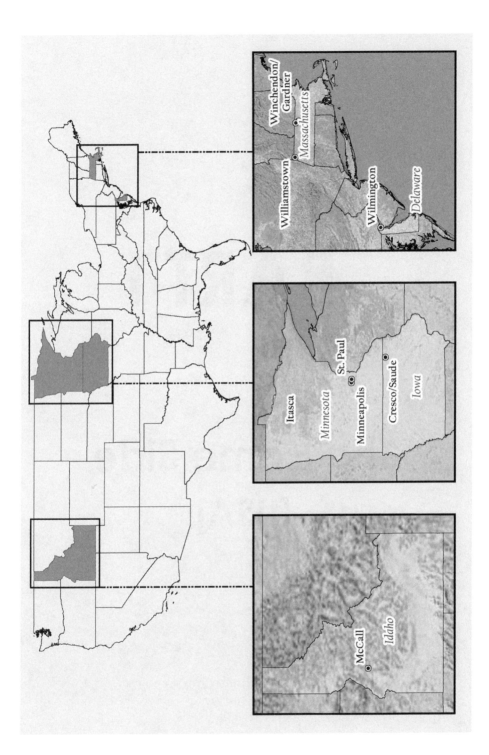

1914-1927

Darkness

O ther than a manger, a humbler birthplace can hardly be imagined. It was a little house on the prairie, just 25 miles as the eagle flies from one sanctified by Laura Ingalls Wilder.

Unlike the Frontier Girl's home in Burr Oak, the counterpart in Saude had pretensions to prairie grandeur: a kitchen, a parlor, *two* bedrooms. But behind the grand façade there was no bathroom, no running water, and no insulation to block Iowa's wicked winter winds.

On that birth day — March 25, 1914 — life within this lowly Borlaug [BOR-LOG] abode reflected the rugged frontier still springtime fresh in memory. Water was hauled in by bucket from a Jack-and-Jill well out back. Clothes were sewn by hand on the kitchen table and washed using a bucket, a bar of home-made soap, and a washboard. Heat came from the kitchen stove that devoured mountains of wood while boiling water and cooking food. Evenings were lighted by a smoky lamp whose wick needed a daily trim like a mustache. Saturday nights a tin tub was hauled up from the basement so all could enjoy their weekly bath.

Civilization had yet to colonize this Old World holdout. Although by 1914 city slickers enjoyed a trickle of electricity, no one hereabouts could switch on a light, let alone a coffee pot. Motors hadn't made their mark either. Unwary vehicles sometimes ventured out for a country drive, but rural roads were crudely graded dirt and downpours turned them into liquid mud. One of the joys of country living was watching horse teams pull fancy-folks' cars from the mire.

America itself had yet to penetrate this prairie preserve, whose residents considered themselves Norway's outliers. Saude citizens nattered in Norwegian and read newspapers written in Norwegian.

Their phone lines linked only themselves; conversing with the barbarians beyond the border being neither necessary nor desirable.

Not even Education dared stray so far from the city lights and delights. The little house's owners, Nels and Emma Borlaug, had reached sixth-grade, the highest on offer forty years back when grade school cost good dollars. Their son, Henry, and his young wife, Clara, who was now struggling to birth her first child in the upstairs bedroom, had reached eighth grade, which many locals considered beyond reason.

Contemplating those events upstairs was super scary. Throughout history births had happened in humble homes and many had produced horror outcomes. With science too incompetent to surmount superstition, medicine remained medieval. That Wednesday Harry Hastings' horse and buggy were tethered outside; but the bag the good doctor had brought inside with him contained no antibiotic, anesthetic, heart monitor, or respirator. Without a tap in the house, even washing his hands was hard.

As the day progressed, both mother and baby faced their moment of highest hazard. An infection, a breach birth, a break in breathing or a hemorrhage would likely denote one death, perhaps two.

Death in those days still made house calls and took an abnormal interest in the young. But this baby joined the world kicking, bawling and full of life. It proved to be a boy.

If the world noted this, it was merely to register the addition of yet another American, of whom there seemed altogether too many: an unbelievable 99 million!

Mother Nature, though, put on welcoming weather. For late March in the zone where Iowa merges into Minnesota the bright sunshine and 55 degree temperature provided a sampling of the spring that should have still been in pre-season training in Florida.

Thus as darkness rolled up the sky that evening the scene within the walls lovingly built by ancestors' hands was calm, quiet and contented. Billets burned cheerily in the kitchen stove wafting heat upstairs to comfort the cradle's occupant and his mother in the bed beside.

Relaxing in the downstairs kitchen, the father and grandparents felt blessed by the safe arrival of their first child and first grandchild. That inaugural member of a new Borlaug generation was here and healthy. It was a miracle. And all was well with the world.

When the time came, the baby was named Norman Ernest. A year passed before the birth was registered – a hand-written note in the Record of Births of Howard County, Iowa.

From the start little Norman Ernest possessed a special charm that endeared all comers. His inner glow manifested itself notably in a cheeky smile and an ice-blue stare that came with a twinkle on top.

The following years saw another basic trait rise into view. Lost out there on the prairie, in the homey homely spot where his grandparents ruled and his parents toiled, Norm Boy Borlaug began developing the dedication that decades hence would serve him and humanity.

From the time he could toddle he challenged himself. As he grew, this congenital competitor scampered up the stairs, across the fields, through the woodlot, down the road. And he was renowned for jumping the stream that lazed across the grandparents' hundred acres.

Given this combo of charisma, devotion and muscular vitality he projected the presence of a movie star. Everyone who met him knew this kid could amount to something. Such a pity Fate had chosen him as the sole boy child of a farmer. Keeping his kith and kinfolk from starvation was his assignment. No question, he'd devote his livelong days to teasing survival from the stubborn soil of Saude, Iowa.

Fate in those days could not be eluded, and during the first seven years Nels Borlaug worked overtime to place his first grandson firmly on destiny's designated path. In this, he acted less as grandfather than god.

Of trim build and average height, the head of the family had a weather-beaten outdoor face, graying close-cropped hair and a white-flecked mustache. The grandson, though, knew the intense arctic-blue eyes reflected the Norse superhero Thor.

Nels often entranced his captive pupil with remembrances of life on the frontier's cutting edge, first in Wisconsin, then in Dakota Territory, and finally — following the Sioux's revival of scalp collecting — in the comforting stability of settled Iowa. He could remember all the way back to Lincoln's time; he'd been six the year the president was shot.

Also while he had the boy within his orbit the grandfather induced yet another basic trait: optimism. Although the Borlaugs farmed in ways familiar to Ancient Romans and no change seemed possible, Nels insisted that a great uplift was in store.

Given his total trust, the boy primed himself to meet some magnificent makeover that lay in waiting somewhere in the unfathomable future. Many years later, he remembered back:

> It was Granddad who most influenced my young life. No one else saw any prospect of change. But if he saw a better world ahead, I had to make myself worthy to meet it.

Former Borlaug generations had farmed wheat. However, in the 1890s spores of a miniature menace that drained wheat's will to live deluged their fields. Stem rust fungus had found the crop's soft spot, and, being irresistible, finished the farm for wheat.

With his known world toppled, Nels Borlaug sought an alternative source of support. For several years he grew flax and sold his harvest for linseed oil. The rewards were fabulous; no Borlaug had ever lived so well. But then the spores of a miniature menace that drained *this* crop's will to live deluged the fields. Wilt fungus had found the flax genome's soft spot and, being irresistible, finished the farm for flax.

By the year of the birth, corn kept the Borlaugs moving forward. Though surviving in Saude soil, corn yielded only 25 bushels an acre, which in 1914 brought the five family members a grand total of $17.50 per acre. That pittance pinned them to poverty's edge. They were basically broke.

Nothing could be done about that. Of the many barriers nature imposed on corn farmers, yield was the most inflexible. Neighbors sometimes bragged of getting 30 bushels. None ever claimed more. Clearly, 30 bushels an acre was the limit God had imposed.

The 40 acres the Borlaugs devoted to corn provided the five family members just enough cash for necessities such as sugar, salt, oatmeal, coffee beans, thread, yarn, kerosene (to light the stove) and, rarely, a few yards of cloth. All those were bought at the Vaala & Natvig General Store in Saude, 3 miles down the road.

Food they had to produce themselves. Their sole splurge was the flour they bought for Grandmother Emma. Every other day she produced a fresh loaf that provided delight with dinner (the midday meal) and supper. Though bread was, in a way, their reason for living, paying good cash for flour made it a guilty pleasure.

In those un-modern days food was neither abundant nor dependable. In 1917, for example, the Borlaugs had to go without their daily bread. The bags of flour that had forever filled the Saude store shelves vanished.

Nothing could be done about that. In August 1916 the northern wheat belt had been ripening a bumper crop, but in September spores of the miniature menace that drains wheat's will to live struck the whole region, leaving a vast rust-colored mass of rot.

With Mother Nature in charge and with flour running low, Americans faced having to forgo bread, cookies, crackers, cakes, pastries, pancakes, doughnuts, rolls, bagels and maybe even the newfangled breakfast cereals. As a stop gap, federal officials banned the sale of booze, not to mention the sale of bread on Wednesdays and Mondays. Hotels and restaurants were restricted to serving no more than 2 ounces of bread.

The absence of flour forced ordinary folk to change their ways. Some embraced Victory Bread. Eating that cracker-like concoction of oats and barley was patriotic because it released whatever wheat remained for our gallant soldiers fighting for liberty and fraternity in France. Obligingly, they'd already been called "doughboys."

Some otherwise sane Northerners bent so low as to eat macaroni like Italians. Others consumed cornbread like southerners, which was considered the ultimate social disgrace.

With no flour in the general store the Norwegians of Saude faced a major mealtime makeover. Norm was 4 years old when his family spent miserable months without Emma's beloved loaves. And the experience of surviving on cornbread permanently marked the mind:

Johnny cake was okay, but not all the time for god's sake!

As Norm Boy approached his fifth birthday an irresistible deluge descended *directly on Americans*. This one was not a fungal spore. Actually, no one knew what it was. Invisible even to a microscope, it was beyond that era's grasp.

In their cluelessness and helplessness people accepted that they'd been afflicted with some unearthly thing. Many considered it the Hand of God come to punish sinners. Indeed, the name for this visitation derived from "Celestial influence."

Influenza (or Spanish Influenza, as Americans called it in regal disregard of its Kansas origin) ultimately killed some 600,000 fellow citizens within about a year. The Civil War — our most traumatic and transformative affliction — had at least spread that much killing over four years.

Beset by this alien entity America was clearly headed downward to doom or the Devil. Local health departments isolated victims in their homes or in crude shelters, leaving them to rot.

Influenza, however, couldn't be contained. It quickly conquered eastern cities such as Boston, Philadelphia and New York, which had sinners aplenty. After that, it developed wanderlust and toured the Midwest where sinners were of course entirely unknown.

Norm recalled the dread pervading the house when in the early months of 1919 they learned that Granddad Nels' brother's household had been stricken:

> The Thomas Borlaug family had ten members, one of whom was my cousin Sina. They weren't allowed outside even to milk the cows or get food.
>
> Thus, each day for two weeks Grandmother Emma carried two big kettles of soup almost a mile to their farm. I went along, but we never dared enter the house.
>
> We placed the kettles on the porch and whisked away the empties. Although they'd already been scoured and scrubbed, Grandmother scalded them for an hour before refilling them with soup next day.
>
> What was it like for all my cousins, my great-aunt and my great-uncle trapped within that small house? That's troubling to think about. We never saw them. However, standing on the porch one day I noticed the curtains flutter.
>
> Sometimes I still wonder about that lost soul peering through the lace. How agonizing it must have been to see me so alive and so blessedly free.

The tiny tot trotting beside the tall severely dressed lady dutifully lugging cauldrons by their hanger handles to cousin Sina's house comprises one of this great life's indelible images:

The two were caught in a calamity they couldn't comprehend.

They were carrying lifesaving soup to stricken relatives.

And they were walking in the terrifying presence of the Hand of God.

In 1919 even the educated lived in the dark because the latest news came from last week's *Decorah Posten* newspaper. Weather was thus a constant source of surprises.

That fall Norm Boy was adapting to school. A single small room serving first grade through eighth grade, New Oregon Rural School Number 8 usually had a dozen students, though as winter took hold farm chores ebbed and school enrollment swelled. One teacher taught every grade, relying on the older students to help the younger. The system was very effective. Kids tutoring each other mobilized the powers of both peer pressure and repetition.

Buses being unknown, children trudged to school together in groups. For five-year-old Norm Boy the walk was a mile and a half *each way.* And when he left home one winter morn in 1919 there was no way to know that a blizzard was brewing beyond the southwest horizon.

Early that afternoon the bone-chilling front whistled in. The teacher lit the oil lamps and cracked open the door to find the nearby road had disappeared. Worse, the wind was rising, the temperature tumbling, and the snow cascading like Niagara.

Along with everything else, one-room school teachers faced fearful life-or-death decisions. That afternoon, an anxious Lena Halvorson (who was 26 but so small and frail she looked like another student) explained that she'd walk six children home in the direction of Protivin, the Bohemian town a mile to the east. The others from Saude, the Norwegian community to the south, had to make it home alone:

> There were about seven of us in the straggling line. As the smallest, I took my proper place in the middle. Children always moved Indian file through deep snow, the biggest boys breaking the trail while the biggest girls stayed in back watching over the little ones, who fitted themselves between.
>
> That order of march was never written down; it just came by instinct, like baby ducks waddling from the nest. And that day the journey was terrible. We trudged through the swirling whiteness, leaning on the wind, blinded by the sleet and struggling against the clinging waist-deep snow.
>
> I was miserable. Icy drafts slipped through my clothes and sliced the skin like a scalpel. It was hard to get a breath. Snow clung to my face, mittens, jacket. The melt inside my boots numbed my feet. I began stumbling. Soon it became too much to bear. Weariness pervaded every sense, including common sense. There was just one thing to do: I lay down to cry myself to sleep snuggled in the soft white shroud nature had so conveniently provided.
>
> Then a hand yanked my scarf away, grabbed my hair, and jerked my head up. Above me was a face tight-lipped with anger and fright. It was my cousin Sina. "Get up!" she screamed. "Get up!" She began slapping me over the ears. "Get up! Get up!"
>
> The other children were clustered round. There was fear in their voices. Some of the young ones were crying.
>
> Finally, Herbert Lee hoisted me onto my tired little legs. Sina took my hand and got me walking again. She was 12, sweet-tempered, and filled with self-assured authority.
>
> I was in tears when we entered the warm kitchen. I knew I'd let

everyone down. But Grandmother Emma was as calm and goodhearted as ever. She'd just emptied her big wood-fired oven and the house smelled of yeast and hot bread.

I've never forgotten that comforting fragrance. No food was ever so sweet as those loaves Grandmother baked the day when I was five and nearly died.

By 1921 the Borlaugs had increased by two; Norm now had sisters, Palma and Charlotte. The grandparent's two-bedroom home being too small to house seven people of three generations, Henry Borlaug spent a year building a replica on the property next door.

In October 1922 the family left the grandparents' home. Their new dwelling also had pretensions to prairie grandeur: two bedrooms, a kitchen and a parlor. But behind the grand façade there still was no bathroom, no running water, and no insulation to foil Iowa's wicked winter winds. Within weeks that omission was sorely regretted: throughout January 1923 temperatures stayed below freezing, with a dozen nights below zero degrees and two plunging to 55 degrees of frost (minus 23°F).

In their cluelessness and helplessness the family accepted such hardships as humanity's fate. All five members toiled for food. Producing enough for year-round survival was a supreme challenge. Weighing constantly on the mind was the upcoming winter months when the fields would furnish nothing.

In preparation for that hungry time, they spent long hours picking berries from the roadsides, and cherries, apples and plums from their few fruit trees. All were quickly boiled, crammed into Mason jars and put on the kitchen shelf. Those glass-encased supplies, together with some bags of cornmeal and a few vegetables surviving in sand barrels in the basement were their wintertime life-insurance.

Though they always managed to avoid starvation, the Borlaugs were largely under-nourished. From November to April, fresh fruits were the stuff of dreams, regardless of special need such as sickness, blood loss or growth spurt.

Little Norm and his sisters each got an orange a year. It was the highlight of the Saude Lutheran Church's Christmas Eve celebration. For twelve long months they dreamed of the special treat from on high. And when the great day arrived, they trooped the two miles to church in a state of exaltation.

Winter was the nadir for nutrients. Beyond the fruits in Mason jars the family relied on carrots, turnips, cabbages, potatoes, rutabagas and onions that hibernated in those barrels of damp sand in the root cellar. Those hardy, barely alive plants in the basement supplied the only fresh edibles *for almost half the year.*

E ight being the accepted age, Norm joined the family workforce in 1922. Adding his muscles to those of his father and three horses gave him a new way to challenge himself.

Other than during a few midsummer weeks when the sun awoke at an ungodly hour, the tiny towhead began in the dark, hauling in wood and water and driving the cows to the milking shed. He always ended in the dark, feeding and watering the horses as the weary old sun ran away and retired to its own slumbers.

Bound to him by empathy as well as equality, those plow horses were his closest friends. Though runts of the equine species, they labored nearly nine months – two working an eight-hour stretch while the third got a day of rest.

Like all energy sources, horses were a mixed blessing. Borlaug lives were devoted to feeding, watering, currying, and anointing sores with oil. And whenever the barn was occupied, which was every day of every year, the family had to haul manure from the stalls and drag in clean straw for bedding, regardless of weather or personal want.

Work woke up as winter wound down. Being out of shape from months in the barn, the horses needed pre-season training. And, like all star athletes, they required tender loving care. Necks were a special problem; any chafing where the collar pressed the flesh would fester once fieldwork began. Thus, every week Norm and his father cleaned the collars and salved the big soft shoulders as if their future depended on them. As it did.

Throughout the spring months those big-hearted 1-hp muscle machines, whose top speed was 5 mph, pulled plows, planters, disks, harrows and cultivators, to prepare seedbeds for oats, clover and corn.

During the summer they pulled the cultivator that ripped out the rascally weeds that constantly tried to overrun the place. In late summer they powered the corn binder that cut and bundled green corn plants, which they then hauled to the silo on a "bundle wagon." Between times they towed the hay mower and subsequently moved the mown hay to the barn on a hay wagon.

In the fall they pulled the binder that cut and bundled oat plants, as well as the dray that in due course delivered those bundles to the steam-powered thrashing machine a group of neighbors hired every September. Later they tugged the grain wagon that toted the bags of oats to the granary. Following all that, those humble heroes spread manure with a smelly machine and (if winter was kind enough to wait) they plowed the fields to get things started for the following year.

But a horse carried a person only when snow was too deep for walking. Usually that meant Norm Boy climbed onto Bob's back and the pair of friends plodded more than a mile down the county road to the community mailboxes at the junction with Cresco Road.

Youngest of the three plow horses, Bob was big, brawny, reddish-brown and a born rebel. Boy and bay were more than buddies: they were a sub-family, being born on the same March day in 1914 and growing up inspiring each other:

> Our friendship was mutual; with a swoop of his nose Bob would nudge me like some co-conspirator hell bent on mischief. He didn't do that with anyone else, and how could I resist? We enjoyed many adventures together. We'd take excursions into the woods, to the fishing hole on the Little Turkey River; and we often took off together to see the relatives down the road.

Not everything was play however. His best pal was after all his business partner. They had collective responsibility for certain cornfields, and sometimes their collegiality was severely tested:

> Bob had an uncanny understanding of when midday was coming up. If I tried to squeeze in an extra pass within half an hour of noon, he'd stamp down a few corn plants as we rounded the far end of the row.

All in all, Bob was a diabolical dissenter with a built-in alarm clock and no loyalty when it came to lunchtime!

On the up side, however, it's only a slight exaggeration to say that Bob induced Norm's fundamental tolerance. Thanks to this huge and gentle workmate he'd forever exude togetherness, loyalty and respect.

Beyond robbing family time, horses stole precious land. At least half the farm's acreage was devoted to growing hay and oats for three horses and a score of cattle and calves. That's why a 100-acre farm was reduced to growing 40 acres of people food.

Actually, harvesting those acres involved the year's worst anguish.

Machinery that peeled away the husk from corn, cut the ear from the plant, and gathered in the harvest needed more horsepower than a horse could offer. Corn had to be harvested by human hand.

The toil that imposed was a torment. Norm and his father began in October, hoping to finish by Thanksgiving. But when weather was willful the job absorbed half the winter. You see, the husk had to be stripped off *as each ear was pulled from each plant.*

Day after day, corn pickers – then called corn huskers – walked the rows while to the right a horse drew a wagon fitted with something approximating a sheet of plywood standing on edge.

On his right hand the picker wore a glove fitted with a hook that sliced open the husk. Then he reached into the opening with his left hand, wrenched the ear free and flung it high over the 12-foot tall plant to hit the plywood "bangboard" affixed to the wagon's far side. As the ear bounced back into the wagon he clicked his tongue, telling the horse to step forward, and grabbed the next corn plant and proceeded to slice open its husk.

An observer would see something like a human windmill, arms waving and a steady stream of corn flying out as the horse plodded forward step by step and the wagon filled ear by ear.

Gathering corn this way burdened lives beyond belief. Across the Corn Belt each acre contained *12,000 plants*. With 40 acres sown to corn, Norm and his father had to handpick and hand-husk almost half a million ears.

The memory of that agony rippled down a lifetime:

> That was true hell. Although we wore cotton gloves and covered our forearms with sleeves torn from old sweaters, the husks still managed to cut and scrape until our hands and arms were raw and bleeding.

Folks in corn country accepted that. But the price it exacted was terrible. Boys like Norm couldn't pursue innate their love of learning when the corn had to be picked. For them, high school was a luxury beyond the wildest underdog dream.

Worse still, the pushy winds of fall commonly knocked the fields flat. Thousands of soggy plants then had to be lifted one by one to locate the ears that always tried to hide underneath. During the harvest season a boy's back ached almost more than his body could bear. And nights were filled with shooting pains that snuffed out sleep.

Norm made this torment bearable by turning it into a mental

challenge. In this case, he approached the agony like an athlete aiming to be America's champion.

He remembered all this with a not altogether regretful sigh:

It sure helped me get through each acre. Day after day for almost two months I'd be bringing in the corn but also honing my technique, strengthening my muscles, timing my performance, and seeing myself crowned the next National Corn Husking Champion of the United States!

1928-1932

Dawn

With the coming of 1928 Norm was approaching his fourteenth birthday and preparing for his future life as a farmer.

Mornings he fed the chickens, separated the cream, hauled skim milk to the pigs, and lit the kitchen stove.

Afternoons (after trudging home from school) he trimmed lamp wicks, picked the bugs off potato plants, gathered ripe fruits and vegetables, hauled hay, and turned the grindstone (so his grandmother could sharpen her kitchen knives).

Evenings he cut kindling and split the firewood they'd need for boiling tomorrow's water and cooking tomorrow's food.

Blissfully unaware of the inalienable rights of those who dwell in the Land of Opportunity, this teen had found his comfort zone.

Then in the spring of 1928, when both eighth grade and education were ending, Sina Borlaug showed up at the Henry Borlaug farm. Since saving Norm from slow death in a snow bank nine years back, she'd become the local teacher.

The sight of such an authority figure on their doorstep panicked the parents, who knew their son was struggling with eighth-grade math. But that Saturday morning Cousin Sina had something different in mind. Gathering Henry and Clara around their own kitchen table, she declared in ringing tones: "Norman should go to high school. As a scholar he's no great shakes, but he's got grit!"

Nowadays urging that a teen attend high school seems kind of quaint; but in farm country in 1928 it caused heartburn, even heartache. Rainstorms still liquefied rural roads and cars hadn't evolved enough to have hard tops or heaters. Driving was thus a fair-weather fancy. The county high school was in Cresco, and even when weather was fair 14 miles was too far to commute.

Sina's proposal thus required Norm Boy leave home and actually *live with* the barbarians beyond the border. Also it required Henry and Clara to find a Cresco family who'd provide him meals and a bed Monday through Friday. And it required them to find the money as well as to run the farm with *half* the necessary complement of male muscle.

Despite all that, they acquiesced. Yes, they'll release their son to the outer world. They'll scrimp and save and find the money. And at age 39 Henry Borlaug will work twice as hard. Norm Boy can have his chance.

I n the fall of 1928, the farm kid who possessed neither money nor prospects crossed his First Great Divide, leaving behind the family and the Norwegian village. It was a leap almost too far. He now lived in a metropolis so huge it housed *3000 inhabitants!*

Coming from a school with 12 students, he was way out of his comfort zone in Cresco High with 300. Half of those were farm kids, and for them the school offered Vocational Agriculture classes. The curriculum was bottom basic because America's leaders figured that farm boys who could read the local paper, write a reasonable letter and tote up a few numbers were educated above their station. Farmers, everyone knew, needed only weak minds and strong backs. And farm boys' only ambition was to follow their fathers.

After the Christmas break Norm returned to Cresco High to finish his freshman year. It was an exciting time. He'd found a new comfort zone. And history had reached its grandest year. For one thing, 1929 promised to deliver the ultimate in technological progress. For another, Herbert Hoover had just been elected president. In March this can-do Iowan would enter the White House. An orphan who'd made good as a mining engineer in foreign lands, he'd campaigned on the slogan: "A Chicken for Every Pot and Two Cars in Every Garage."

Folks in farm country were ecstatic. Indeed Americans everywhere were ecstatic. Hoover would deliver both food and fortune. A then-popular hit song captured the prevailing mood:

> *Blue skies are smiling at me;*
> *Blue skies are all I see.*

During the spring of 1929 Norm encountered agricultural science, thanks to a newly appointed Vocational Agriculture teacher. Fresh from Iowa State College in Ames, Harry Shroder was a fertilizer believer.

Around Cresco, that seemed like heresy. God had made Howard County fertile; no field hereabouts needed force-feeding. Science's recent revelation about soil fertility was a fanciful error.

The class members were thus underwhelmed when Shroder walked them a few blocks down the road and had them prepare a series of small plots borrowed from a friendly farmer.

One plot was left untouched; the rest were treated with differing combinations of nitrogen, phosphorus and potassium salts. Then corn was planted evenly across the area.

A t that time Norm failed to see science or even school as important. His sights were fixed on sport.

Most of his classmates were similarly obsessed. Two years back, Cresco High had captured the Iowa State high-school football championship. A major contributor had been a quicksilver running back named George Champlin, who'd become team captain and town hero.

Given that shining example Norm went out for football. Though a bit on the light side, he was well coordinated and years of farm work had added strength and sinew and fashioned a sturdy body.

Then, after the fall football season was over, he signed up for winter wrestling. It seemed a good way to keep fit for the next football season. A couple of afternoons a week he'd stay at school a few hours to practice and participate in meets.

Sadly, that didn't work out. His very first meet delivered the wrestler's curse: boils. Wrestling mats, being too big and bulky for easy laundering by hand, tended to amass sweat, skin and *Staphylococcus*. Thus after a session squirming on the mat a knee, neck, backside, or elbow could erupt in a painful swelling:

> During my first couple of years I suffered boil trouble. It hurt like hell but nothing could be done. Anyone with a boil was barred from competing until nature had run its course. Unfortunately nature had no appreciation for the significance of sport . . . I was out for the season.

Wrestling, it seemed, would get him nowhere. But he was far from discouraged because his focus was actually the baseball diamond. His path to the top was the Big Leagues.

This fantasy infected millions of male minds thanks to the modern marvel that served up disembodied sensations. Radio had begun broadcasting in 1921 and, by some means beyond understanding, sent sound into your senses. It was tremendously exciting, but you could experience it only at night and only through earphones.

Now, eight years onward, there were loudspeakers and a 50 kilowatt Chicago station that reached across Middle America *during daytime* when baseball occurred. Play-by-play suspense was the sensation addicting all those susceptible males. It was new and oh-so subversive:

> Every Iowa farm boy loved WGN, which broadcast the Chicago Cubs on summer afternoons. What a joy! After unloading a wagonload of hay I'd dash inside for a drink of water and a chance to catch the score. The Cubs then became a major part of my being. Deep down, I knew that one day I'd be their second base.

Given that planetary plan, Cresco High's signature failing was the absence of baseball. That was downright un-American! How could he develop the skills and savvy to make the Cubbies?

An alternative was needed. Though northeast Iowa had an amateur baseball league, you had to be 18 to play. So, while still a high-school sophomore, he began his own league.

That wasn't so hard. Even back then he inspired trust. In Saude and surrounding villages — Protovin, Spillville, Jerico, Lawler, Alta Vista, Fredericksburg — he found interested teens. Together they worked out a roster of games for the 1929 season. Then each went home and recruited friends to form a village team. Each also arranged with a local farmer to provide a field. In Norm's case Carl Natvig helped out by providing the "ball park" on Oak Valley, his farm almost within Saude's shadow.

Games were played Sunday afternoons. When recalling them years later he expressed surprise at the upshot:

> We were just squads of farm kids aged fifteen to eighteen. The Saude players were Norwegians except for the three Seery brothers, who were Irish and came from Schley. Other teams were Bohemian [Czech], German and Irish.
>
> The facilities were very poor. The Saude home ground was a cow-pasture with no dirt diamond and grass that grew too long. Bases were sand-filled sacks. Bats and gloves and balls were well-worn.
>
> Yet we soon began attracting spectators, even cheering sections. By season's end fans were coming from miles around,

and our exploits were the talk of the neighborhood. Looking back, I can see that this was a surprisingly tough and talented group.

I didn't realize it at the time but these clashes on the baseball diamond helped unite northeast Iowa's immigrant communities, which were so isolated their phone companies served only themselves. Villagers used their own languages and seldom needed to talk with outsiders. However, all took a keen interest in their baseball team's prowess against the rival villages.

Saude's biggest rivals were the Bohemians down in Spillville. We played them regularly and during my senior year our game was incorporated into Spillville's Fourth-of-July Celebration and was played at Dvorak Riverside Park, beside the Turkey River.

Though the afternoon proved to be hot as the devil, no one in the crowd of several hundred seemed to mind. Indeed, the conviviality between the Bohemians and Norwegians made that my most memorable Independence Day. Sadly we lost in extra innings, however the action proved so thrilling that someone later said it was as good as the fireworks.

Best of all, by day's end we all felt part of *America*!

That same spring, the grandest of all years was indeed delivering the ultimate in technological progress. That's when Saude farmers learned of a new kind of corn seed. A bushel of that seed was said to yield as much as *100 more bushels of corn*.

Such productivity seemed beyond belief, but it came with a catch: *you had to buy the seed and you had to buy it every year!*

That outrageous demand sowed resistance, doubt, even hostility. The general consensus was that seed that had to be bought could never be worth the cost. Most of the Borlaugs felt that way:

> In the late twenties Dad, Granddad and my very voluble Uncle Oscar got highly exercised over the issue of whether to buy hybrid corn seed. It was the first time I'd heard any family members yell at each other. And it was disturbing.
>
> Only Oscar was for trying hybrids. The others declared we should stay with Reid's Yellow Dent. Its seed was free . . . we collected it from our own fields. How could you possibly do better than that?

Norm's Uncle Oscar, a lifelong bachelor who then managed Nels Borlaug's farm, had a rebellious streak. He'd first worked on the rail line known as Milwaukee Road and then had gone off to settle in South Dakota, living for several years in a hole-in-the-ground house near the town called Winner. A free thinker, Oscar Borlaug believed in anything modern, and devoted his spare time to studying the textbooks Cornell

University used to teach economics. He wanted to keep up.

However, even agriculture's boosters lacked Oscar's enthusiasm for hybrid corn. And at first the worrywarts prevailed. Across the Corn Belt even as late as 1935 hybrids were sown on barely one acre in a hundred.

Nonetheless, a few mavericks risked their reputations by bucking popular opinion and buying the newfangled seed. Typically they doubled their former take. Moreover, the pushy winds of fall failed to topple the stiff-stalked plants. To males the greatest blessing was the absence of the shooting pains that snuffed out sleep.

Hard on the heels of hybrid corn came two more modern marvels. A dozen years back Henry Ford had created a mechanical horse. The farmer's son knew what he was doing. Steel-wheeled Fordsons rolling off the assembly line broke the power barrier that had capped food production at the level of four-footed horsepower. His replacement had the power of 20 horses. It could far exceed 5 mph, pull loads horses could never budge, and motor on from dawn till sunset with nary a rest for food or water.

Despite that, country folk resisted: Why on God's green earth should any family admit a metal monster into its midst? A horse was friendly, alive, a known quantity.

Nevertheless the tinny trespasser kept propagating, evolving and spreading like a live thing. Within two decades, tractors sent the farm horse into history.

Like hybrid corn, this motorized marvel boosted food production beyond imagining. For one thing, the 75 million acres required to feed America's 21 million horses and mules were released to feed 45 million humans. Without breaking a single acre of virgin soil the tractor doubled production of the nation's basic staple.

The Borlaugs' steel-wheeled Fordson arrived that spring of '29. Norm's father and grandfather shared this hand-cranked helpmate that imbibed kerosene and resented working during the cold months. Only occasionally between October and April could it be coaxed out of hibernation to drive the circular saw and cut tree limbs into billets small enough to appease the wood stove's appetite.

In itself, that was a revolution, and the tractor provided the first portable energy source. The power companies then refused to wire up rural America, declaring the distances too great and the people too poor to provide proper profits. Thus the tractor carried electricity's load in farm country, powering water pumps, corn grinders, mills that ground oats into animal feed, augers that filled granaries and choppers that sliced corn plants for silage.

After the Fordson arrived Norm experienced those wonders:

> That little gray tractor produced no manure, so flies were no longer a bother and we could keep it near the house. It worked without a feed of oats morning, noon and night. Greatest of all, it seldom needed salve or soothing and never got a rub down, so we were freed from tending animals every day of our lives.
>
> In time, inspired engineers devised a corn-picking mechanism that could be fastened to a tractor's power take-off. What a godsend! The two-month horror of harvesting, husking, and heaving hundreds of thousands of corn ears was no more. Tractor-powered devices gathered the crop and elevated the cobs into the crib so easily young men like me forgot the shooting pains that had burdened sleep during every previous harvest season. With a tractor shouldering the brutal burdens corn picking seemed almost a lark.

By September 1929, when he returned to Cresco High for his sophomore year, Norm was rising 15 and felt at home in the great metropolis. He'd even glimpsed an incredible and impossibly bigger world on the few times when he had no homework and could scrape up a dime to visit the Opera House on North Elm to see a movie.

When Harry Shroder again walked the Vo-Ag students down the road to see what had transpired over the summer break they remained underwhelmed. By then their plots were almost ready to harvest, and the students were overwhelmed with amazement when they saw what they'd wrought. A few pounds of powdered plant food had crashed the age-old yield barrier. Norm's family had sacrificed everything and never surpassed 25 bushels an acre; with almost no effort he and his classmates got 50!

This shattered four social conventions: A bunch of clueless kids had proved the traditionalists wrong. The ceiling over farm life had nothing to do with God and everything to do with the ground. County soils were less fertile than common knowledge claimed. And farmers now could force Mother Nature to yield extra food.

Norm would never forget these lessons. Nor did he forget the paramount message that rural prosperity depends on a muscular seed and on the fertilizer that brings out its best.

As the 1920s crept toward their demise a pair of *off-farm* technologies made their mark. Both had to do with transportation.

Before this point, trains and Model T Fords moved farm products. Now the truck began muscling in. Though primitive and puny, trucks were cheap enough for locals to own, and they both carried small loads from farm to market and provided a speedy delivery for perishables such as vegetables and dairy products.

Trucks thus opened vast new horizons, but an even more fabulous vision was also emerging: concrete strips connecting the states. Rural folks initially considered this mere Washington meddling. Millions who'd dealt with dirt strips considered concrete roadbeds utterly absurd. Worse still, the authorities were giving roads numbers. What a waste of taxpayer money! Everyone knew where their roads went.

The first pavement to penetrate Norm's orbit was being constructed when he went to high school in 1928. Highway 63, running from Minnesota into Iowa, passed within nine miles of the farm. The sight of construction crews laying that concrete ribbon drew crowds of sightseers from far and wide:

> Several times we went over to admire this marvel. By today's standards it was narrow, primitive and unsafe at any speed, but we'd never seen a surface so smooth or solid or seemingly safe. Now we could drive worry-free whatever the season. We'd never considered such a possibility; driving had forever been fraught with the fear of plunging into bottomless mud right around the next bend.
>
> This narrow band of concrete had huge social consequences. Beyond mobility and access to better food, it endowed us a kind of nobility. This is where we first sensed the concept of the open road, and that expanded vision had an electrifying effect. The horizon that had always been close by was gone. Now we were part of the big wide world where all the action occurred.

The wonders that arrived during that grand year generated greater harvests and more wealth than rural regions had ever known. Farm families found themselves vaulted into the Land of Opportunity, which they'd sometimes heard about but never seen. Now with money to share with shopkeepers, they could carve out their own futures. Fate could no longer consign them to dead-end lives.

Norm's dad sowed the whole hundred acres to hybrid corn. He incorporated fertilizer. He fired up the tractor to till the soil and attack the weeds. And each acre yielded 52 bushels, more than double its previous best.

Now selling grain by the ton, Henry Borlaug stashed away a cash reserve, and began experiencing the good life. To him and all those like him, the greatest uplift was liberation from animal care. With no cows to coddle or horses to handle, they could pursue personal interests — a trip to town, say, or a big-band concert across the county line. Nothing like that had been known in farm country before.

Norm sums up the feeling of freedom:

> Only those who experienced it can appreciate the blend of excitement and satisfaction in having your life's prospects made over. Farm families had seen their frontier expand but now, with no animals to care for, they could go out and explore it. Suddenly we could shape our own fate without the old restrictions. We could get an education; maybe even a profession. The possibilities seemed endless. That sudden perception was so overwhelming it amounted to a change in consciousness.
>
> For the Borlaugs this amounted to a dream come true. Previously, the prospect of better times had been merely a family faith, one that most likely would never eventuate in our lifetimes. Now, however, it was clear that Granddad had been right all along. His fabled future had arrived. And it was even more fabulous than anything we'd dared wish for. The solid wall around rural life had virtually vanished in the mists; the larger world was ours for the taking!

Those years had delivered so many technological triumphs that the 1920s can be said to have made modern America. Food is, after all, a fuel more basic than any produced by industry. Though Iowa's corn harvests had never topped the divinely decreed 30 bushels an acre, the new seed and the supportive technologies lifted the state average to a staggering 75 bushels an acre.

Moreover in scaling such heights America's biggest crop lifted millions of poverty-stricken rural families into the middle class. Nothing like it had happened in farm country. Anywhere. Ever.

All in all, the 1920s' magnificent rural makeover secured the food supply that set up America's subsequent rise to greatness.

This was the inspiring scene as 1929 approached its Use-By Date. The old order had died; a new order was being birthed. Life was movin', groovin', improvin'. The grand year had delivered on its promise. For good measure, it had also delivered the yo-yo.

But late in October something mean supervened: With terrible thousand-mile tentacles Wall Street reached out and ravaged the rural regions that had no idea what or where Wall Street was. Plunging stock prices pulled down millions of hard-working Midwesterners who didn't know a stock from a stocking and had just gotten a taste of the good life and were savoring the glory of opportunity.

This evil force even pulled down the blue sky's happy smiles. A new hit song now captured the prevailing mood:

> *Once I built a railroad.*
> *I made it run; made it race against time.*
> *Once I built a railroad; now it's done.*
> *Brother, can you spare a dime?*

When young Borlaug began his sophomore year at Cresco High life was disoriented. More than that, life was dissolving. Millions of underdog dreams were dying as people fell pell-mell back into poverty and home detention. The taste of Heaven had been sweet but it had been oh so brief.

As 1929 tottered off into history the only thing that now sprang eternal was despair. Having raised hopes beyond reason, then having delivered a wondrous new order, this year ravished all it had inherited and all it had provided. History quite rightly booted it off the stage and into disgrace.

When 1930 opened its eyes and looked around it was clear that its predecessor had also ravished the future. But as Norm finished up his sophomore year in the spring and as he worked on the family farm through the long and blistering summer, it was apparent that 1930 had no more technological triumphs to deliver.

In September his junior year began with a surprise: Cresco High had hired a new principal, and this one also coached wrestling.

Short and barely 135 pounds David Bartelma actually seemed like a giant, having been selected as an alternate on the U.S. wrestling squad for the Olympic Games. To kids in little Cresco this star had descended not from the teacher's college in Cedar Falls (60 miles south) but from the heavens!

Bartelma proved a master of mind games. He treated his charges more like brother than boss. And he challenged them to attempt the impossible. And to that end he promoted a five-point code of conduct:

> *Give your best . . .*

Believe you can succeed . . .
Face adversity squarely . . .
Be confident you'll find the answers when problems arise.
Then go out and win some bouts!

Coach Bart drove home those five points with taunts. "There's no damn messing around here," he'd yell during wrestling practice. "Give the best God gave you, or don't bother competing!"

Taken all round, Bartelma and wrestling gave the 16-year-old Borlaug his first taste of talent, and it was terrific. Out on the mat he became fast, agile, tricky, strong, and the terror of the takedown:

> Wrestling changed my life. It made me mentally tough. Given my small size and small hands I had to focus very hard . . . if my thoughts wavered I got humiliated fast. Thus I learned to never give up whatever the odds.

In the fall of 1930, when he was starting his junior year, Norm made the Cresco High varsity football team. Notwithstanding modest size (140 pounds, including boots, leather helmet and sopping locks in wet weather), he played guard.

This junior year was not without incident. In the spring two of Cresco's three banks padlocked their doors, sealing forever the depositors' hard-won savings. With it went the Borlaugs' cash reserve together with their new-found dreams. That summer, Norm lost hope of ever being somebody. He couldn't even stay at home — the farm being too small and too poor to gainfully employ both father *and* son. And there was no other place to find work. America was imploding. Across the nation headlines and deadlines had given way to breadlines.

A new hit song now provided collective spiritual reassurance:

> *Who's afraid of the big bad wolf*
> *Big bad wolf, big bad wolf?*
> *Who's afraid of the big bad wolf?*
> *Tra la la la la*

Though composed for "Three Little Pigs," a short Walt Disney cartoon, its popularity soared. People sang it to keep their spirits up. They were sure the wolf it referred to was Wall Street.

In September 1931 when he returned to Cresco High for his senior year and his final fling with formal learning, he found he'd been elevated to captain of the football team.

As custodian of the town renown, he let everyone down. That fall the team went 2 and 8 — its worst showing ever. Although three key players were lost to injury, Norm's brain never overcame the shame.

On the wrestling mat during that winter things went better. In the District Meet, which included high-school wrestlers from several northeastern counties, he won the championship.

By the spring of 1932 he ranked among Iowa's best, reaching the finals in the State High School Tournament.

Also competing in Des Moines was a fellow team member, Ervin Upton, who reached the finals in the next weight-class down (135lb). Success in the state capital converted these local lads into Cresco heroes. And in the outcome they became training partners and good pals.

This, his final lap of high school happened in the Great Depression's bleakest year. Members of the Class of 1932 dared not discuss the futures. None of them had a future. Cresco High was graduating them into a society that had lost its moorings and was adrift.

Norm, for instance, had no chance of a profession and no chance of college. His grades had been good — he'd been listed among the school's outstanding students and had won the American Legion Citizenship Award as well as the Athletic Coaches' Medal of Honor. But in 1932 grades had lost their credit rating. College took only cash. His family was broke. And the end of twelfth grade meant the end of everything.

Following the graduation ceremony at Cresco High Norm and Erv Upton remained in town and spent the night with their pal Bob Smylie. All three played football. As the team's left tackle, Bob lined up beside Norm, so they enjoyed a special telepathy and empathy.

Bob had arrived just the year before. His father had been Superintendent of Schools in central Iowa. Collapsing tax revenues had, however, forced the councilors to abolish the position.

In the mad hope of stumbling over some means of sustaining themselves, the Smylies headed off and after 200 miles ended up in remote Cresco, where they operated a one-pump gas station on a corner of Highway 9.

Desperate for every cent, they adopted a then-unique business strategy: 24 hour service.

Bob got the graveyard shift. The station had a tiny loft, and whenever a vehicle pulled in he'd roll off his camp cot, scamper down a ladder, crank a heavy handle, pump a few gallons of gas, and clamber back up to the cot. On typical nights a couple of trucks might stop and buy a few gallons at 10 cents a gallon.

That garret over the gas station forever haunted Norm's memory:

> It was almost bare. Bob had unfolded a couple of camp cots, but could offer us nothing more. He was burdened by appalling poverty. When Erv and I returned to our homes next day, we left our friend living in that crummy little loft. He had nothing to look forward to except being woken up all through the night. I felt a deep sadness.
>
> From such utter deprivation Bob Smylie had no chance of amounting to *anything*.

After graduation in May, he lived out the rest of that bleak year working around home to pay for his food and board. For cash he toiled for the neighbors, who dispensed a dollar a day for cutting fence posts, thrashing oats, or filling silos with chopped green corn plants – all done the old way, using muscle power: his and the horses'.

In the early weeks of 1933 he heard with surprise that Iowa's colleges would hold a wrestling meet in tiny Cresco late in February. He asked if he could compete and, to his amazement, the sponsors crafted a special category: "Unattached to Any Institution."

Powered by latent bitterness and with a body honed by hard labor, he out-pinned, out-pointed and out-escaped all comers until the final bout wherein he faced a star who the week before had won the All State College Tournament. Norm had never been on a campus, while his opponent was a senior at Iowa State Teacher's College.

Despite the seeming mismatch, the struggle proved torrid enough to end in a tie. Then during overtime — on a close, even disputable call — the referee awarded the other youth an escape.

From that defeat's dark depths sprang a miracle. As the dejected loser trailed off the mat the opponent's coach whispered: "If you'd like to come to Teacher's College next fall, I'll try to find you a job."

Those seventeen words changed everything. This single, seductive, very vague offer was enough to convince Norm his months of struggle had paid off. Right there, standing in his cotton shorts and sweaty singlet before the excited crowd with cheers echoing around the Cresco High gym the prospect of a fine future instantly blossomed into rosy brilliance before his disbelieving eyes.

In seven more months he'd go to Teacher's College!

Later reality struck, precipitating a hysterical hustle for money. For one thing, he ran lines of traps through the woods behind the house, and managed to catch the odd weasel, muskrat and skunk. The pelts were dispatched by parcel post to a rough-and-tumble Kansas City dealer who sent back small thin envelopes enclosing a dollar bill or two.

Nights he secured a trap in the stream behind the house. It seemed a silly obsession until one morning he beheld a mink. That pelt brought $10! It was not unlike hitting the lottery when you'd hit rock bottom.

In March when the weather finally decided to show some sympathy for suffering humanity, Norm again approached the neighbors, only to find they were down to paying 50 cents for a hard day's toil.

Nonetheless, throughout that summer he beat himself up cutting their trees into fence posts, thrashing their oats, chopping their green corn plants. He did it with vigor. There was nothing to lose; this was his last farm work. He'd spend the rest of his days as a science teacher and athletics coach at a high school somewhere in the great Hawkeye State.

Then in June a letter from Cedar Falls arrived. His application to Teacher's College had been accepted. A job would be found to help him meet personal expenses.

He replied, expressing deepest gratitude and confirming he'd report on time in mid-September. Of that no doubts were entertained: This was his chance for a profession. He'd never get another; during the Depression few people got even one!

Having hoarded $50 from the pelts and the pennies from the neighbors, he enjoyed a fragrance more heady in 1933 than any other year: the scent of success. Of the quarter-million lost kids in America he was among the handful to get a hand up.

On a September Saturday about a week before he needed to report to Cedar Falls, George Champlin's brown Model A roadster rattled up the driveway.

This was a puzzlement. Norm had never met the quicksilver running back, who'd graduated before he got to Cresco High. But everyone knew this hometown hero now played for one of the greatest college teams, the University of Minnesota Gophers.

But what was he doing all the way out here at the humble Borlaug home on a Saturday afternoon?

Champlin quickly made his point. "Norm," he blurted, "I've just been talking with Dave Bartelma. He says you're a good lineman. Tomorrow I'm leaving for Minneapolis . . . early football practice. I've been asked to find players for the freshman squad. Come with me and I'll get you a try out."

This was all so sudden, so thrilling, so preposterous Norm could only stammer: ". . . B-B-But I'm going to Teacher's College . . . I'm leaving next Friday!"

Stimulating his stammer was the breathtaking possibility of attending *a real university*. But common sense quickly returned. Patiently he explained exactly why he couldn't possibly go to Minnesota. Champlin, however, countered with canny answers to every concern:

Money. George explained that, compared to Cedar Falls, Minneapolis offered many more chances for finding work.

Academic requirements. No problem; Bartelma says that with grades like yours you'll be accepted . . . you won't even need to take the entrance exam.

Accommodation. George had a room near the campus. It was real expensive — $20 a month — but there were two double beds, so the rent could be shared among four.

Commitment to the Teacher's College. Again George had a slick response: "Drive up with me and see for yourself," he said, "If you don't like it, you can hitchhike home."

Then the gridiron star tossed his long bomb: "Erv Upton's coming."

That proved the game-winner: A flustered and severely shaken 19-year-old teacher-in-waiting mutely nodded acceptance. If his friend Erv could make the Gophers, why couldn't he?

Champlin barked at him to start packing . . . he'd be back *tomorrow*!

Understandably, Norm's parents were dismayed that a virtual stranger had dropped in out of nowhere and had in mere minutes disrupted their son's future.

Norm himself was worried.

One family member, however, was over the moon. Sunday afternoon, Nels Borlaug came over from his house next door, linked arms and marched his grandson out the gate to where George

Champlin stood beside his fancy Ford.

Then from a pocket the family patriarch hauled a frayed leather pouch and spilled its entire contents into his grandson's hand. "You'll make more use of 'em than I will, Norm Boy," he said.

There were eleven silver dollars.

1933-1935

Hunger Pains

Heading for university without having applied seems silly to us nowadays; doing so with just $61 was quite absurd even in September 1933. Out-of-state tuition would take $25 and from the remaining $36 he needed to pay for lodging, books and food.

Champlin, however, squelched all fears. "You'll have no trouble," he said. "Just you wait and see!"

Having retrieved Erv Upton from his home near Oak Lawn cemetery, the three headed north up the half-finished concrete highway that today is Minnesota 52.

George Champlin's Roadster being a two-seater, Norm and Erv took turns sitting in the rumble seat that opened like a jackknife from the sloping back. Out there in the breeze and bright sun they sensed their liberation. But whenever the road reverted to dirt or oiled gravel breathing became difficult, which they might have considered an omen.

The final stretch of the 160 mile trip brought Norm face to face with his first city. To him, Minneapolis seemed like a theme park. On every side were astonishments: streetcars, traffic, sidewalks, shop windows a block long. Towering over everything was a 32-story skyscraper, known as the "Washington Monument of the Midwest."

But beyond mind-boggling the grand metropolis was also mind-numbing. Its noise, confusion, and bustle short-circuited the brains of innocents who'd known only country stillness. Its streets were dingy, dirty and downright dowdy compared with the clean, green farm fields. And it displayed the Great Depression's trademarks: broken windows, faded signs, boarded shop-fronts, peeling paint. In the depths of shop doorways bodies, including tiny ones, could be seen huddled like sacks of grain.

The frightening reality was that America had lost its moorings and was adrift. Some 15 million citizens had no work; 35 million had no income; untold millions had no home and no food. Money had become a mythical substance. Hunger's shadow haunted the land. Breadlines stretched for blocks, and every crust was critical.

Like other cities Minneapolis sported garbage-ghettos wherein families fashioned their own shelters out of packing crates, cardboard and scrap metal. People loved slapping the president's name on things; and these suburbs of squalor — usually located near the town dump for easy access to food and building supplies — were universally known as "Hoovervilles."

Upon its arrival in Minneapolis the brown roadster seemed to have been dipped in dust. Four blocks from campus — near the railroad yards and in a village-like enclave known as University Dinkytown — Champlin swung into 15th Avenue SE and pulled up before number 505.

A complex of three three-story, red brick buildings, the Kearsarge Apartments proved plain but pleasant. The corner unit's second floor housed Champlin's room. Apart from the two beds, there was a small wooden table, four not-too-sturdy chairs . . . nothing more.

Having dumped their bags and peeked at the astounding setting the boys found themselves hustled back downstairs. "We must get to the coffee shop," their galvanic guide declared, "before the other kids grab all the jobs."

Located nearby and just a block from campus, the University Coffee Shop seated 75 customers and boasted three U-shaped counters and a row of booths down one wall. That night the manager was too busy to break in raw recruits. "Come back tomorrow morning at seven," Spencer Holle barked: "Work an hour, get a meal."

Those words brought relief. Food was all they sought. The stuff of life was worth much more than money.

On their return to the apartment Champlin exuded his customized optimism: "Well, you've got a place to sleep and a place to eat," he boomed. "In a few days you'll report for football practice, pay your fees, and enroll. Then you'll be A-okay."

At six on Monday morning Erv and Norm hustled off to their new calling. The experience proved daunting. Spencer Holle, a former hammer thrower who'd almost made the U.S. Olympic team in 1928, was big-boned, muscle bound and very demanding. His intimidating presence did nothing to help Norm's nerves, concentration, or grip on the crockery. Bustling in and out of the kitchen with platters of fried eggs and buttermilk pancakes the anxious rookie scrambled his orders.

The evening stint brought no improvement. As the dinner hour wound down, George Champlin dropped by to check on his protégés, and Norm overheard Holle say in slow and terrifying tones: "Either I'll make a waiter out of Borlaug or I'll kill him!"

Suddenly the new recruit forgot his fright, found his focus and fathomed out how to properly serve food and remove dirty dishes.

By Wednesday, Champlin had wangled Norm a second job parking cars on campus. Whenever the cavernous Northrop Auditorium hosted a symphony concert, a lecture, a convocation, or performance Norm earned tips by driving patrons' cars into the garage under the Adult Education Center next door.

The auditorium, commonly called "the Midwest's Carnegie Hall," was popular. Typically he worked twice a week and earned a couple of dollars. Maybe that seems inadequate, but a month's take paid his share of the Kearsarge Apartments rent.

Life had turned out grand. He now had food and lodging. Not without a stab of guilt, he wrote to the Iowa State Teacher's College. Sorry, but he wouldn't be coming to Cedar Falls at the end of the week.

Within hours of slipping the letter into the mail box at the Dinkytown Post Office on 4th Street SE he had reason to regret his hasty action. After perusing his transcript, the admissions officer declared him ineligible for the University of Minnesota. He was missing a year of science and a year of math, and could not possibly be admitted.

This was a mere technicality. For purposes of admission, ninth grade records were ignored. That year, Norm had scored well in both science and math, but now those scores couldn't be considered. The University of Minnesota would neither accept them nor him. He was told to take the make-up test. It would be held next Saturday. Then the relevant authorities could judge whether he was worthy.

That Saturday as he trudged back to campus for the test of a lifetime, he was a bundle of fears. Quite right too: the questions proved familiar, but a year's absence from school had softened the brain synapses and the answers had made their escape.

He flunked.

That did it. The professor in charge of testing and matriculation declared Norman Borlaug to be not University of Minnesota material. To Dean E. Williamson this Iowa oaf had proven himself doubly unfitted.

Norm was in full agreement:

At that moment I considered myself a complete flop.

Here again history could have gone awry. He would have packed his bags, headed to Saude, and – as a son of the soil was supposed to do – lived out his days growing corn to feed and finance his family. What alternative was there?

While preparing to hitchhike home in disgrace, his biggest regret was turning down the Iowa Teacher's College, the only school he was good enough to attend.

Thank goodness for George Champlin and his giant heart. Unfazed by the setback, he marched his dejected adherent into an assistant dean's office and shouted: "Something's wrong with your testing up here in Minnesota. Give this guy another chance. He's not as dumb as you think!"

Norm nearly died of embarrassment, but the words did not dismay the assistant dean. Frederick Hovde, a 25-year-old chemical engineer, Rhodes Scholar, and renowned quarterback of the 1928 Golden Gophers had been entrusted with starting a new kind of college to help promising youngsters sucked down by the Great Depression's social undertow. Remedial classwork would prepare them for admittance to the university. Or so it was hoped.

Dean Hovde thus was unfazed by the suspect transcript and accepted the Iowa rube, allowing Norman Borlaug entrance to what was then known as "Junior College of the University of Minnesota." In time, this experimental venture would spawn today's national system. Borlaug was thus a Junior College pioneer.

As for freshman football, he felt obliged to try out. But the Gophers were still a national powerhouse, and one glance at the goliaths of the defensive line made clear he needed a sport safer to life, if not limb.

Accordingly, he and Erv Upton enrolled for wrestling and were shocked to find that their sport counted for nothing in Minnesota. The coach was a local lawyer who donated two hours a couple of afternoons a week. He was sincere, but even by Iowa's high-school standards, distressingly deficient in wrestling savvy.

Soon thereafter Norm took an afternoon off to walk around the downtown area. Crossing the Mississippi by the Washington Avenue Bridge he wandered westward into a squalid section called the Warehouse District.

When the noise of a crowd attracted his curiosity he strolled around a corner to see several hundred men surging against a tall fence. They were clearly striking drivers but were screaming angry obscenities and acting like hooligans.

Inside the fence, behind high wire gates, a line of guards stood shoulder-to-shoulder, each clad in black peaked cap and black uniform and each grasping a black club. Behind them was a line of white milk-delivery vans.

The imminence of conflict proved irresistible. Having got himself exactly across the street from the gates, Norm spotted a photographer hoisting a tripod onto the hood of an old touring car. For balance, the man rested his foot on the canvas roof. When that proved inadequate he levered himself up.

Then his foot ripped through the canvas and, as if on cue, the gates swung open and the black-clad guards charged the crowd, Billy-clubs flailing. The first casualty was the camera; the second its owner, who emulated a heap of red wreckage staining the pavement.

Realizing the danger, Norm tried to wriggle away, but in recoiling from the attack the mass of strikers had pinned him against a warehouse wall. The charging deputies surged directly toward him. But just when they and their nightsticks were about to crack his head they pivoted sideways in what seemed like a prearranged move to open the road for the trucks to get out and go on their scheduled rounds:

> I was freed from the crush only after the milk trucks had gone past. That's when the pickets took off down the street, screaming with frustration. Minneapolis got its milk delivered that day; the batons had beaten the strikers both ways.
>
> The strikers, however, didn't realize they'd lost the skirmish. They kept on yelling as if their lives depended on it, which was certainly so because no job meant no life in those days. However, they were also yelling because the scene was so horrifying.

Bodies and blood were scattered and spattered over the street.

By then, the company guards were back behind the gates. Again shoulder-to-shoulder, they stood stiff and seemingly unmoved by the sickening sights their own hands had created.

Ambulances arrived, but no police that I saw. However, I didn't stick around long. I took off running.

For a pupil from the placid plains this was a soul-searing experience never to be forgotten. Throughout a long life he'd tell his listeners:

"Hungry people are angry people."

A s payment for working the breakfast rush, the University Coffee Shop allowed waiters to take a cup of coffee, five prunes and two slices of toast. One morning, shortly after starting the job, Norm glanced up from this grand repast and noticed a pretty girl sitting nearby.

Margaret Gibson was bright and vivacious and looked . . . well, nice. Her cloud of thick black hair was strongly curled, with a sheen where the light struck. Her skin was smooth and healthy, giving an impression of well-scrubbed. Their eyes met. She smiled and asked what he was studying, and he noticed that her voice was low and cool. Embarrassed, he stammered he wasn't in the university at all — just Junior College. And he had no idea of what he was going to do. She smiled again.

Unlike the introvert from Iowa, Margaret was sophisticated, sure of herself, outgoing. Her brother George had captained the most famous of all Golden Gophers — the 1929 National Champions. Nothing more was needed to confirm an ethereal origin.

The coffee shop's owner, Augusta Holle (Spencer's mother), had hired Margaret as a waitress. The job was just for food of course, and from time to time while eating their pay the young acquaintances talked of their backgrounds, their dreams, and this and that.

Soon the boy whose only treats had been the odd movie in Cresco found himself sitting beside Margaret quite often.

Junior College was hardly challenging, and from the start he considered it a waste of time. After acing the first-quarter exams, he called on Dean Hovde and requested a transfer to the university. The request was denied on the grounds that he'd been there only 6 weeks.

That stirred the furies, and Norm dedicated the second quarter to super-serious study, and again aced the exams. During his return visit he sat rigid with tension as the deity behind the desk scanned the scores seemingly forever with furrowed brow.

Norm concluded that the slim figure fingering his fate was deciding how to yet again refuse his request. But finally a momentous verdict emerged: "Well Borlaug, you can transfer to any college you want. Which will it be?"

Knowing that his real career was with the Chicago Cubs he offered an almost flippant reply. A few days earlier a friend had hauled him five miles across town to see the university's second facility. The St. Paul campus was dedicated to agriculture, home economics and forestry, and he'd fallen in love with it. "The College of Agriculture," he blurted. "I'll major in forestry."

This outburst served only to re-furrow Dean Hovde's brow. Forestry was then a kind of campus cult. Clean-cut young men from the finest of families swaggered around campus displaying unkempt beards, checked shirts and hobnailed boots. It was a youthful protest against the establishment and the hard times it had spawned.

In addition, though, Frederick Weyerhaeuser had founded the world's largest forest empire in St. Paul. Anyone seeing his mansion on Summit Ave knew that the woods could dispense wealth. And during the Depression anything with that power was priceless.

For a long moment Dean Hovde seemed to be bracing himself to issue another rebuff. Then he relaxed, leaned halfway across his desk, locked eyes, and nodded. Yes, he said, suddenly grinning, Borlaug could enter the College of Agriculture.

This was the next great turning point. As Norm hitchhiked southward for the Christmas break he felt his spirits and confidence soaring. The coming year would launch him into the real university as well as into his new field of study. Not only that, baseball season was coming up and he'd go out for the freshman team. He'd soon be on the road to his predestined place of employment: second base at Wrigley Field.

At the farm reality crashed him back to earth: Granddad Nels had contracted cancer of the stomach. The tumor was inoperable. Now 74, the family patriarch was too weak to leave his bed.

Just after New Year, as Norm said farewell, the old man grasped his wrist. "Education puts power into a man, Norm Boy," he said, glaring as though by look and touch he could transmit his own determination.

"Governments come and governments go, but if you've got a good education no one can take that from you!"

A second setback struck when he returned to Minneapolis. During the Christmas break the Holles had closed the coffee shop. This was a body blow to existence itself. Now he needed to find a way to eat. And he had to do it fast. He was already hungry:

> Before anything else I had to find food — and not just for myself . . . Margaret Gibson also depended on that coffee shop.
> The university had no dining halls, so Dinkytown contained many restaurants. But finding work proved difficult. We did the rounds, almost begging for the chance to wait tables.
> At odd times one would let us in, but whenever business was slow the managers would shake their heads when they saw us standing in the doorway.
> For us, that was terribly disappointing. We were living meal-to-meal, so it meant we went off to class hungry.

Few Americans then got three meals a day, but Norm was getting one or none. The empty stomach turned into yet another challenge of will. Trouble was, there seemed nothing more to try; nowhere to turn. Hunger had him beat. He prepared himself for the inevitable defeat: he'd hasten home — famished, flummoxed and a failure in the foreign world, not to mention in Margaret's eyes.

For a few weeks coupons kept the two of them them alive. Some were clipped from the *Minnesota Daily*, the university newspaper; others came from a boy he'd met in the coffee shop who'd acquired a roll of the magical coupons (exactly from where Norm didn't want to know). Three coupons and ten cents bought a bottle of milk and three hamburgers at the tiny, crenellated White Castle Restaurant just off campus.

The hamburgers were only bite-sized and were meant to be eaten in multiples, but they normally cost five cents apiece, so providing three with a bottle of milk for ten cents was a contribution to those hungry *and* unhealthy times.

And what a contribution it proved. Without White Castle he'd have foregone the rest of his life and headed home *just to eat*. Though the company's generosity filled the need for just a few weeks, it kept the career from coming unbuckled:

> Thank God for those little burgers. They got me through the worst stretch of my young life! They allowed me to stay in school for the few weeks that made the difference.

For the long haul, though, he couldn't live on hamburger handouts. But what else was there?

Again he decided that the situation was hopeless, and once more prepared himself to hasten home. Just the day before he planned to pack his bag and slouch back to a life of ignominy, the answer materialized as if Heaven sent. That evening, Scott Pauley burst into the apartment whooping the magic word "Food!"

Scott was a fellow student whom Norm had met in chemistry class. He was bright, cheery, fun to be around. Margaret also enjoyed his company, and several Sundays that spring the three had wandered into the countryside around the campus, identifying trees and admiring the glistening waters of the lakes.

This was the friend who'd introduced Norm to the farm campus. The afternoon they'd taken the streetcar to St. Paul the autumn sky was dulled a milky gray. Norm, however, found the somber scene glowing with promise and prospects — not from the intellectual ferment within the facilities but from the peace and quietude without. This campus — so near the hoovervilles and hooliganism — was clean and restful. Serenity was what catalyzed his interest in forestry, not rebelliousness or reveries of wealth. He felt happy out here in the quietude beyond the chaos.

Scott shared these feelings, and his outburst had an impact difficult to overstate. For his own sustenance he waited tables and bussed dishes in a dining room of a well-to-do sorority. That evening he'd been asked to find a second waiter.

Now he marched his hungry friend three blocks along Southeast 5th Street to Alpha Omicron Pi where the House Mother announced that Norm could start the next day. For pay, he'd get *all he could eat*!

Mrs Nichols was unaware of her offer's significance to our story and to Norm:

I've often said it was the greatest compensation I ever received.

Now he had food, he had rent money (still earned by parking cars), and he was in the university proper. Only the wallet ran on empty. Of the $35 scraped together during winter break when 1933 merged into 1934, tuition had absorbed $25. Not even he could make it through a college quarter on $10.

That March, having defeated Herbert Hoover, Franklin Delano Roosevelt was sworn in as president. Next day, he began providing financial relief to help Americans weather the Depression. One of those, a federal program nowadays largely forgotten, will save our storyline.

According to author Robert Caro, FDR's wife conceived the idea. "A civilization which does not provide young people with a way to earn a living," Eleanor Roosevelt declared, "is pretty poor." Then this most formidable of First Ladies pressed her husband for a program to help youngsters stay in school. "We have got to [make] these young people . . . feel that they are necessary," she explained.

The president resisted. There was no special problem of young people, he said, just a problem of society. Did she expect him to provide cash relief for everyone? Why, next all the 40-year-olds would be demanding government handouts!

But Mrs Roosevelt knew her husband's weak spot. Those young people, she quietly noted, were about to become voters.

All resistance then evaporated. Losing the next generation of voters was quite unthinkable. "There is a great deal to what you say," he replied, and surely his eye must have emitted a rascally twinkle.

Some weeks later when signing the National Youth Administration into law "the friend in the White House" announced, "I have determined that we shall do something for the nation's unemployed youth. They must have their chance."

A portion of the NYA funds were set aside to help needy students stay in school. The University of Minnesota established an office to screen candidates for its portion. Norm's finances proved so appalling he was immediately accepted and sent straight to the entomology department.

There, department head C.E. Mickel explained that he'd have to pin insects onto boards for a graduate student studying the jack-pine sawfly, tidy up after professors, and be generally available for other work around the department. In return, he'd be paid 18 cents an hour in tuition chits. And he could put in 15 hours a week.

Did he want the job?

Did he ever! $2.70 would cover the week's tuition.

Thus the financial impediment was overcome for less than $3 a week. It was thanks to the grand lady in the White House. It required that Norm add another 15 hours of toil to every week. But in the long run it made all the difference.

Now he had food, he had funding, and of course he had Margaret Gibson. Occasionally on weekdays they met on campus; Sundays, they spent an hour or two together.

More than that was not possible; no more time slots remained. Margaret actually feared his maniacal schedule would damage his health. "Norman," she said, "you really must slow down; you'll kill yourself!"

Her concern was commendable. Each week the NYA and sorority jobs absorbed 36 hours. Around those he had to fit a full schedule of classes, homework and independent study. Travel took more hours: some classes were in Minneapolis, others five miles away in St. Paul; the trip between the campuses absorbed 30 minutes and the streetcar ran only every half-hour. Beyond all that, he spent an hour a day in the gym staying in shape for wrestling.

By now, though, baseball took no time at all. That spring he'd been admitted to the freshman squad, and during the early weeks ranked among its most promising hitters. Then there arose an exquisitely agonizing conflict: the team practiced *every* weekday afternoon. And on three of those he had a forestry lab class. What to do?

> I was playing well enough that I probably could have gotten out of baseball practice for those three days, but two days of practice per week didn't seem enough to master professional level skills.
> Suddenly I had to confront a career choice: baseball or forestry?
> In one of the saddest days of my life I turned in my uniform. It was among the most difficult decisions I've ever made. The dream of playing for the Cubs was over; my one chance at the highest of all callings was gone.

It was such a blow to youthful pride that sixty years onward those words emerged dripping with disappointment.

While fretting over Norm's health, Margaret failed to realize that his manic pace was actually fueled by the fear of flunking. During the Great Depression failure was a paramount fear, and he had but one chance to avoid academic annihilation: the upcoming winter-quarter finals. These, his first exams in the university proper, would determine his destiny. It was not unlike sudden-death overtime. A completed pass was essential.

Then in mid-March — just as he prepared for the last exam — his throat began burning. Soon he began feeling hot all over. Finally the throat tightened so he could barely swallow his own saliva.

After struggling through the chemistry final he took his agony to the health service, and found himself whisked into the University Student Hospital. Strep throat.

Death then had myriad tentacles that have nowadays lost their grip. Strep was one. In 1934 there was no treatment, let alone cure. For two days he lay on a cot, boiling with fever, frustration and fear. The pain rose and rose until it became almost unendurable. His wits began to wobble. But the hospital provided nothing more than warm salty water for gargling.

Only one of its staff wanted to do more:

> The intern on my case was bent on cutting out my lymph nodes. The guy wanted to document some detail for his thesis. I'm sure he'd decided I was dying. Heck, I'd decided that too. And it didn't matter; living with such pain wasn't worthwhile.

In all his long life this was the sole experience with apathy. Only the intern's morbid quest jerked him out. When Caifson Johnson appeared on the second day Norm croaked an urgent plea: "Get this intern out of here; he wants to carve me up!"

The wrestling team's light heavyweight scurried straight to the Athletic Department and collared the Assistant Football Coach, George Hauser, who was also an MD and member of the Student Hospital staff. "Please go over and look at Norm Borlaug," Johnson gasped out. "He's in real trouble."

Soon Dr. Hauser was bending over the cot, kneading the neck and peering down the red, raw throat. "You're a very sick young man, Borlaug," he said with obvious unease, "but we can't do more. It's up to you. You've got to make this on your own!"

Norm now had to wrestle with the miniature menace that was draining his own will to live. He turned the tussle into a mental challenge. "It'll take more than this to knock me back," he told himself. And in a few days the fever abated a trifle. Then he felt a trickle of energy flow into his ailing interior. Slowly stepping back from the graveside, he retrieved his throat from the devil. Soon he could swallow saliva and even indulge a smile.

He'd been extremely lucky. Sometime afterward, the wrestling team visited Kansas State and after the Friday-night bouts the team's heavyweight complained of a sore throat. Saturday, he was delivered to the student hospital in agony and abject terror. Sunday, the boy died.

I n those years, forestry was barely a science and was considered a not altogether reputable subsection of horticulture. Norm's training was more like something people might expect to find at a trade school. He had to exhibit proficiency in identifying, measuring, pruning, doctoring and planting trees; not to mention proficiency in thinning forests.

He and Scott spent that summer of 1934 at the Itasca Forestry Camp in northern Minnesota. The School of Forestry ran a training program there where the Mighty Mississippi is merely a creek with high hopes. These two sophomores shared an army barrack, sleeping on cots, washing their clothes with bar soap on wooden washboards in tin tubs, and boiling coffee over open fires, woodsman's style. They loved it.

It was at the Itasca Forestry Camp that Norm learned to use a surveyor's transit. He made triangulations, altitudes, and azimuths as well as laid lines of pegs identifying places for fences and plots for tree trials. His training was very old fashioned, but it was quite proper for a forestry career.

Little did he know it would help keep the world's food supply from collapse.

T he quarter he'd spent in Junior College had scrambled his school schedule and put him out-of-synch with the normal academic year. However, during the remainder of 1934 he completed his freshman year. By January 1935, when his sophomore year began, he'd mastered the curriculum and college life.

Then during the exam-preparation period late in April 1935 a secretary called him from the classroom and told him to report to the dean's office. There, Edward Cheyney explained that Norm's father had telephoned. He should call home.

It was the worst phone call he ever made. The voice from faraway Cresco was even softer than usual. Granddad Nels had passed on.

Norm was lost for words. He'd known it would come of course; leaving home after Christmas, he'd felt it might be the last goodbye. Still, the shock was tough to take. "Look, Dad," he said. "I'll come straight away. I can take the exams next quarter."

Suddenly the voice hardened. "You'll not do that, Norman. Your grandfather was very pleased at how well you're doing. He wouldn't want you to interrupt your work for *anything*."

Getting through finals was a struggle. However, as a memorial to

Granddad Nels the boy called upon his deepest reserves.

Easing the way was his remembrance of their last conversation when the old man had grasped his wrist and said: "Education puts power into a man, Norm Boy. Governments come and governments go, but if you've got a good education no one can take that from you."

S oon thereafter the lawyer who moonlighted as a wrestling coach declared he was quitting. That was bad enough, but not a single soul in the Twin Cities wanted the lowly, unpaid, twice-a-week coaching of a sport that attracted little interest.

Then one afternoon when the wrestlers were sitting around the mat agonizing over their beloved sport's demise Norm had an idea. He mentioned it to Erv Upton, who backed him up. The others acquiesced; so he dispatched a brief note to Cresco High.

Within days the reply was in hand: David Bartelma would love to coach University of Minnesota wrestling, just as long as he could also study for a doctorate in psychology ("a subject," Norm noted wryly, "in which he needed no higher learning").

The boys then approached Frank McCormick, the athletics director.

Thus it happened that in September 1935 Coach Bartelma breezed into town and U of M wrestling rose from the dead. Candidates were selected for the different weight-classes. A season schedule appeared. Stomachs were prodded, biceps pinched, muscles strengthened in the weight room. In Norm's case the results were not encouraging. "You've been eating too much up here in Minnesota, Borlaug," Bartelma brayed. "Got to get you down to a hundred and forty-five, *and keep you there!*"

From the start the coach's view stretched beyond the horizon. The boys had dreamed of having some fun and winning a few bouts; Bartelma wanted a program that could compete with the nation's best. He also wanted it backed up by youth wrestling leagues to provide a talent pool the university could plumb forever.

On this latter point he needed to generate interest in high schools, where wrestling was unknown, misunderstood, or maligned. But Coach Bart was not dismayed. He had an idea for that, too:

> Bartelma sent three of us — Erv, Caifson Johnson, and me — to Parent-Teacher Association meetings all around Minneapolis. We spent several evenings a week at it. He'd hand us bus fare and thirty-five cents for dinner and off we'd go.

Most of the parents we met had no conception of amateur wrestling, and confused us with professional showmen bouncing around boxing rings.

We were getting nowhere until we sought out the football coaches, explaining that by coaching wrestling during the winter months, they could ensure their players remained in top shape for the football season.

That football connection made the difference. Within a year, high-school wrestling meets were being held in several parts of the city. Those, in turn, led to district contests and eventually to a state championship.

Under Coach Bart's fiery influence, U of M wrestling caught on quickly. Indeed, it soared high enough to approach football in the Gopher stratosphere.

Seeing his sport climbing back from collapse was satisfying, and these days were filled with interest and good fellowship. Among athletes he befriended was a future governor. That was not apparent at the time. Norm knew Orville Freeman as a rising football star. It was good that the two got to be locker-room buddies. At a vital point in the decades ahead their paths will again cross and mutual respect will mean a lot.

At the time, though, neither Norm nor Margaret could foresee all that would transpire. Life looked bleak; the Great Depression refused to retire gracefully into the shadows of history; Norm's situation may have improved, but it was far from a bed of roses:

> For me, the fall semester of my junior year raced by and the new year of 1936 loomed ahead. By then Margaret Gibson and I were seeing each other regularly. She'd remained a student in the Department of Education, but that December she ended her formal studies . . . unable to tolerate the scrimping and scraping any longer. "I'm sick of going to bed hungry," she said.
>
> Her brother made it possible. Bill Gibson edited the University of Minnesota Alumni Magazine and had learned that his printer needed an assistant proofreader. Thus it was that Margaret left school. Colwell Press paid her a pittance, but at last she could eat. And that was the main thing.
>
> I was doing better too, although still facing financial difficulties. By then, the National Youth Administration had assigned me to a new job: cleaning cages and feeding mice, rats and rabbits at the Department of Veterinary Medicine. It took two hours, which I squeezed in before dawn. Three mornings a week I'd rise at three-thirty and ride the university streetcar to the St. Paul campus. That after-midnight service was called the "Owl," and I

got to know it far too well.

One freezing January morning I stupidly left my overcoat on a seat outside the animal house. When I came out, it was gone. For the rest of the winter I had only a thin jacket and my varsity sweater. I joked about my carelessness, but Margaret worried I was going to get sick.

Truth be told, I did too. Surviving a Minnesota winter without an overcoat seemed suicidal. But, though very cold and very miserable, I fortunately stayed healthy.

At the time the jacket was lost, he could not know that the winter ahead would deliver 36 consecutive days with sub-zero lows, including one that will plunge to 66 degrees of frost (minus 34°F).

1936-1937

Forester

During the spring of 1936, around the time of his 22nd birthday, Norm realized he either must find a job or drop out of school. To Margaret Gibson he wondered idly whether his practical forestry skills might secure him employment during the coming summer.

Margaret considered it a grand possibility. On a typewriter borrowed from another girl in her apartment house she pounded out letters to Forest Service field offices nationwide. Night after night.

That was much more than Norm had in mind. "I'm just a junior," he said, "No one will hire me."

Margaret replied that it was worth a try, and when slipping each letter into the mailbox at the Dinkytown Post Office on 4th Street SE she kissed it good luck . . . 55 kisses in all.

Then with the gullibility of greenhorns, they awaited a glut of responses.

In the outcome there was only one: The U.S. Forest Service field office in New Haven Connecticut would pay $100 a month for three months work. He could come when ready.

Following finals in May, Norm hitchhiked eastwards toward the great Atlantic. His spirits were high: by the time school started in September he'd have a whole $300!

His maroon sweater with the big gold "M" advertised his university connection, and netted him free rides. He made Connecticut in three days, despite the 30 mph highway speed limit and the two-lane roads that writhed around every hill and wriggled through every town.

The Northeastern Forest Experiment Station was located on the Yale University campus and its director, Edward Behre [BEAR-AH], assigned

45

him to a research forest 90 miles up the Connecticut River Valley.

Then Behre handed over the bus fare, and, with a reassuring handshake, a friendly grin and a cheery wave, dispatched this fledgling forester to the extreme northwest corner of Massachusetts.

On arriving at Williamstown in the beautiful Berkshire Hills Borlaug was alone with his first command. Despite being only 22 years old, he'd been assigned two local men paid by a federal program for out-of-work adults, and two Boston boys sponsored by the Civilian Conservation Corps.

Managing those CCC youths was especially gratifying. Though having almost completed their teen years, they were savoring the wonder of being employed, of being wanted, and of being away from the folks – all for the first time.

He and the four coworkers were required to repair a run-down hill tract recently deeded to the Forest Service. Formerly a scenic showcase, the Hopkins Forest was centered on a manor house with at least ten fireplaces and rooms that seemed to follow one another forever. But by the time Norm arrived the grand structure was suffering.

Back in 1924 the owner's widow, Theresa Hopkins, had moved away. Lacking children, she'd deeded the property to nearby Williams College. Sadly, she also sealed the house so tight that by Norm's time moisture and mold had wrought its ruin. During those twelve years, the foundations had caved and the once beautiful show home had been condemned.

The four square miles of farm and forest surrounding the sagging central feature were hardly more promising. After a dozen years of abandonment, it was a wreck of rotting fences and riotous foliage.

The only safe accommodations were in a carriage house. Norm and the boys occupied what had previously been the hayloft over the horse stalls.

As one corner of the estate belonged to three states, Behre envisioned the Forest Service developing the place as a regional field station. For the cleanup operation he'd provided a surveyor's transit and six sets of hand tools.

To extract order from this messy manor Norm and the crew inventoried the vegetation, planted hundreds of white pines to foil erosion, and laid out sites for tree-growth trials. They also drew a map highlighting the different land forms and began a boundary survey.

All this occupied June, July and August. Then, just as Norm was preparing to pack his bag for the return to Minnesota, Ed Behre called from New Haven and asked him to stay on three more months. Norm was of two minds because the new academic year was about to start, but an extra $300 during Depression days was a treasure too tempting to deny. Devil be damned; he'll delay his studies!

Ed Behre then mentioned he was sending a second forester . . . one who'd just received a Masters from the University of California.

This was doubly disconcerting news because Norm remained an undergraduate, and a mere junior at that. In the upshot, though, Merlin ["Dick"] Dickerman neither pulled rank nor resented reporting to a minor partner:

> Dick and I had a great time. We shared the sleeping loft above the barn attached to the carriage house. Our accommodations were so poor that to this day I feel sorry for the horses who'd once occupied the barn downstairs. Its walls were so drafty the snow blew through and piled up in the stalls. Some even swirled up through the ceiling and infiltrated our quarters on the upper story.
>
> The addition of Dick gave us a six-man squad, and together we finished a topographical map as well as a vegetation map highlighting the different plants in the Hopkins Forest. Our major achievement, though, was the boundary survey.
>
> The group got good at surveying: hacking through the under-growth, setting up the transit, and pegging out the lines. By happenstance, the last stretch was a long steep slope that ran right up to the intersection of Massachusetts, Vermont and New York. That point, belonging to three states, was so submerged in tangled undergrowth that I'm sure no one had seen it since the 1800s.
>
> On the morning of the survey's final day Dick bet me that we wouldn't come within three feet of the "Tristate Corner."
>
> However, in clearing the last bit of bush we uncovered a five-foot-tall granite cairn erected in British times. And the line my transit indicated was less than *two feet* off.
>
> That was a great day, made even greater by the bottle of bourbon Dick conceded. In 1936, that meant more than you'd think. The constitutional prohibition against liquor sales had been repealed and for the first time in our adult lives we could buy liquor legally.
>
> The Jack Daniels we shared that evening seemed like ambrosia. Yes, we'd found the secret spot where three states met; more important, though, we were free to toast our discovery!

Come December his six months stint was up. He took the bus back down the Connecticut River Valley. In New Haven, he picked up his magnificent paycheck. Then he headed out on highway 34, thumbing his way westward. The maroon sweater with the big gold "M" again worked its magic and got him free rides as he wended the roads that wandered toward Saude.

Arriving home in time for Christmas, he discovered the Borlaug place transformed. Civilization had finally colonized the Norwegian enclave.

This surprise was thanks to a novel partnership between the farmers, the Feds, and the power companies. Since 1933 this three-way self-help operation had strung wires into farms across the American countryside. The farmers erected the poles and wired up their own districts and their own houses. The Rural Electrification Administration supplied wire, poles, transformers, insulators and the rest. And the power companies supplied the electricity at reduced rates.

During 1936 area farmers had wired the district for electricity. Thanks to this amazing collaboration Norm's parents and sisters had left the ancient world behind. Clara Borlaug no longer needed a mountain of wood: the wood-fueled stove and the washboard had gone the way of the work horse. On Mondays, she washed clothes with water that — quite incredibly — flowed hot from the tap. A real bath had been installed to replace the old tin tub that only made Saturday night appearances. A sewing machine mended and made clothes. Portable heaters warmed rooms to meet the desires of the moment (luxury unimaginable). And radio teased and eased the mind before bedtime.

The effect on Norm is hard to recreate. In the last seven years, he'd seen lives mirroring those of Caesar's serfs made over not just with trucks, cars and concrete highways, but also with abundant food thanks to fertilizer, farm machinery and improved seed. Now electricity has completed the magnificent makeover, and made life grand.

Early in January 1937, refreshed in mind and with a fortune resting easy in his pocket Norm left home and hitchhiked back to Minneapolis. With all his newfound wealth he could control his own destiny. He thereby quit working for tuition chits, though he continued serving meals to sorority sisters for "all he can eat."

He even treated Margaret to occasional movies. During his six-month absence she had risen to become Assistant Proofreader for Independent Press, a small publisher of books, magazines, pamphlets and folders. When they snatched a few hours together the couple sometimes talked of the future, but he decided to secure his profession before taking the relationship further. That seemed to make sense: the economy remained distressed and not even $600 could last forever.

As to wrestling, it was a pleasure to find that he was still listed as a member of the varsity squad. This was a signal honor because in two years Bartelma had worked wonders. The squad now competed with Big Ten and Big Six wrestling powers. One upcoming contest promised to be a clash for the ages: the University of Iowa was coming to town!

Knowing that the reigning national champion presented an extraordinary challenge, Coach Bart assigned Norm to a lower-than-normal weight class, hoping to impart a strength advantage. "You'll have to starve yourself," he explained; "spend hours in the sweatbox and drink nothing for the last two days."

Cutting weight like that proved agonizing. The sight and scent of the heavenly repasts he served young women, who often left their portions untouched, made it worse.

Finally, his craving overcame his common sense:

> I waited tables at the sorority but scarcely ate or drank a thing — not even coffee. Handling food was sure hard, but my mind was fixed on the scales at the gym. And the damn things weren't cooperating. After the third day I stopped drinking water.
>
> That evening Margaret and I took a walk together, and she later told Scott [Pauley] I'd been extremely irritable.
>
> Early on the afternoon of the University of Iowa meet I spent an hour in the sweatbox. Bartelma came by and joked I was idling my time away while the others were hard at training. To me, there seemed nothing funny about it. For four days I hadn't eaten a decent meal, and the brass weight on the scales said 136. . . . I stared at it in disbelief: Oh hell, still a pound to go!
>
> Right then, one of the other wrestlers put his hand on my arm. "Let's see how you've done, Norm."
>
> Without even being aware, I swung round with a fist at the ready. "Take your hands off me or I'll break your arm!" I was about to smash his face when Bartelma stepped between us. "Take it easy; take it easy," he said, opening the sweatbox door and pushing me toward the showers.
>
> Standing under the cold water I was overcome by shame. "I'm sorry," I told the coach. "I behaved badly."
>
> He replied in soothing tones: "It's understandable," he said, "Don't worry. . . . it's over now."
>
> I went back, sweated away the last pound, and won my bout.
>
> The win brought no pleasure, however. At the following buffet I

wolfed down a mountain of food but was too troubled to rejoice. It should have been a festive occasion; we'd scored an improbable victory over the reigning champs. But I left early. Had to get away.

Margaret was living in a small apartment near mine, and as we walked home I told what had happened: "A friend just laid a hand on my arm, and I went berserk," I said.

"You know, a hungry man can be as violent as a hungry beast!"

E arly in 1937 the Forest Service offered Norm a summer position as a firewatcher in Idaho. He was then in the first half of his senior year and, although the job required no special preparation, he took the National Junior Forestry Civil Service Examination to prove his commitment to forestry. His score was among Minnesota's highest.

Thus the day after finals ended in May, he and Scott Pauley headed west in Scott's decrepit old Dodge. Scott was headed for Montana's Flathead National Forest; Norm was to report to the Idaho National Forest, a vast wilderness within Idaho's self-proclaimed "Inland Empire."

In Butte, Montana they split up, agreeing to meet in West Yellowstone three months hence. Before heading home, they'd take a peek at Old Faithful.

The Idaho National Forest was managed from McCall, a mountain hamlet bounded on one side by a gorgeous lake and on all others by tree-clad slopes. It seemed like paradise, except that people in paradise would surely have demanded sidewalks. McCall's main street was lined with the raised wooden-planking only wild-west movies still approved of.

In this quaint and woodsy spot, the Forest Service ran a firefighter boot camp. Veteran rangers trained Norm and five other youths to extinguish blazes, maintain telephone lines and radio links, and survive alone in the wilderness.

After two weeks dishing out hard knocks and hard lessons, and repeatedly probing for psychological frailties, the crusty drill instructors ignited small blazes and assigned a student to each. Norm happened to ace his trial by fire.

Finally, compasses and maps were passed out and the trainees were dumped individually in separate sectors of the wilds. Norm was the only one to make it back unaided.

A day later he faced three of the hard-bitten foresters he later called "shellbacks." They were very demanding, but they were also practical, positive and properly prepared for the unforeseen:

I was put through quite a grilling. The questions mostly focused on moral issues and mental stability, which came as a surprise. But my answers must have been satisfactory. When the session was over the senior ranger stared at me: "Borlaug," he said, "we're assigning you to the most critical post in the system. Our whole fire-protection network will depend on you."

Perhaps understandably, Henry Shank, the Idaho National Forest supervisor, failed to explain that Norm would occupy the most isolated lookout in the lower 48. Out there, this 23-year-old novice will be 45 miles from a trail, still further from a road. For three months he'll survive by his own wits. He'll be responsible for protecting a seemingly limitless forest domain. And he'll be beyond any kind of help.

Three days later he was driven to Big Creek, where Dan LeVan, the fire dispatcher, worked out of a tiny ranger station. LeVan provided a horse and dispatched him into the nation's biggest "Primitive Area," which stretched to the north and east. As guide, Norm had an almost mute packer on another horse. Three much-burdened, complaining, very loud mules toted his supplies.

The little expedition worked its way through the massive ranges ringing Big Creek. There being neither roads nor trails they picked a path tree by tree, streambed by streambed and mountain pass by mountain pass.

On the afternoon of the second day they reached the northeast slope of Cold Mountain. Here, high above the wilderness' heart stood the only structures in the whole vast region. Amid a scraggly grove of pines was a tiny log cabin. A few yards behind that stood an outhouse. And a hundred yards farther up the slope aluminum poles soared skyward, holding up Norm's designated workplace: a metal cube seven by seven by seven feet.

That evening, having stored the supplies on the cabin shelves, he climbed the ladder that zigzagged upwards between the aluminum legs and pushed up the trapdoor in the floor of the metal box in which he'd spend the next 100 days.

Though barely big enough to stretch out in, the workspace seemed expansive because he was 70-feet high in the sky and walls of windows commanded endless views all round.

Dominating the interior was a table fitted with a compass rose and something like a sniper-rifle sight that swiveled. Attached to the table's pedestal was a crank-type telephone. And on the floor was a tiny footstool with feet wrapped in insulator glass. During electrical storms he'll be inside Idaho's finest lightning rod and has to stand on that footstool to avoid getting fried as hundred-million-volt charges take a shortcut to the ground through the metal around him.

F rom his perch 8084 feet above sea level he could look to the far side of the Chamberlain Basin, a vast tree-covered alpine meadow tucked into the core of the Continental Divide. The scenery stretching to the limits of sight was his to protect:

> My duty was to watch for smoke and phone in any sighting to the Fire Dispatcher at Big Creek Ranger Station. Then, if Dan LeVan instructed, I'd go out and deal with whatever was causing the smoke *by myself*.
>
> Sending me out to fight a forest fire may seem foolish, but I was the only trained person within the Primitive Area. Helicopters and smoke jumpers were unknown in 1937. Thus, no other immediate help was available.
>
> Crazy as it may seem, I was required to keep the fire controlled *for several days*. The Forest Service needed that much time to round up a crew, get them into the Chamberlain Basin by horse, and keep them fed and supplied by mule.

Next morning, with barely a murmur, the muleteer vanished. Norm was now alone amidst the vast stillness *for the next three months*. He must learn to survive single-handed. He must find water. He must clean himself, his clothes and his cabin. And he must cook camp style:

> Overall, my diet was simple: canned meats, beans and vegetables as well as bacon and a few basics such as flour and cornmeal. Mostly I lived on baking-powder biscuits, made each morning in the oven of the wood-stove in the cabin. After suffering through weeks of those, an urge for fresh bread became an obsession. I cut off a portion of my block of Fleishmann's Yeast and added it to the flour and water mix. Then, I kneaded the dough and left it overnight as Grandmother Emma had done. It was a total failure. The bread was like a slightly soggy brick; the altitude and the nighttime cold inhibited the yeast. I went back to making powder biscuits and eventually ate so many I got to hate the damn things, and cut back on eating.
>
> An old prospector named Charles Mahan saved my sanity. "Matty," as we called him, had built a cabin in the hills across the

Chamberlain Basin and the Forest Service had installed a telephone so he could report any smoke he might see.

The phone was strictly for emergency use, but Matty was lonely and called a different lookout each evening for a chat. "How ya doin' up thar?" he'd say in his cracked old-timer voice. When I complained about the bread, he told me to get a pencil and he'd explain what prospectors do in the high country.

Soon I had a jar of batter warming beside the stove. By continually topping it up with yeast, flour and water I kept it in a high state of fermentation. To make bread I'd ladle out a few big spoonfuls and knead them into the dough. The result was sourdough. Up there, above eight thousand feet, the bread still didn't rise fully, but it sure tasted great.

Norm quickly appreciated why he'd been probed for psychological frailties. But after those days of self-doubt he grew more comforted than concerned. The place — so massive, majestic and mind-bending — became like home. Due to its splendors, surprises and scary denizens, however, he'd never ever underestimate the power of nature. He was, after all, sharing the territory of rattlers, mountain lions, bears and lightning bolts.

During the first month the days were cool and damp, and might even have been boring, had he not needed to clamber down a thousand feet to the bottomlands and repair the winter-ravaged telephone line. Once that was working he had the voice of the fire dispatcher beyond the massive mountains for reassurance.

Dan LeVan's evening phone calls were a special comfort in July when the thunderheads appeared. These black-hearted castles of cumulus darkened his world and loosed liquid as if a plug had been pulled.

Early in August the skies cleared, temperatures rose, and the air turned thirsty enough to suck up all the rain before the soil could get a sip.

The fire season had begun. From his eyrie atop the seven-story metal poles Norm watched charcoal-colored cloudscapes drift toward him, shooting hundred-million-volt sparks onto the natural powder keg he had to protect.

It was far from comforting:

Many an afternoon, I'd watch as a dry thunderstorm crept toward me. One memorable one started eighteen "smokes" . . . I counted each with mounting dread.

Smokes were low-intensity ground fires that grazed on leaf litter beneath the trees. Some lived for days before dying discreetly. The eighteen Norm watched were a long way off, and he was infinitely thankful when they learned to quit smoking on their own.

Had they been closer he'd have had to take action. The trick was to keep the fire on the ground. The main trees, such as pines and spruce, had bare trunks and didn't mind embers creeping through the neighborhood. Alpine firs, however, had foliage that swept low enough to entice an ember to a higher calling. Norm's challenge was to work ahead of the skulking cinders, lopping off every fir limb that might excite ambition. This was critical because once a fire got the taste of dry treetops it could not be stopped. A single sagging fir branch could induce an inferno in the forest crown.

To prevent such a catastrophe he had only a special hand tool whose head had both axe and adze. It was called a Pulaski.

By mid-August, summer's end was in sight and things had gone so well he was dreaming of Margaret, Minnesota and meeting Scott in West Yellowstone. So when Dan LeVan phoned and asked him to stay *three more weeks* it hit both heart and head like a hammer.

But Norm knew that the fire dispatcher faced disaster. For days a towering plume of smoke had been billowing up from the neighboring watershed. And during their evening phone conversations he'd learned about the tragedy playing out beneath that smoke.

For the first time the Forest Service had relied on aircraft. Not for two more years would it test the suicidal notion of parachuting men into a wildfire's path. Here, it sent crews into Acorn Butte Valley on horseback and parachuted their food, water and supplies from the sky.

It didn't work. Most packages burst on delivery; the rest disappeared amid the underbrush. At the time LeVan asked for Norm's help he had 200 men battling a blaze without food, water or medical supplies.

Norm therefore remained at his post. But the days dragged until LeVan gave the all clear. That was on the evening of September 12, a Sunday.

Sunrise, September 13 Norm stepped from the cabin to fill his canteen at the seep he'd found nearby. This was a truly glorious morning — the one in which he'd begin the long march home.

Then, far off in the northern dawn shadows, he spied a curling wreath of ruin. Racing up the steps to the observatory, he swiveled the compass platform, took a quick azimuth, cranked the phone, and reported the bearing. Next, following LeVan's instructions, he headed out toward the plume of white with his shovel, daypack, canteen, and Pulaski, not to mention fluttering fears.

The smoke was miles off, and reaching it turned into something akin to a trek through treacle. For almost six hours he scrambled over the Chamberlain Basin's treed bottom, hoping he was heading in the right direction. Finally he smelled smoke and climbed a spruce. Though even at 40 feet nothing was visible through the tall timber, he could sense the direction the smell was coming from.

Rangers at the boot-camp had not taught tree climbing, and for good reason. Norm had about six feet to go to reach safety when the branch under his left hand broke, tumbling him to the ground, legs doubled-up beneath his body. This was serious, deadly serious. Anyone incapacitated here might never be found, other perhaps than by fire, thirst or a grizzly.

Fortunately, he landed in a pad of needles. Shaken but still sharp-witted, he dusted himself off, and proceeded toward the smell souring the sky up ahead.

At last he located the source: a stand of Engleman spruce that was relatively sparse and almost devoid of alpine firs. The fire was hugging the ground and creeping northeastward. Hustling back and forth in advance of its leading edge, he hacked off any fir frond that might excite a spark.

Through the afternoon he struggled with the flames, the firs and the fluttering fears. Then at about 4 o'clock, a ranger arrived on horseback from the far side of the Chamberlain Basin.

The pair then turned from defense to offense, scratching little firebreaks in the needles ahead of the greedy glow. When the final flickering threats seemed destined to die they patrolled the scorched perimeter seeking places where an eager ember might effect an escape.

At about 7 o'clock the ranger suddenly remembered Norm's situation: "Hey," he said, "you'd better get going."

That curt dismissal came as a huge relief. Racing against the sunset, Norm scampered back to Cold Mountain, grabbed his belongings, filled his canteen and, as the sky fell, turned his back on his summer abode.

By the lingering light he headed down one of the spidery drainage lines traced on his map, intimidated neither by the gathering night nor by the massive mountain range between him and Big Creek.

For a while inky darkness made it impossible to step out safely. Near bursting with frustration, he rested up, sitting astride a boulder.

Then a full moon rose to light the land, and he moved onward, hopping from rock to shadowy rock back down the now-dry streambeds, through the mountain passes, and finally picking a path tree by tree.

Driving him onward was the fact that he should already be in West Yellowstone; that fear of letting his friend down was so all-consuming he pressed on through the night, stumbling into Big Creek Ranger Station about nine the next morning.

Imagine the apparition that appeared out of nowhere: eyes bloodshot, feet blistered, clothes grimy — to say nothing of the stink of smoke and sweat. Ranger LeVan took one glance and barked: "Hell, you go to the crick and take a bath. We'll get you some breakfast; then you're going to bed. I don't care where you have to go, you're not going today!"

Though fagged in body and brain, Norm was furious at being sent to bed like a naughty boy while his friend waited in Wyoming. He spent the day in a cot, but in anger rather than slumber.

Next morning, he grabbed a ride with a young cadet, and fled toward the liberating sensibleness of civilization.

In McCall, however, events took a surprising turn. Hank Shank revealed that a Junior Forester position was coming available in January. It was his if he wanted it.

That changed everything. He instantly calmed down and without a second's hesitation accepted the offer. A delighted Henry Shank, informed his new recruit he could start right after graduation.

This was a crucial decision. Great Depression be damned! He had a job; he had a future; four months hence he'll be working right here in McCall. His first day on the Forest Service payroll would be January 15, 1938. Before then, he merely needed to complete his last quarter of college.

And he nurses a secret hope that a certain someone will be by his side sharing the endless joy of Idaho's Inland Empire.

The meeting in West Yellowstone proved uneventful. Scott had also been delayed, and had just arrived. Forsaking the chance to see Old Faithful, they lit out immediately for Minnesota.

Getting across Montana and South Dakota took an age. Scott's decrepit Dodge couldn't top 25 mph. Finally they creaked into Minneapolis late in the afternoon. Norm took the streetcar straight to Independent Press in the Warehouse District, not far from the scene of the milk-truck riot.

Standing outside the building at 89 10th Street S, he surprised Margaret as she emerged. Grasping her hand he explained he'd landed the perfect job. His career was settled. There was no reason to wait any longer. "Will you marry me?" he said.

Having neither money nor any desire for a fancy wedding, they accepted Margaret's brother, Bill Gibson's offer of the sitting room in his house in the nearby suburb of Robbinsdale. There being no need for delay, they scheduled the event for the coming Friday, September 24.

Norm phoned his father and mother, but with the harvest in full swing they couldn't come. His sisters Palma and Charlotte, however, said they'd take the train.

On that Friday Margaret quit work at noon and treated herself to the luxury of a hairdresser. Bill Gibson's wife Lois took her shopping to complete her trousseau. And at seven that evening the Lutheran minister was at the front door. Behind him stood Norm clad in a suit right off the rack at the local haberdasher. Scott Pauley was best man.

In the simple room with its couch and chairs and flowery wallpaper, the two exchanged vows. It was brief, quiet, tender.

After a super meal put on by Lois, Bill drove them to Margaret's apartment in Dinkytown. And next day, Norm hauled his meager possessions over from the Kearsarge Apartments, just four blocks away.

Honeymoon? They'd soon honeymoon a lifetime in Idaho. For the four months between times Margaret's apartment would do just fine. But he nonetheless promised her a honeymoon when such an indulgence would be possible.

Well, that's what they told themselves. But even as a temporary shelter, this single room — containing a table, two chairs, a daybed, a stove and a sink in the corner — was hardly enticing, despite the snappy curtains, decorative crockery and vases of fall flowers Margaret had added.

Less than two weeks earlier Norm had been alone in a seven-foot cube seven stories high, and his companions had included million-volt bolts of electricity from the sky. With a guilty grin he settled into domestic bliss. What did it matter that the bathroom was down the corridor and shared with another family?

The future was now plain. His last few Bachelors courses would occupy the next three months — October, November, December. Then they'd head to their private piece of the Promised Land.

By the final quarter of his senior year he'd dropped in and out of school often enough to scramble his coursework beyond rational recognition. "Borlaug," Dean Cheyney said jokingly, though with a note of anguish in his voice, "your schedule is so loused up I can't understand the first thing about it. Why don't you either go to work or come to university?"

Forest pathology was among the dean's top worries. By taking extra courses Norm had made up his missing credits but now, merely three months from graduation, he was just getting around to this tree-disease course designed specifically for sophomores.

Then one afternoon when the semester had less than six weeks to run something strange occurred. That particular lab section started out quite uneventfully. The professor distributed thin sections of wood cut from a diseased pine and told the students to sketch the blotchy blue stains a fungal intruder had pushed out between the tree cells.

Then as the class members peered down their microscopes, a dignified-looking gent ambled in. Neither tall nor imposing, he wore a commonplace tweed jacket and carried a pipe loosely in one hand. His face, though tinged with grayness around the temples, was handsomely good-humored. Yet, for all his downhome demeanor, the man radiated an aura of authority. This power emanated notably from a piercing gaze and a voice that stabbed like a steel dagger.

Actually, with every student eye glued to a microscope, the intruder attracted little notice until he stopped at the sophomore next to Norm. Peering over the boy's shoulder, he started firing questions . . . not about the blue fungus, but about the wood. What species of pine was it? Why did this part stain and not that? What is this cell? What is that?

Fortunately Norm was ignored, but his young companion quickly collapsed like a rag doll. And no wonder: Elvin Charles Stakman [STAKE-man or STAKE for short] was a campus colossus. Dean of the Department of Plant Pathology, he was renowned for discovering great things about wheat disease as well as for daring students.

A month after that episode, on a day when Norm was *just two weeks* from heading for the western wilderness, he noticed an announcement tacked to a campus bulletin board. The Sigma Xi Society was sponsoring a special lecture entitled "The Little Enemies that Destroy our Crops." This same professor Stakman would discuss rust diseases affecting cereals.

Norm had no interest in cereals, yet he decided to attend. Certain rusts affect pine trees; perhaps he might pick up some useful insight. This casual decision was a mere matter of chance. Only years later would he realize that it was the pivot about which everything turned.

Stakman's subject was wheat stem rust. That fungus, Stakman said, had felled food supplies as far back as the great plagues of the Old Testament. Even in the 1930s it still could not be stopped. Every August saw wheat farmers scanning their fields for any hint of its presence. A reddish look and sour smell were harbingers of failure, and perhaps foreclosure and financial ruin.

He referred to the 1916 rust epidemic — the one that forced the Borlaugs to consume Southern food.

He reached beyond science to portray humanity's dependence on plant health. Hunger, he warned, was humankind's oldest companion; every society lived within its shadow. Historically, food shortages had been the worst killers. All too often hunger's weapon of choice had been crop diseases, and the greatest of those was wheat stem rust.

Even in modern 1937 this scourge remained the protean enemy, forever changing its chromosomal clothes to circumvent whatever variety wheat farmers planted. Though then quiescent, rust was merely awaiting the right moment to reappear. Somewhere in the years ahead the fickle fungus would slash the food supply as it had so many times before. Preventing that should be people's greatest priority.

"Rust is a shifty, changing, constantly evolving enemy," Stakman thundered during his peroration. "We can never lower our guard. Rusts are relentless, voracious destroyers of man's food, and we must fight them by all means open to science!"

As Norm listened, his imagination soared. In later years he commonly referred back to the scene in the cavernous Northrop Auditorium:

Stakman lit up the skies that night!

That evening while Margaret cooked supper Norm quoted passages from his notes:
"Rust is a shifty, changing, constantly evolving enemy."

"We can never lower our guard."

"Rusts are relentless, voracious destroyers of man's food, and we must fight them by all means open to science."

"Biological science, crop disease, soil infertility, human population and world hunger, all are interwoven."

This cosmic vision brought to mind the possibility that he himself might try to suppress crop disease. He mentioned the idea to Margaret, but they both knew it was a flight of fancy. Within the month they'd be heading west on the Northern Pacific Railway.

As to the bargain struck with Hank Shank in Idaho, Norm held to his part. He'd made up the classes missed because of the three weeks' wait in the wilderness. He completed his degree on time. The Department of Forestry awarded his BS at the scheduled ceremony on December 18, 1937.

His progress seemed hard to believe. Nine years back, Cousin Sina had given him the chance for a high-school education. Now he was the first of his family to have earned a college degree. He'd become a forester. He had a wife to support. And in a month or so he and Margaret would reside in the western woods.

Everything had come out for the best.

1938-1944

Problem Solver

The year 1938 had barely begun when the Borlaugs' world turned upside down. That day Norm stood in the apartment staring at the letter in his hand. Postmarked "McCall," it revealed that unexpected budgetary problems had arisen; funds had been cut; the Junior Forester position could no longer be offered. Could he hold off coming to Idaho until June first?

He felt his heart fall to his feet. What could he do now? College was over; the Depression was not. He was broke. And now January's rent money was due – a whole $30!

Everything in the young couple's mutual compact seemed to have shattered. For days they discussed their plight without finding an answer. Finally, it became clear that they had to stay put. At least Margaret has a job in Minneapolis. He took the decision hard:

> As a breadwinner, I'd failed before even getting a chance to begin.

Margaret tried to ease the wounded pride. There must be other jobs around, she said; all he needed was something until June. Then in a flash of inspiration she recalled his enthusiasm for the Sigma Xi lecture. "That professor you told me about . . . couldn't you take courses with him?"

She laughed away his doubts. "Oh come now, Norman," she said. "I'll go on working. We can make do on my wages."

With no other option, a very dispirited and very downcast forestry student approached the cereal scientist who just weeks before had crumpled his classmate like a rag doll.

Years would pass before Norm could properly appreciate Stakman's contributions. As a young forester in January 1938, he resented the fact that cereal research dominated the Plant Pathology Department. But at that moment, thanks to Margaret's urging, he approached its most daunting proponent.

Despite an open door policy, Stakman seldom allowed the lower life forms a sympathetic hearing. Leaning forward on his office chair, as if on the point of rising, he heard-out the nervous youth. For long minutes he remained rigid, fingering his pipe but otherwise unmoving. Then, fixing the frightened supplicant with his birdlike gaze, he shook his head and loosed a series of blasts:

"Fill in a few months between jobs, Borlaug? That's a pretty poor reason for staying in graduate school.

"You should know better. "You'll have to get more serious than that!"

There was a pause while these words were digested. Then the steely voice hardened and the lacerating sentences continued:

"What exactly do you want to study?

"Do you have any idea?

"What is your career goal?"

Norm explained that he sought to stay in forest pathology.

"Look here, young man, you do that and you'll lock yourself into a single profession. You'll lock yourself out of everything else."

Stakman paused again; he was shaking his head with resignation, almost disgust.

"You're young . . . keep your options open . . . USE A LITTLE COMMON SENSE!

"Get a broad education, and leave the specialization until later.

"Forgo forestry and study crop science.

"Take plant pathology and round that out with agronomy, genetics and soil science.

"Then you'll have a breadth of perspective that'll serve you well in your future. And you can always return to forestry should you want to."

Finally Stakman threw in his kicker: "Put away this idea of taking higher education in dribs and drabs!" He jerked his pipe stem toward the perplexed plaintiff. "Aim for your Master's degree and I'll go to bat for you. Play about, and you must go somewhere else to find help!"

Norm gasped; had he heard right? Was he being offered a job? How could that be? This was the Great Depression, and this man knew nothing about him. They'd never met before!

He'd never considered going for a graduate degree. The idea was scary. But such an offer could not be refused during those dismal days when dollars had disappeared like dinosaurs. Quickly he nodded assent.

Norm slouched home to tell Margaret that they'd not get to live in Idaho's Inland Empire with all its wonders, wildlife and woods. It was very sad, but he had no alternative. What he did have was a job . . . and two more years of study.

Stakman's assistantship paid tuition and provided a modest stipend. In turn, Norm spent 10 hours a week peering down a microscope barrel at bits of greasy glass and counting how many rust spores he saw.

Each spore was about the diameter of a human hair — a red blob cloaked in fine spines that through the microscope looked like a microbial pincushion.

It was only then that Norm came to appreciate the Stakman's stem-rust discoveries.

During several decades Stakman had pulled off four major feats.

His first discovery came from assaying the greasy microscope slides. Each spring for almost two decades, this prestigious professor sent hundreds of boxes — each containing 24 Vaseline-smeared microscope slides — to every state from Texas to North Dakota. Most ended up in rural grain elevators, and during the prime rust period the operators hung out a slide a day. Other boxes went to Army- and Postal Service pilots, who held the slimy slides up in their open cockpits, noting down the date, altitude and location.

Particles blowing by stuck to the Vaseline, and back in St. Paul Stakman's students counted the rust spores. It was tedious but it produced a day-by-day image of where rust was and in what amount. Over time, they'd shown that wheat's greatest enemy annually migrated to Mexico, just like ducks and geese. The great rivers of high-altitude wind that each fall flow from Canada to Mexico and each summer flow from Mexico back to Canada carried clouds of stem rust.

In his second feat he'd shown that rust was a muddle of over 300 strains. And those genetic variants used their winter playground in Mexico to mix and mate and evolve ever nastier weapons for draining wheat's will to live. Thus the spore showers raining down on North America each summer had constantly changing infectious powers.

In his third effort he'd created wheat varieties with the exquisitely rare, mysterious and almost mystical ability to deny the microbe access to its innermost tissues. His most recent creation, a variety called Newthatch, was even then ushering in a new era of reliability for the world's top food crop. No wheat plant could resist every rust race, but Newthatch thwarted the four most devastating races and was standing tall amid trillions of the worst spores raining down during the 1930s.

Stakman's fourth contribution was to meld his former students into a cooperative distant-early-warning force located in wheat lands around the world. His several dozen students from the Americas, Europe, Australia, Africa, and China remained ever alert for the reddish look and sour smell that indicated rust. When such signs appeared, the one on the spot identified the rust strain, and the others donated seed of any wheat they thought might save the threatened crop.

The professor and his loyal students were thus insuring the health of the food supply, nay of civilization, and they did it as a voluntary contribution solely out of respect for each other and for humanity.

As his Master's thesis topic Norm investigated the red stain commonly seen in the wood of box elder trees. Following Stakman's iron-clad demand he took classes in genetics, plant pathology, plant physiology, and cytology. He also took a memorable course in plant breeding. The professor, Herbert Kendall ["HK"] Hayes, emphasized that plant breeders *must develop their crop in the place where it will be grown* and nowhere but *the place where it will be grown.*

Being so new to the subject, Norm never questioned that general rule of thumb that crops were location-limited and had to be bred for each place and each planting season.

During the remainder of 1938 and the first half of 1939 the young couple enjoyed domesticity. Both had jobs. Margaret remained a proof reader at Independent Press. Norm not only earned his tuition by peering down Stakman's microscopes, he conformed to Stakman's demand that he *"commit to being a* proper *graduate student."*

Then in June 1939 a puzzling letter arrived from the nation's capital. There was fear in the phraseology. The U.S. Government needed experienced forest-firefighters. Norm was requested to again man the fire-lines.

This missive caused much mischief. He talked it over with Stakman as well as with Clyde Christensen, the professor overseeing his box-elder research. Finally, following much high-level deliberation, the U of M agreed to let Norman Borlaug put his studies on hold *yet once more*. Their approval, however, came very grudgingly; this rackety Iowan had solemnly pledged to stay a proper graduate student; now he was proving unreliable all over again. Why did he have to be so maddening?

For Norm and Margaret the choice proved maddening too. They'd been married less than two years and the U.S. Forest Service wanted his services *for six whole months*. After they'd spent a week agonizing over whether he should stay or go, Margaret told him to go. It was, after all, his country that was calling.

His country had called because the previous September one of history's most violent hurricanes had descended on New England. Before then, the region had been renowned for its tree cover. Now almost 300 million century-old oaks, elms, pines, beeches, birches, maples and walnuts had been uprooted and heaped across five states. The situation seemed hopeless. Workers couldn't reach, let alone unravel, the tangles of branches, trunks and roots that were braided and knotted together. And now in 1939 every passing summer month raised the possibility of blazes breaking out amid the sun-dried tinder.

Though New England threatened to become a raging inferno, it had no trained forest firefighters, a breed unique to the west. That is why the Feds had requested a rackety Minnesota graduate student's help.

In June he reported to the Forest Service office at Gardner, Massachusetts and was dispatched to Winchendon, a likable town hard upon the New Hampshire border. There, he was designated "Foreman of Laborers" at the hundred-man camp known as DA-14.

As before, he had to convert a mix of older workers and jobless youths into crews capable of clearing and cutting fire-lines through trashed trees. Chainsaws being unknown and tractors unavailable, everything had to be done with axes and two-man hand saws.

The 25-year-old student again bonded with his workers, some of whom were much older and some much younger than he. The bonding was helped along by his evening wrestling lessons and contests in which he sometimes yelled out challenges like Coach Bart.

Despite the pay (less than $5 a week), harsh conditions and hard labor, the men and boys relished the work. In those hopeless and heartless times it was pure joy to have something to do, let alone something important.

The living arrangements were like those of a New England summer camp. Crews and supervisors shared army barracks, slept on cots and washed their clothes with bar soap on wooden washboards leaning like ladders into tin tubs. They were awakened each morning with a bugle call to breakfast. And their meals were served in a military-style mess.

As before, Norm reported to Forest Service professionals who, like Hank Shank, were demanding but also practical, positive and properly prepared for the unforeseen. New England's recovery, however, had been entrusted to the Works Projects Administration, whose director (Harry Hopkins) was President Roosevelt's political advisor. Accordingly, many New England camp managers had been selected for party ties rather than professionalism.

This led to friction between the professionals who knew what to do and the political appointees who didn't. The manager directing the neighboring Camp DA-13 at Ashburnham had obtained his appointment through Boston's labor bosses. The man was prickly, quirky, emotional, loud and incompetent. The fulltime foresters hated his petulance almost as much as his ineptness. Three had quit in as many months.

One afternoon Norm got a telephone call and was requested to come to Gardner right away. "Look, Borlaug," supervisor Dean Rowland said, "our patience has run out. We can't afford to lose any more foresters, but we can't fire that director because he's a political appointee. How about going over and working for him? We need someone with a calm temperament who knows what he's doing. Will you try it?"

Norm packed his kit, and moved the eight miles to Ashburnham.

He found that the site had formerly been a highway winding through a tall, dense, very beautiful forest. Now the sylvan giants were scattered like pick-up-sticks. Cleaning up that mess was a horrendous challenge, but he and the prickly boss got along fine. Norm's new crew of about 20 men and boys steadily cleared away downed debris.

Though fire was not expected, Norm divided the men into two-man crews and for an hour or so each evening put on a special training in Western firefighting methods. Two months later it proved prescient:

> It was about lunchtime, and I was in charge. My boss had gone off somewhere. Suddenly we saw smoke and then some sparks.

The situation demanded instant action. It was early October; the downed timber had been drying for over a year and all around us flames were roaring skyward like a bonfire.

Within mere minutes, the blaze exploded to encompass several acres. With a breeze from the south urging it on, there was a good chance it would consume thousands more acres. It might even get out of control and prove unstoppable.

I was out on the fire-line directing every man in sight. There were about a dozen, and we were trying to pinch off the northern front where the flame was spreading. The heat singed our faces and stung our eyes. Because my novice workers had never considered confronting anything so terrifying they were very skittish. I had visions of them running away and our worksite starting New England's Big Blowup. And I'd surely be blamed.

There was only one thing to do. We needed outside help, and rapidly. So I radioed Gardner and Winchendon.

Within minutes my boss stormed into the already chaotic scene. He'd heard my call on his own radio and was offended because I'd asked for reinforcements without his permission. He strode past me and addressed the crew, loudly countermanding my orders. It was already hotter'n Hades and a catastrophe could result if we let those leading edges get out of hand. I yelled at the crew to ignore him. And without another word I pitched in and worked like the devil.

The men looked first at him and then at me . . . and went back to deflecting the fire-line. Working side-by-side, we collectively contained the flames in a rough but steady and organized way.

That rejection of his rank left my boss livid. He was so beside himself he refused to join our fight. In fact, he stalked off and I never saw him again.

After perhaps half an hour, truckloads of new crews began arriving from Gardner and Winchendon. Soon we had maybe 50 firefighters. And by late that afternoon the flames were finally under control.

A few of us patrolled the area through the night, but thankfully the wind died at dusk and there were no flare-ups.

First thing next morning, even before snatching some sleep, I went straight to Gardner. "I've had enough," I told Dean Rowland. "I'm going back to school!"

The fall semester of 1939 was the best interlude the young couple had had. Norm completed his classwork and his investigation of the fungus that reddened box-elder wood. At the same time he taught a survey course on basic biology and natural resources at the Junior College (or General College, as it was now known). Helping out the school that had given him a second chance when he was desperate gave him great joy. He was both paying forward a debt and affirming that the yokel had made good.

Home life was flourishing too. After three years crammed into Margaret's single-room they'd moved into Thatcher Hall, a new university apartment block built to house married graduate students. Here they enjoyed *two* rooms as well as reasonable rent!

The Master's degree was awarded in St Paul in May 1940. His parents attended — outwardly bewildered, but inwardly radiant over their son's stunning success in the barbarian world beyond the Saude border.

S takman had by now softened his attitude toward the student who'd once seemed so rackety. He went so far as to urge Norm to pursue the supreme scientific degree, a doctorate. He had funds earmarked for flax and offered a scholarship.

Norm happily committed himself to flax research for the simple reason that he'd avoid rust research, which would have meant involvement with wheat, which above all, he wanted no part of. No sirree! With the rest of Stakman's students working on wheat, a recently re-treaded forester could never compete for the few job openings after graduation.

Thus in the spring of 1940 he tackled *Fusarium lini*, the fungus that had bedeviled Granddad Nels' flax plants in the 1890s. Half a century onward it still turned soils "flax-sick," finishing them for flax.

For starters, Norm established that *Fusarium lini* occurred as a muddle of races. In that regard it was not unlike wheat rust.

Then, following Stakman's precedent with wheat, he began a search for flax plants with the exquisitely rare, mysterious and almost mystical ability to deny the microbe access to their innermost tissues.

In this, his first encounter with crop disease, he seeded hundreds of flax varieties into flax-sick soil. Though the field ended up looking like a disaster scene, the handful of survivors made him happy. Despite seeming half dead, they possessed some hidden inheritance that helped them avoid total destruction. He saved their seeds and plowed in all the other dead and dying plants to concoct a super-duper flax-sick soil for the next round of the "survival of the fittest" challenge.

That fall, the St. Paul campus' Athletic Director buttonholed Norm: "I've got all these kids with nothing to do in the evenings," Marshall

Ryman said. "Let's start a wrestling program."

For the next two winters Norm coached wrestling at the University Farm School, a unique institution that allowed rural high-school grads to sample college during the winter months. Following the October harvest, students trickled into the St. Paul campus, took a handful of courses, and trotted home happy when farming's relentless demands required attention in April.

Given his own tortuous history Norm was a huge fan:

> University Farm School was a great thing. It benefited a critical portion of Minnesota's youth and did a huge amount of good. I'm still mad as hell the university abandoned it after World War II.

The fact that the University Farm School wrestling coach was unpaid did nothing to diminish his zeal. As always he relished the chance to push young people and raise their performance. "There's no damn messing around here," he yelled. "Give the best God gave you, or don't bother competing!"

His wrestlers competed against high school teams, which by then were legion. Just five years following Bartelma's arrival at the U of M, 260 high schools had embraced wrestling and the sport was part of growing up Minnesotan. Norm recalls the encounters:

> We had some good times with the Farm School squad, and even won some meets.

Though his research was not supervised by Stakman, Norm routinely participated in the professor's seminars, many of which were conducted in a field beside the Plant Pathology building in St. Paul. He began as an outsider, suspicious of everything to do with wheat. Soon, however, he caught the spirit of the man and the significance of his mission, and became a lifelong devotee:

> Looking back, I can see that Stakman's program was unique. During that era students came from across the country as well as from around the globe to study with him.
>
> Stakman did more than teach to the textbook: he produced cereal caregivers. These self-contained "general practitioners" were capable of diagnosing disease and counteracting it wherever they might be in the world. Much of their skill was learned during his outdoor seminars in which he required all of us to interpret the symptoms of scores of wheat diseases and to recommend remedies.
>
> In the fields next to the departmental building Stakman

maintained 40 acres of diseased wheat plants. It was a sort of wheat hospital ward, where he made us diagnose smut, scab, rust, blast, blight, bunt, wilt, mildew and the rest. Every Saturday afternoon the students and faculty trailed through those acres of sick and dying plants. Stopping at each one, Stakman would stimulate arguments over what we were seeing. The sessions sometimes went for hours; and sometimes got very heated.

This was his style. His laboratories and classrooms were open intellectual forums full of fire and light. He threw out sharp-edged thoughts like grindstones throw sparks. He thus illuminated young minds, but often enraged his peers; more than once the rhetoric turned so rancorous that fists got clenched in preparation for use.

Stakman's Thursday evening seminars were also amazing. In fact, they were the most stimulating and wide-ranging academic discussions I've ever attended. Since those distant days I've often said that you only had to audit his seminars to get a rounded education. Into the immediate scientific issue he integrated history, geography, current affairs, philosophy and whatever else engaged his probing, catch-all mind at that moment.

Two of the Stakman students Norm met at this time became close friends.

One was a quiet Minnesotan who was not easy to know. Although a year behind Norm, Joseph A. Rupert had begun as a forester before succumbing to Stakman's blandishments and switching to agriculture for his master's degree. Strangely, Joe and Norm had more than career path in common: they thought alike and looked alike – so much so that outsiders commonly considered them twins.

The other was a doctoral student who also studied flax. Albert H. Moseman was confident, outgoing and easy to know. He and Norm shared research findings, compared data and collaborated on experiments. Theirs was a partnership of mutual benefit — Norm's specialty being plant pathology; Moseman's being plant breeding and agronomy.

In the spring of 1941 Norm sowed his few surviving flax seeds into the doubly deadly dirt patch he'd previously concocted. A few germinated, and in midsummer he cross-pollinated their flowers to combine their different survival powers.

And at season's end in October 1941, he saved their seeds. Those second-generation survivors had gene cocktails capable of fending off multiple wilt strains. They opened a new era for the crop that then produced linseed oil and linen, but nowadays also produces flaxseed for food supplements.

Just when he was preparing to write up his doctoral dissertation he was summoned to Stakman's office. There, he found one of his former undergraduate forestry instructors, which seemed strange because he barely knew the man. Several years before, Frank Kaufert had moved up in the world to direct a biochemical laboratory at E. I. du Pont de Nemours & Company, which was somewhere way off on the East Coast.

Then things got truly weird: Kaufert explained he was returning to become Dean of Forestry. The company he was quitting had a peculiar policy of letting successful scientists nominate their own successors. He wanted to put Norm's name forward for the position he was vacating in Wilmington. Was Norm interested in going to work for a big corporation in Delaware?

This was a stunning revelation:

> I couldn't believe the incoming dean would consider me a suitable replacement for himself. That didn't seem right. But then he explained I'd control my own research and have an annual salary of $2800! On hearing that, I struggled to keep from grinning. The sum was so enormous.

Stakman offered reassurance: The flax research would be wrapped up in a month; the dissertation could be written during the evenings in Wilmington; the doctorate could be awarded next year, 1942.

Norm said he needed time to talk it over with Margaret, explaining that they'd never thought of going east.

Within a week another DuPont scientist showed up. Wendell Tisdale explained that the lab was new, well equipped and dedicated to finding ways to grow more food and protect forest products. Tisdale was the lab's director; Norm would be its resident microbiologist.

This didn't help matters. Norm was now concerned that DuPont's core business was chemistry. It was famed for developing Cellophane, Rayon and especially Nylon, which had been on the market barely a year and was sensationally changing the look of women's legs. What chances for advancement would a microbiologist have in a chemistry company?

He kept raising his unease with Margaret, who was much more positive. She noted that he had no other prospect. "At the very least," she said, "it's a good place to see if you like working in industry."

In the end that argument prevailed. Margaret then withdrew $300 from her savings (built up dollar upon dollar from her minuscule assistant-proofreader paychecks) and bought her boss's father's old car.

Early on the first day of December, a Monday, the young couple left Minneapolis and, with rising spirits, headed eastwards in a purring 1935 Pontiac. That broad-shouldered, tan-colored, boxy conveyance was their only significant possession and it contained everything they owned.

By today's standards, travel in 1941 took forever. Highways were cramped, crooked and clotted by country towns that padded the payroll by fining lunatics reckless enough to zoom down Main Street at 26 mph.

Pulling into Philadelphia late the following Sunday afternoon, both Norm and Margaret were relieved that the week-long almost 2000-mile journey snaking across half the nation was nearly over. All but the last stretch — the recently opened, astoundingly modern, Pennsylvania Turnpike — had been by two-lane roads bejeweled with stoplights.

Now Wilmington lay just down the Delaware River; in 30 miles they'd discover the delights of East Coast living.

In the heart of Philadelphia a crowded sidewalk caught their attention. This seemed unusual for a sleepy Sunday afternoon. Moreover, the gathering radiated a strange kind of nervous energy.

Then a nearby newsboy shouted out the evening headline: "Pearl Harbor Bombed!"

That Sunday Japanese planes had bombed Hawaii and sunk the pride of the U.S. Navy along with more than 2000 sailors.

Instantly, America lost its mind. Anticipating invasion of the mainland, the Army designated the three Pacific-coast states as the "Western Combat Area." College-football authorities moved the New Year's Day Rose Bowl game to the safety of Duke University in North Carolina. San Franciscans lined their streets with sandbag walls thick enough to withstand the pre-invasion blitz. Government agencies distributed 50,000 gas masks so West Coast women could protect themselves from the enemy's poison gas. National Guard troops cut slit trenches into pristine California beaches. And fearful Feds hustled citizens of Japanese descent into inland camps so they couldn't tell the invaders where to go.

The jittery mood spread eastward, where Norm experienced it:

Early in 1942, DuPont sent me to Pensacola, Florida to check on some tests of antifungal agents. Months before, samples of wood, fabric and paint had been treated with various organo-mercury compounds and placed in contact with soil. My job was to record how well each of the different treatments had done.

Wartime travel was always tedious, but this was my worst trip. The train was so overloaded even the aisles were crammed with passengers, ninety percent of them soldiers.

Then as we pulled into some place in rural Georgia the sound of smashing glass reverberated from up front. Suddenly, a maddened crush of humanity came screaming and struggling toward me. Next came a wave of sensation . . . invisible but unmistakable: the breathtaking stench of ammonia. I instantly knew it was not to be feared and shouted for everyone to relax. But panic had taken charge. Soldiers near me broke windows, and crawled out. Thank goodness we'd by then reached the station.

For some reason, a passenger at the front of our car had been carrying a bottle of concentrated ammonia. I guess in preparing to detrain he'd dropped it. In the outcome that poor guy had to run down the platform for his life. He could quite easily have been strung up by locals convinced he was a saboteur delivering poison gas. In that part of the country there was no guarantee anyone would wait for the cops; with the furies stirred up by war, lynch-mob mentality was back in force.

On May 6, 1942, a new Federal agency opened for business. The War Manpower Commission had to balance the competing labor needs of agriculture, industry and the armed forces. It was a tricky business because all were vital, all had priority and all needed manpower. Borlaug was among the first it classified as "Essential to the War Effort."

What may sound like an honor was more like hostage taking. The Feds now ran his life, freezing his salary and forcing him to stay affixed to his desk until otherwise instructed. His plight was far from unique; during those years Washington determined what millions did with their days. It was an un-American age . . . national survival was at stake.

Even private life became regimented, though more by personal choice than public necessity. On the home-front volunteers filled in for the boys who'd gone off to fight. Many 12-year-olds, for instance, picked crops on local farms. Norm did his bit too:

With millions being called up for military duty, those of us still in civilian life had to fill in. I, for example, spent three nights a week substituting for Boy Scout leaders who were away in uniform.

Someone needed to keep the activities going. Although I signed on as a Troop Leader, I eventually was elevated to Neighborhood Commissioner, with authority over several Wilmington troops.

As 1942 progressed Norm was twice ordered to cross the Delaware and report to Fort Dix for induction into the Army. All that kept him from combat was his Federal designation "Essential to the War Effort."

By then he was managing contracts of global consequence. Indeed, his modest laboratory provided support to all the services, many of which were running into greater threats from microbes than military might. In the Pacific Campaign, for example, bugs were felling more marines than bullets.

Such problems were DuPont's to solve . . . and on the double. Every few days Norm would glance up from his desk to find an agitated officer from the Quartermaster Corps, the Navy, the Marines, or the Army glaring down and demanding he fix some frightful difficulty from a distant fighting zone that "was holding up the whole war." The typical order ended with: "Find the answer before the end of the week!"

Among the incidents he often recounted was the one late in 1942 when a Marine colonel and a Quartermaster Corps captain marched in bearing cartons of canned rations — tomatoes, he thinks. They explained that the marines on Guadalcanal were desperate for food and supplies, yet the Navy couldn't deliver the goods because Japanese warships controlled the nearby seas. To keep its fighting force from starvation the Navy was speeding destroyers in close to shore, and sailors on the decks would pitch cartons of rations overboard, trusting the waves to wash them into the shallows. The cartons, however, quickly came unglued, dumping their contents straight to the bottom. "Fix that," the Marine officer barked. "Before the end of the week!"

Cardboard boxes were then bonded with sodium silicate, a weak and soluble adhesive. Luckily, Norm found a DuPont chemist who suggested polyvinyl acetate, an insoluble adhesive immune to water, damp and mold. The military services adopted it, and as far as he knows, polyvinyl acetate still seals cartons and food-can labels. At any rate, cartons no longer fall apart on humid summer days (nor do labels float off beer bottles in the ice bucket, formerly a truly troublesome affliction).

Given the South Pacific's hothouse climate, molds were messing up seemingly everything: corroding electrical equipment necessary for radios, ships, bulldozers, jeeps, trucks and aircraft;

turning camouflage fabrics dazzlingly obvious; beclouding the inside surfaces of binoculars; rotting tents and sandbags and exposing troops to weather and weaponry; decaying medical supplies and endangering the wounded; cracking conveyor belts and hosepipes and destroying engines.

Soon there were too many challenges for Norm alone. The company hired Elizabeth Horning, a recent PhD from Rutgers University. There, just up the railway line, she'd been isolating soil molds and assessing their potential for curing disease.

To handle the never-ending battlefront demands, Norm and Betty Horning created a "Jungle Room." Heaters kept the air inside at 90 degrees and troughs of water kept it sodden. Both floor and walls were seeded with fungi and bacteria capable of degrading any part of man or machine: skin, hair, toenails, leather, wool, cellulose, rubber and whatever else might hinder or help the war effort.

Among products tortured in that hellish hothouse were electrical and telephone equipment, sandbags, trousers, paints, and fabrics. DuPont's own chemists adopted the room to evaluate the worst that rot, mildew, decay and corrosion could do to Rayon, Nylon, Dacron, and other wondrous materials that then were regarded as too vital to victory to share with civilians.

Within a short time the laboratory ran out of technicians; the former ones having been whisked off to war. Stand-ins were needed, and they couldn't be male. DuPont recruited girls just out of high school. Norm had to teach them microbiology, virtually overnight.

Home during that second year in Wilmington was as calming as the laboratory was creative. Norm and Margaret lived in quiet comfort on the third-floor of the apartment building at 1407 Delaware Avenue. Despite their serenity, though, life was not all pleasure:

I still had to write up my PhD research results. Stakman and Christensen [his box-elder research advisor] kept sending notes: "Get that thesis written before you go into the armed forces—or you'll never finish it!"

Thus, in addition to working at the lab and taking care of home life, I had to also put in long nights of writing. Trying to squeeze in even a little relaxation was impossible. But the wartime atmosphere was all the incentive we needed to stay focused. In those days we all felt invigorated and willing to work without complaint.

During that winter Margaret announced she was pregnant. With excitement, they awaited the great moment, imagining what their expanded future would be like and trying out names. As the due date approached, they settled on Norman or Norma Jean.

The baby, born on September 27, 1943, was a sparkly, blue-eyed daughter. She was quickly shortened to Jeanie.

Other than the Boy Scouts, Borlaug had avoided outside activities, but in the fall of 1942 he learned that the Phytopathological [plant disease] Society was holding its annual meeting in nearby Philadelphia. Trains from Wilmington were quick and convenient, so one afternoon he snuck out to sample a couple of hours of lectures.

He was here indulging in a little nostalgia, having heard that Stakman would attend, along with another of his students, George Harrar.

Harrar [ha-RAR] had earned his doctorate in 1935, before Norm got to graduate school. The two had never met, but Norm had heard breathless tales of "Dutch" Harrar, who combined a commanding presence, an iron will and an engaging charm.

Following the afternoon's final session, Norm happened to pass through the hotel's main lobby as Stakman and his charismatic colleague sauntered in from the other side. The professor introduced them. "This is fortuitous," Harrar said, "I've been wanting to talk with you." He waved toward the bar: "Let's go have a drink."

Over a beer Harrar, as was his habit, came straight to the point. "You know," he said, "I'm working with the Rockefeller Foundation. In a couple of months we're starting an agricultural research program in Mexico. Stak says you'd be a good person to have on our staff. We need a pathologist to help with the diseases of corn and beans and wheat. Why don't you join us?"

"Well," Norm said, "I'd like to consider it, but I'm under government control. The War Manpower Commission says I have to stay where I am, and there's nothing I can do about that."

They had another beer, after which he traipsed off home and pretty much forgot the offer.

Eighteen months later the competition for labor was lessening, and in May 1944 the War Manpower Commission officially freed anyone 30 years or older from employment restrictions. As he'd passed that cutoff point on the 25th of March, Norm could now accept a raise . . . even change jobs.

Though that was liberating, he did nothing about the job on offer below the border.

Then one day Harrar telephoned. He happened to be visiting the Rockefeller Foundation headquarters on West 49th Street in Manhattan; would Norm come up? There was something to discuss:

> I took an afternoon off and rode the train to New York. George laid out a grand scheme of lifting the poor people of Mexico out of hunger and poverty. It was exciting and inspiring. Again he asked me to join. This time I explained that while I was no longer under federal restrictions my work was still war related, and he'd need to contact my chiefs at the company.

So Harrar did exactly that, to the intense annoyance of DuPont's executives. Wendell Tisdale immediately called Norm in. "We understand why you're unhappy here," he said, assuming Norm was pursuing an outside career because of displeasure with his paycheck.

That assumption was understandable. Almost everyone working for Norm was earning more than he was; some, including Betty Horning, earned twice as much. Actually, though, he felt lucky. He explained to Tisdale that he was only concerned about advancement in a company built around chemistry.

A few weeks later this notion arose again in his mind and he took his concern to the division chief, explaining that he didn't seem to fit in well now that war work was winding down.

"No, no," John Woodhouse replied, "we want you here. If you feel out of place in research you can go into sales." Then he added a special inducement. "Seeing how well you've worked and considering the injustice of your salary, we'll give you two afternoons a week to go up to the University of Pennsylvania and take graduate courses in chemistry."

This seemed perfect . . . it settled all doubts. Norm called New York, only to find that Harrar had already returned to Mexico. So he left a message: he was grateful for the offer but would remain stateside.

It would have happened, too, but on George Harrar's next visit to New York, he called again. This time, he wanted to come to Wilmington and bring a Rockefeller Foundation vice president with him.

"Sure," Norm said, "that's okay."

"But we want to talk to your boss."

"Well, I don't know about that. Security is very tight and getting into the Experiment Station could be difficult."

Heedless of the warning, Harrar and the foundation's VP showed up, wangled their way through the security screen, and collared Norm's boss. A microbiologist by training, Wendell Tisdale appreciated the grandeur inherent in helping a hungry nation lift its food production. "If Borlaug is important to you," he said, "we should not stand in the way."

With John Woodhouse, however, the fireworks flew. In temperament, both Harrar and Woodhouse were explosive. Norm made the introductions and scuttled from the room. Later he heard that an ugly confrontation ensued. Among other niceties, the infuriated executive charged Harrar with unethical behavior: "I resent you coming down here and hiring away our employee!" Woodhouse had yelled across the table.

Nonetheless, the decision ultimately came down to Norm and Margaret. And it wasn't easy. On the downside, he'd have to leave his country and live in a foreign culture. He'd have to take the job sight unseen. He'd have no technical support because Mexico was a scientific wasteland. And he'd have to sacrifice all material advantages because his annual salary would be $3500, which, after four years of wartime inflation, no longer seemed excessive.

To colleagues, the decision was a no-brainer. Norm should NOT throw his career away like this. Immured in a technically primitive society he'd lose his professional edge . . . he'd fall behind the curve of advancing knowledge. He'd be unhappy. He'd never get another job stateside. He'd become an exile.

But after mulling it over he decided to go.

Margaret agreed. She'd noted a special sparkle in his eye whenever the prospect of uplifting Mexico's feeble food supply came up.

There was only one catch: She was again pregnant, and wartime Mexico seemed hardly the best place to bear a child.

She'd have to stay in Delaware a while longer.

PART II

The Near Side
[The Americas]

1944-1945

Breaking Hearts

On crossing the Rio Grande in October 1944 Norman Borlaug was driving Margaret's boxy tan-colored Pontiac. And he was doubly troubled. For one thing, he seemed to be deserting his family. Back in Wilmington his wife was suffering in a cramped third-floor walk-up, caring for their year-old daughter and enduring pregnancy's final weeks. For another, he seemed to be deserting his native land just when Uncle Sam was hounding Americans to "work round the clock" and "do more to win the war!"

Awaiting him on the Mexican side of the International Bridge he found Edwin Wellhausen, one of three young agronomists the Rockefeller Foundation had already sent to Mexico. Wellhausen had driven up from the capital of Mexico City to welcome their fourth and final team member.

Norm was then 30 years old, bone-lean, with eyes as blue as ever. His movie-star presence was, if anything, heightened by a new and barely suppressed enthusiasm. He was eager to put his science to work and lift Mexico's impoverished farmers out of hunger and poverty.

A little older and much mellower, Wellhausen was an ex-farm boy of average height and slim build who never stood out in a crowd and seldom offered opinions. But he was a crop-production genius and had been charged with studying "native Mexican and American strains of corn and beans with a view to the production of improved hybrids." In the foundation's Mexican agricultural program he was the star.

As the new friends traveled the rocky thousand-mile road to the capital city they saw the problem they were expected to solve. Misery was manifest. The wheat crop was harvested by sickle and manhandled in sacks that weighed up to 50 kilos (110lb). Yields were typically 200 kilos an acre, an amount that pinned millions of families on poverty's edge.

The friends could see that Mexican society had lost its moorings and was adrift. Inadequate food production was the underlying cause. Absent high-performing crops, four out of ten rural Mexicans lived on a few cents a day. They had to fashion their lives out of nothing, and dwelt in adobe huts without sanitation or running water. Absent electricity, they cooked over smoky open fires burning sundried corn cobs.

Mexico then had a modest population – 22 million; it was rich in oil and mineral resources; its government was stable and every six years its male populace elected a new presidente. But in 1944 a volcano was rumbling beneath the society. Hunger's shadow haunted the land; malnourished children could be seen throughout the rural areas; and fear of famine was rising among the public. Already much of the wheat and corn for tortillas was imported. And with the main suppliers, the U.S. and Canada, waging world war those staples were harder to get.

After three days Borlaug and Wellhausen reached Mexico City. Norm checked into the project's designated digs, the Hotel Geneve [HEN-eh-vah] on the street named Londres. This upscale establishment was just four blocks from Viena 26, where the Rockefeller Foundation had its main office.

The Mexican Agricultural Program comprised the first foray against foreign hunger since John D. Rockefeller endowed the foundation in 1913 "for the well-being of people throughout the world."

Since then, the New York institution had spent millions fighting foreign diseases, including malaria and malnutrition affecting Mexican children. But the world's richest foundation clearly had limited interest in uplifting Mexico's miserly food production. It had sanctioned $45,000 for the construction of an agricultural research station and $147,800 for general expenses during *both 1944 and 1945*. It had, moreover, entrusted the task of transforming this country's food supply to just four young and inexperienced American agronomists.

Officially, those four were embedded within the Mexican Department of Agriculture and were required to focus on the Bajío, the farming area that provided Central Mexico's food and that was peopled by millions of impoverished farmers. Beyond all that, the quartet was to train enough specialists that Mexico could continue developing its food supply unaided. Since it had but a handful of agriculturists with Masters Degrees and none with a doctorate, the four newcomers were expected to start the agricultural science profession from scratch.

The project's leader, George Harrar, had been designated the agriculture department's Plant Pathologist and Chief of Special Studies. His responsibilities included keeping the research fields free of diseases and pests. Fluent in Spanish and body language, Harrar still projected his legendary raw energy. As an undergraduate at Oberlin College he'd set the Ohio state record for the quarter-mile dash and been subsequently dubbed "Flying Dutchman." Close colleagues called him "Dutch."

Borlaug was considered Harrar's helper. His formal title was Assistant Plant Pathologist but, being a mere forester, he was generally regarded as the project's handyman.

On visiting the research site at Chapingo, 25 miles east of the capital, Norm expected to find a functioning research station. Instead, he found no greenhouses, no equipment, no technicians, no field-hands, no fields. All that was visible was a crude adobe cabin Wellhausen had thrown up the year before. That clay edifice, with fabric roof and dirt floor, was known as the Tarpaper Shack.

The land extending out half a mile around the Tarpaper Shack was even more dismaying. Instead of neatly groomed research fields those 160-acres were a riotous tangle of untamed weeds and scrub.

Plainly the four young scientists were expected to also create a research station from scratch. And that would be far from easy. Wartime priorities meant they had no tractor, and a quarter-square-mile of wasteland couldn't be cleared and leveled by hand.

Moreover, there seemed to be a deeper, unfathomable problem. Five months earlier, a small patch had been cleared and Wellhausen had sown test plots containing North America's finest corn and bean varieties. George Harrar had similarly sown test plots containing Stakman's finest wheats, including the famous Newthatch.

Now the results were apparent. From a distance the plants looked strong and healthy, but up close it was clear that they'd produced almost nothing edible.

Assuming worn-out soil to be the root cause, Harrar told his newly arrived assistant to repeat the planting someplace where better conditions would expose North American wheat's stellar qualities.

Thus it came about that Borlaug and Wellhausen loaded Margaret's creaky old Pontiac with packets of America's finest wheat seed and headed eastwards for the fertile highlands of the sunny state of Puebla.

There in the hills above the city of Tehuacan they found a well-tended farm that seemed ideal. Though neither spoke Spanish, they managed to sweet talk the owner into loaning them part of a field for the next five months.

As they returned to the capital Norm was suffused with satisfaction. This was his first foray into food production. It was his first hands-on meeting with wheat. And he'd sown his boss's prime seed in a prime part of this hungry land.

Marching into the Hotel Geneve he was aglow with the joy of his blossoming professional career and of being back where there was hot water, clean sheets, reasonable food, and people who understood what he said. That radiance lasted merely a minute:

> As I picked up my room key the desk clerk handed over a note that had been waiting several days. The first words shunted aside all sense of elation. The clerk's crabbed scribble summarized a phone call from Wilmington. Margaret had given birth to a son, Scott. She was well. But there was some trouble. A letter was on the way.
>
> After an agonizing hour of desperate dialing and cajoling operators in two languages, one of which I couldn't understand, I finally got through to Wilmington General [Hospital]. The hospital staff made no effort to help: Margaret was unavailable. Her ward had no phone. She was sleeping. No, they wouldn't wake her. No, they wouldn't provide personal information. Nothing could be done. Call back tomorrow!
>
> Next morning in a state of panic I visited the downtown office and discovered Margaret's letter. It had been written under great stress. The sentences were rough and broken. But my eye latched onto two strange words: *spina bifida*.
>
> These I didn't understand, so I hurried down the corridor and collared George Payne, the physician managing the foundation's malaria team.
>
> "What is spina bifida?" I asked.
>
> In turn, he inquired why I wanted to know. He was usually outgoing and very friendly but on hearing of Margaret's note, his manner turned stony and strictly professional. It was a birth defect. In some cases the spinal column was exposed. There was danger of sudden movement paralyzing the legs and bodily functions. There was risk of infection . . . and of hydrocephalus. "I'm terribly sorry, Norman," he added, "but I have to say that at

best it's bad. At worst, it's tragic."

This knowledge was almost impossible to bear. It emptied my mind of everything else. Mexico be damned, I had to get to Delaware. Fast.

There was no option but to fly. Trouble was, I was out of cash. So was everyone else. Though George Harrar could advance a loan from operating funds, he was traveling in the U.S., and well beyond reach.

This was as big a frustration as I ever faced. It was agony sitting in the office that morning and confronting the phone. Knowing I couldn't get to Delaware for love nor money made everything so much worse. Another age passed before the various operators got me through to Margaret.

Sadly, I explained that there was no way to get out of the damned place until the boss got back.

"That's okay, Norman," she said. "Don't worry too much. Being here won't help. I can cope. But come as soon as you can."

Three days later Harrar returned, and Norm took the next plane out. The 2500 mile flight proved a trial. Passenger planes then featured propellers, and he endured two days in a noisy, cramped, bucking DC-3 that flew at 150 mph and stopped often for fuel. Then, having taken a train from downtown Philadelphia to Wilmington and a cab to 1407 Delaware Avenue, he climbed to the third floor.

As the door marked 3B swung open Margaret's ashen face appeared and he saw her palpable relief. They stood and hugged, saying nothing for an age. "I made the decision, Norman," she finally whispered through the tears. "There was no more time. They wanted to cut Scotty up . . . but the operation sounded too desperate . . . I thought it best to let nature take its course."

Though born in Wilmington General, baby Scotty was scheduled for transfer to the Alfred I. du Pont Hospital for Children, a state-of-the-art pediatric facility a few blocks away. The exposed spine, however, precluded even so short a trip.

Worsening the parents' agony was Wilmington General's insistence on restricting the isolation ward to hospital staff. Neither Norm nor Margaret were allowed to approach their offspring.

That was bad enough, but neither knew what to do next. They couldn't even discuss the future; there seemed to be no way forward.

Then they got a huge break. Norm had dropped by DuPont for a chat with his former co-workers, and over lunch Wendell Tisdale offered him his old job back.

"Yes," he exulted to Margaret that night, "I'll be a microbiologist . . . or a chemist. We'll stay in Wilmington. We'll be with Scotty. I'll work in a laboratory, and we'll all have proper medical care!"

By now, however, Margaret knew him better than he knew himself. She'd seen him radiant with the joy of his blossoming hunger-fighting career. "My husband has a future," she said. "My baby has none. You go back; I'll come when I can."

Two days after Christmas 1944, for the second time in three months, Norman Borlaug headed for Mexico City. He spent another two days in cramped, bucking, noisy DC-3s that between fuel stops slowly plied the skies. This time his mind was trebly troubled by guilt.

During Norm's absence, quite by accident, Wellhausen had located two junked TD8 International tractors. Neither would run, but a week or so later Ed had heard that a nearby villager had maintained Mexican tanks as an army cadet. Vicente Guerrero discovered himself standing on his own doorstep being hired by a gringo scientist who was barely understandable and who seemed to want him to create one live crawler tractor out of two dead ones.

Norm arrived back to find the Tarpaper Shack surrounded by a muddle of metallic body parts: large ones strewn on the loose dirt outside and small ones — screws, nuts, chains, belts, bolts, cables and springs — strewn across the hard-packed dirt inside.

His colleagues lounged around; helpless, disheartened, fearful that their grand endeavor would never make the start line. Meanwhile, with the care of a surgeon transplanting tissues, the one-time tank doctor reassembled the best bits of two bulldozers.

On the day of reckoning the uneasy onlookers gawked as the improbable medicine man climbed aboard, pulled the decompression lever, engaged the starter, and got his heavy-metal patient breathing on gasoline fumes.

After allowing it five minutes on life support, he tested the vital signs by pushing the decompression lever and easing out the throttle to switch fuels. In its Lazarus moment, the iron giant coughed and spluttered, and began imbibing its staple diet, diesel.

Finally, Guerrero selected first gear, hauled on the lever that lifted the blade from its place of rest, and inched back the main clutch lever. Here was the moment of truth. The nervous onlookers held their breath; the rusty crawler treads screeched their disapproval. Then the steel-ribbed treads grabbed the ground and the beast inched forward.

At that, the observers jumped and clapped and cheered. Their euphoria erupted from relief more than pleasure. The military mechanic had given them their life back.

As team handyman Borlaug became a bulldozer driver. After scraping away the scrub and leveling the 160 acres he morphed into a surveyor. Peering through a transit, he laid stringlines and pounded in rows of pegs that defined fields, roads, fences, water channels, and drainage pipes. Finally, he climbed back aboard the bulldozer and graded those roads, dug the water channels and installed the drain pipes.

While all that was underway Wellhausen dug a well, installed a pump and sent water surging down Borlaug's freshly dug ditches and into the flat fields and welcoming soils of the group's very own experiment station.

Wellhausen's first research crop of corn and beans was planted that December, just in time for the winter growing season.

Late in January Norm tracked down a rental apartment on the second floor of an apartment block at Sierra Guadarrama 61-2 in Mexico City's attractive upscale suburb of Lomas de Chapultepec. It was near the ancient citadel the Marines' Hymn calls "The Halls of Montezuma" but whose Aztec name really means "Grasshopper Hill."

Having put down a deposit, he bought a bed and four chairs, and moved right in. "We have our first home in Mexico ready and waiting," he wrote his wife. "Come when you can."

Despite a vow to stay by her baby, Margaret could feel her resolve wilting with the weeks. Though DuPont paid for its *ex-employee's* very sick child's hospital stay, Norm's new salary couldn't cover apartments in two countries. Also the sight of the son deteriorating behind the window was agonizing. Then, halfway through February tests revealed the onset of hydrocephalus. That swelling on the brain meant Margaret faced a month . . . two months . . . maybe a year of endless heartbreak.

During the last visit the doctor gently guided her away from the glass divide. Rest assured, he said, little Scotty would receive the best of care.

Margaret then had to confront a wrenching, staggering, stupefying sense of grief and guilt. Later she said the worst part was walking onto the platform, climbing aboard and staying put while they pulled out of the Wilmington Train Station.

As the steel wheels thrummed away the miles separating her from her suffering son she sat, hurting, hunched and head down, holding little Jeanie tight. That contact, according to her recollection, saved her sanity.

On arrival in Mexico City a week later, Margaret was exhausted less from the 2500 mile rail ride than from the misery pervading her mind.

Though unpretentious, the apartment proved functional. It had a kitchen, a dining room and *two* bedrooms! When she arrived it reeked of bachelor barrack. Within days, though, it had been scrubbed down, washed out, tidied up, decorated and fitted with furniture. Refashioning those rented rooms began her long climb back to happiness with herself.

For little Jeanie the new home proved nearly perfect. She quickly befriended the neighborhood kids, most of whom spoke only Spanish.

Now almost 18-months old, Jeanie and her happiness were crucial because she'd become the link holding the family circle together. Through their love for their toddler each parent came to cope with the horror of having never hugged, kissed, caressed or even cooed to her brother, now slowly succumbing in confinement far away and unaware he had a family and was loved.

Also helping the healing process was Mexico City's sunny upland clime, then among earth's most salubrious. Winters were warm enough for crops to thrive, and in March, when Wellhausen's plantings were nearing maturity, Norm was squatting among the beans searching for signs of disease or insects, when a coarse shout rang out.

Looking up, he saw George Harrar striding toward him yelling: "Norm, I've got too much administrative work to handle . . . I want you to take over the Wheat Program . . . Run it any way you want . . . I'll give you all the help I can — when I can!"

This took Norm aback. He knew nothing more about wheat than what Stakman had revealed in his classes and outdoor seminars beside the Plant Pathology Department in St. Paul. Now he was expected to make Mexico capable of producing all its daily bread. That was a stretch. Yields here were among the world's worst. America and Canada averaged 1100 pounds an acre; Mexico averaged 750 and disease epidemics sometimes slashed that nearly in half. There was not even a wheat specialist to confer with. Convinced the crop could *never* succeed, the government had abolished that position in 1943.

Hoping to find help, Norm dropped in on the agriculture department for whom, formally speaking, he worked. Its administrators, however, proved uninterested in him or wheat.

Then on a whim he dropped by the building next door. Here, he enjoyed a rapturous reception. The irrigation department was staffed with graduates of U.S. engineering schools and they disclosed plans for a massive project to irrigate a wide, dry, alluvial plain in Sonora.

Sonora was a state at the top end of the country, just below Arizona. Not even Mexicans knew much about it; most dismissed it as their country's badlands. The engineers, however, believed their project would turn Sonora's Yaqui Valley into the country's breadbasket.

Of that, Norm was skeptical. From Stakman's lectures he knew stem rust would sooner or later savage any wheat planted thereabouts:

> We established great working relations that day. Irrigation was probably the most efficient government department; its engineers were professionals who really knew their stuff. From the start we both sensed we could work together toward a great end. They could irrigate vast tracts of good wheat land but couldn't keep the crop healthy. That's where I might make a difference. Without healthy plants their great project would be next to worthless.

Though this was an exciting prospect, Sonora lay far outside the zone in which the foundation was permitted to work. Back at the office he raised this difficulty and was summarily squelched. "Listen, Norm, keep your mind on the job!" George Harrar barked. "Our problem is in the Bajío. This is where the poor farmers are. You must get that clear!"

Harrar had reason for concern. An American foundation working within the Mexican government created sensitivities, especially given the widespread suspicion of gringos. Breaking the rules of engagement might get the Rockefeller Foundation kicked out of the country.

Nonetheless, Borlaug decided to go for broke. Early in April he challenged his boss:

> Dutch, the Yaqui Valley is Mexico's most promising wheat area, and I'm going to take a look. If we can lick stem rust up there every Mexican will be better off. We should at least consider working in Sonora. *It's the right thing to do!*

This did not go over well. The team's forester/handyman had been on the job seven months, and had already caused considerable administrative difficulties. Both men lost their cool until — surprise, surprise — the one who blinked was the ever-confidant, seemingly infallible director. "Okay, okay," Harrar said. "Take a quick trip up there and look around. Nothing more than that, though."

This concession was issued in a voice so overladen with angry overtones that Norm knew he'd alienated his esteemed boss.

Although Mexico had only a rudimentary airline industry in 1944, Norm was able to take a United Airlines DC-3 to the Pacific Coast at Mazatlán. Then, following a night in a cheap hotel, he boarded a Fokker Tri-motor for the haul north into the wilderness known as Sonora. At noon the ancient winged boxcar (top speed 118 mph) settled sedately on a runway that was merely a sliver of dirt beside a tiny town most people called Cajeme [cah-HEM-ee].

Having written to a local research facility, he was relieved to see its assistant director awaiting him. Norm, you see, had no idea where the place was located and couldn't ask for directions.

As the dilapidated government pickup passed through Cajeme township, he noted the unpaved streets and false-front stores; this place looked like a mockup made for shooting Wild West movies. It was raw. It lacked even a graveled road. And it seemed swathed in insignificance and hopelessness.

Then that dusty main street took him out into the Yaqui [YAH-kee] Valley that stretched westward beyond the limits of sight. Though this broad, flat plain was part of the Sonoran Desert, green patches of irrigated land stood out among the cactus and mesquite. After a few miles they turned onto a side road squeezed between the main canal and a drainage channel. Barely a track, it amounted to a seven-mile obstacle course fitted with car-swallowing potholes that had to be individually outwitted.

The Yaqui Valley Experiment Station had been plopped out there on the far side of nowhere by a dotty governor who'd viewed it as a vehicle for driving Sonora up and out of dust and destitution. That had been back in the 1930s, and upon seeing the impressive stone-pillared entrance Norm felt his spirits soar. By the end of the half-mile driveway his spirits had hit a new low. Once this had been a thriving operation developing livestock, horticultural crops and wheat, but no longer:

> The place looked like hell: Fields sprouted more wild oats than wheat . . . canals hosted weeds rather than water . . . cattle, sheep

and hogs had gone for someone's dinner . . . farm machinery had emigrated in an equally mysterious manner . . . fences had fallen . . . and a large experimental orchard had shrunk to a few figs and oranges and a solitary grapefruit.

The buildings were in no better shape. From the outside they resembled bombed-out Berlin: windows shattered, doors askew, screens tattered, roof tiles torn off. The laboratory block was befouled by rusting equipment, rotting seeds and musty mounds of moldy old documents.

I never saw a more dismal scientific facility . . . and I've seen plenty of dismal ones.

The driver quickly dumped his awkward and unintelligible guest. Norm then dropped his bedroll and pasteboard suitcase and set out through the shimmering surroundings.

Wheat fields were all around but as he drew near he saw the farmers' surprise turned to suspicion. What was this gringo doing out here in the desert heat asking about their crops in such frightful Spanish?

That first afternoon ended in frustration. Farming in the Yaqui Valley was tenuous. Families lived in shacks on their land, eking out frugal existences. Wheat was harvested sack by sack. The scene seemed familiar: these people were basically as broke as the Borlaugs had been with 25 bushel-an-acre corn.

Pinning Sonora's wheat farmers to poverty's edge was the fact that the great rivers of high-altitude wind flowing south from Canada deluged these fields with stem rust spores every winter. Only one wheat variety had proven capable of surviving the onslaught. Sadly, that variety, Barrigon Yaqui, made poor pasta and bad bread. The harvest mostly ended up in soda crackers, and the growers' paychecks were so pitiful that every year more were switching to flax. Half had already made the change.

Having trudged back to the old experiment station in the gathering gloom of evening Norm found that the place had no sanitation, no running water, and little protection from the elements or wildlife:

The communal kitchen was so filthy I took over a long-deserted staff house, arranged a few stones outside, then lit a fire and heated a can of beans by burning old corn cobs. Finally, after sweeping some dead rats out of the staff house I unrolled my bedroll on the stone floor. During the night live rats ran over the bedroll. I pulled a coat over my head but slept very fitfully.

Next day, stepping out into the soft dawn glow, he set off to explore farms farther out across the khaki countryside. Late that morning he stumbled across small fields of two mystery wheats that stood out amid the dismal Barrigon Yaqui. He subsequently learned that this pair – Mentana and Marroqui [marrow-KEE] – had thrilled the wheat specialist whose position the government had abolished two years back. That specialist had, however, subsequently changed his mind after Mentana succumbed to stem rust and Marroqui failed to yield much grain.

Borlaug nearly rejected them too. But with nothing else to show for his trip, he stashed a seedhead of each in envelopes he'd brought.

Next morning he headed homeward. Despite accomplishing nothing of consequence, he felt strangely elated:

> When we rose out of Cajeme I looked down on the vast expanse of the Yaqui Valley and my mind wrestled with a new concept. The Rockefeller Foundation wheat program needed to change. By solving the Yaqui Valley's stem rust problem we could give Mexico all the bread it could eat!

Back at home base Norm and two young assistants – José Guevara and José [Pepe] Rodríguez – toured several states across Mexico's midsection. The wheat crop was ready for harvest and Norm drove the little green pickup truck from farm to farm. Wandering through randomly chosen wheat fields, he and the students yanked seedheads off any unusual looking specimen.

They had plenty to choose from because these fields were sprinkled with various nameless wheats whose seeds the farmers saved and sowed year after year. The area was a mix of tall and medium stems, bearded and beardless heads, red and white grain. Some plants were overripe, others still unripe. Most were to some degree diseased.

Following a ten-day search, the trio had 8500 envelopes, each of which enclosed a seedhead bearing 200 or so seeds.

May brought the opening of the summer planting season. Norm, José Guevara and Pepe Rodríguez prepared a "survival of the fittest" test for the 8500 separate seed lots. Actually, they seemed to be mere dreamers because they had no way to accomplish the task. Given its weight and steel-ribbed treads, a TD8 bulldozer could not be used to prepare fields for seeding.

Absent any alternative, the three turned themselves into beasts of burden. Fastening a strap about his chest, each in turn tugged a nursery-plot cultivator while another guided the tines that tilled the turf and tore out weeds.

Although the soil was loose and the furrows were shallow, acting the ox was the ultimate human low. Beneath the unfeeling Mexican sun 7000 feet above sea level the body streamed sweat, the back burned, the rope flensed the flesh. Yet these boys of burden persevered at pulling the plow until two short rows (each featuring 10 to 15 seeds) had been sown for all 8500 selections. The task absorbed more than two weeks and involved over 5 miles of sod-busting by biceps.

After accomplishing all that, they created a small "crossing block" comprising 49 wheat varieties sown in 49 very short rows all clustered together. When the plants flowered in July Norm would blend their genes in hopes of securing a new and hopefully more reliable base of stem-rust resistance. Slated for that great midsummer mating were:

- The Mentana and Marroqui seeds he'd carried home from Sonora;
- Mexico's top three commercial wheat varieties;
- Seed from 38 envelopes Stakman had mailed from Minnesota; and
- Six seed lots from a Texas A&M professor, Edgar McFadden.

Although Borlaug would later attract devotees like a diva, during that summer of '45 Guevara and Rodríguez remained defiantly distant. Norm later chuckled about it:

In the beginning they came to work dressed in suits and shiny shoes. By going to college they'd earned a place in society, and they wanted everyone to know.

He himself always wore khakis and work boots, and the first lesson he imparted was that working with your hands was as honorable as working with your head. For a while it was a hard sell. "Dr Borlaug, we don't do these things," Pepe Rodríguez growled in frustration one day. "You should draw up the plans and take them to the foreman, and let the *peones* do the work."

At that point Borlaug lost his temper. "If we don't do things ourselves," he snapped, "how can we advise anyone? How can we ever be certain of our ground?"

Thanks in part to the power of those words, but more to the power of his example, the students took to wearing khakis and boots in the fields. Elsewhere, they hid the embarrassing evidence that they were manual laborers. In time, though, khakis and work boots became points of personal pride. They had caught the Borlaug bug.

Seeing he was managing almost 9000 rows of wheat plants, Norm was relieved when George Harrar assigned him two more helpers.

That the newcomers wore skirts was a surprise because no Mexican woman had ever before participated in agricultural research. Machismo barred females from professional life, and of course they could never be trusted with the vote. By now, though, sexism was triggering shame. Within 12 months — that is, in 1946 — Mexico's smarter half would finally get to cast a ballot.

Still and all, the right to vote didn't mean the right to work, so Harrar took it on himself to bring gender justice to agricultural research. His problem was finding candidates. Trainees such as Guevara and Rodríguez came from the local agriculture college, but being partly operated by the Army it remained a mainstay of manhood.

Lacking any alternative, Harrar approached the National Polytechnic as well as the Autonomous University and hired two recent biology graduates. Angela Melendez and Marta Zenteno made their mark on history working alongside Borlaug surveying endless rows of wheat during the long hot summer of '45.

In July when the plants began flowering, Norm swarmed over the crossing block's precisely arranged rows, cross-fertilizing each of the 49 lines with each of the others, and doing it both ways — i.e. with half designated males (providing pollen) and half females (receiving pollen).

At season's end, he and his assistants strode the 5 miles of rows containing the 8500 mongrel wheats. Rust had won Round 1 by a knockout. That October, *every one* of the nameless plants as well as the best local commercial varieties had angry red, yellow, orange or black ulcers pitting their stems or leaves.

Clearly, the national food supply was in mortal danger. Crops occupying 1.25 million acres were vulnerable to collapse. The famine people feared was just a fungus away. And only he knew it.

At first glance the American wheats had fared little better. The seeds he'd planted for Harrar in the fertile highlands of the sunny state of Puebla had failed to produce anything edible. And at Chapingo, 45 of Stakman and McFadden's 49 gifts had succumbed. The others, however, had withstood the spore showers, not to mention the summer heat. To Norm the sight of those four was inspiring:

> That summer of '45 four plants showed good resistance to stem rust. By our later standards, they were not high yielding but they surpassed Mexico's existing wheats. So I decided to start with them.

In addition, the flowers he'd cross-pollinated in July had yielded 140,000 seeds containing myriad new gene combinations. But genes are shy, and take their time in exposing their qualities to view. Not until he'd planted and replanted the seeds sequentially for several seasons would they reveal their true selves.

While working at home base during the summer months Norm had continued talking up the importance of Sonora. The Yaqui Valley, he insisted, offered nearly a million acres of flat land ranking among Mexico's most fertile. When the irrigation project was fully operational Mexico's wheat-growing area would almost double. The effect on hunger, however, might be nil because the current wheat variety was essentially worthless. An improved and stem-rust-safe replacement could make Sonora into a food cornucopia. The Yaqui Valley might produce all the wheat Mexico could eat. The Mexican Agricultural Program had been sent here for just such a purpose. It should take the lead.

Logic, however, was out of its league. "Sonora doesn't need our help," Harrar declared in his most armor-piercing tones. "Our focus is the Bajío . . . *That's where the poor farmers are!*"

Between them, relations were worsening. The chief's sharp stare now turned passive as he pulled up the poker face previously used only against pushy Mexican officials. It unnerved Norm the rest of his days:

> Sometimes I couldn't tell what George was thinking behind that cold glare.

Then one night the remedy came to Norm's mind. By using the derelict old experiment station up in Sonora he could fit in a second round of research *during the winter*. He could, in other words, help the irrigation engineers without affecting his designated duties.

On the negative side, this sequence would strain family ties. *For half the year* he'd be marooned in solitary confinement at the country's top end. Except for a few weeks at Christmas, Margaret and Jeanie would live alone in the Mexico City apartment.

On the positive side, however, he'd squeeze in an extra round with rust and make progress twice as fast. His chances for foiling the famine and calming the fears rumbling beneath the restive society would thus improve. Maybe too the top brass in New York would never realize he was AWOL half the time.

The possibility that his mischief might not be visible from so far around the curvature of the earth changed the equation. George Harrar agreed to a test run.

However when operating in the distant desert, a thousand miles from the Rockefeller Foundation's area of operations, Norm would receive no financial support. He'd be provided no special facilities. He'd have no staff, no accommodations, no farm machinery, and no vehicle. He'd be alone, without wheels, implements, technical help, or formal recognition.

1946
Breaking Rules

I n November 1945 Norm moved north to establish the 1946 winter
planting and begin his double-decker life. This also started his life as
the Lone Ranger of wheat research. By working in Sonora he was not
only bucking his family's interest and his foundation's interest, he was
breaking a cardinal wheat-breeding rule. Professors and textbooks were
in universal agreement that wheat was location-limited. Varieties,
therefore, must be bred in the place *where the farmers intended to
grow them*. And they must be bred *in the same season the farmers will
use to grow the resulting crop*.

But Norm paid no heed to location or season. He carried the winning
seeds from Central Mexico's summer crop a thousand miles north and
grew them in Sonora during winter. And he planned to carry the new
winning seeds back south to grow in Central Mexico during the
subsequent summer.

From his days in graduate school, and especially from HK Hayes's
plant-breeding course, Norm knew it was wrong to wrench seeds out of
their comfort zone season after season, but he was in a race with stem
rust. To him, speed took precedence; above all else he must beat the
fungus to the punch. Perhaps the resulting varieties would turn out less
than great, *but they'd survive*. And survival counted most.

In Sonora he found the crummy old calamity post as foul and
frustrating as ever. The place still lacked many windows. It had no water
for drinking; no water for bathing; no electricity; no sanitation. And he
had to cook his own meals on an open fire fueled by sun-dried corn
cobs.

The best spot for sleeping was the loft above a ramshackle storage shed. Climbing the ladder, he unfolded a canvas cot amid moldering sacks of long-abandoned grain. As one of the ground-floor walls was merely wire mesh, he shared his shelter with mosquitoes, mice, rats and snakes. Decades later he still shuddered at the recollection:

> Thank God I'd been a forester and had learned to live alone in the wilderness. Without that I'd either have quit Sonora or gone completely mad.

The outdoor facilities were even more limiting than the indoor ones. There were none. Lacking machinery, he began by sowing his fields with hand and hoe.

On the third day, as he hoed lumpy soil over rows of seed, he spotted an imposing character striding toward him. The man had a powerful build, a barrel chest and strong rough hands. Despite lines bitten deep into his weathered face, he seemed in ruddy health. Strangely, under the sombrero he wore a suit. Stranger still, from below his properly pressed trouser cuffs there peeped a pair of dusty work boots.

"Buenos días, Señor. I am Aureliano Campoy." The English was good, though clipped and accented. "I live there," he jerked a finger back over a shoulder to a farm house across the road from the entrance gate. "I see you work like a peon. What is it you do here? And why do you work on the Lord's Day?"

Borlaug said he needed to work every day, including Sunday, and he hoped to create better wheats for farmers, a claim that elicited a snort.

In a letter home Norm mentioned the incident to Margaret:

> I don't think he believed me but I know he was very curious. I had seen him watching me work from across the road. I told him I was making new wheats for farmers and — glory be! — he will let me have his tractor and some implements next weekend.

Two Saturdays later Norm was driving Campoy's Farmall tractor, and focused on plowing straight furrows, when a Chevrolet sedan swept through the stone gates. He watched in fascination as the driver extricated herself. Big-shouldered, heavy, with strong arms, bare and freckled, the lady was no longer young but remained eye-catching.

She beckoned him over. "You must be the crazy American my foreman has been telling me about," she declared. "I'm Cathy Jones, and I hear you're without transportation. I'm heading to town for groceries. Care to ride along?"

There and then he grabbed the chance to not only acquire the week's meager needs but to also converse in colloquial English.

By December Norm had sown a five-acre test of the four survivors of last summer's sizzle and spore storms. Two of those came from Stakman and two from the Texas professor, McFadden.

He also sowed plots containing the 140,000 seeds gathered from last summer's crossbred plants. These he planned to herd forward for several years in hopes they'd eventually expose plants that will do more than just hold the line against stem rust.

And he sowed a new crossing block wherein (at flowering time in February) he'll cross-pollinate Round 1's four survivors with Newthatch and other commercial varieties that might instill better behavior.

By mid-December the seedlings were emerging and, with three-week's freedom from fieldwork, he headed south for Christmas with the kinfolk. As the twenty-year-old Tri-Motor took to the skies his previous exhilaration revived: The winter trials were underway. A friend had made his fieldwork possible; another friend had made his personal life possible. Even wheat was getting friendly.

The exhilaration proved fleeting. On reaching the apartment all sense of satisfaction collapsed when, in Margaret's strained face and troubled eyes, he read the sorrow beyond words.

They held each other, close in their grief . . . and relief. Then Margaret slowly disengaged herself. "I prayed he'd go in his sleep, without pain," she said. "And they said he did. He never had a chance, poor little thing."

She described how the phone had rung, and how she'd wanted to rush to the airport and fly to her baby's side. But the doctor had advised against it. It would be best, he said, to keep the memory as it was.

There was sense in that. Also such a trip would have depleted the funds they'd set aside for the funeral and final hospital bills.

Borlaug tried to console her. "It will get better with time," he said.

But both knew this particular year-long pain would never cease.

That night he lay sleepless and again perilously close to cracking. This was another testing time: He'd not had a single professional success. He'd jeopardized his family's health, happiness and hopes. He'd alienated his esteemed boss. And now there was this engulfing sense of loss for the son he'd neither touched nor talked to — and who'd died so far away he couldn't even attend the burial or pay final respects.

In a scientific paper written decades later, he recalled the despair:

> Many times during the [first] four years, frustrated by unavailability of machinery and equipment, without the

assistance of trained scientists, traveling over bad roads, living in miserable hotels, eating bad food, often sick with diarrhea and unable to communicate because of lack of command of the language, I was certain I had made a dreadful mistake in resigning from my former position.

That Christmas break proved critical for soothing the roughed-up psyches. During those few weeks the family was together in a condition outsiders might judge "uneventful." Deep down, though, Margaret was reassembling her emotional topography. Jeanie was mastering the mechanics of motion. And the man of the house was, by slow degrees, gaining back self-respect.

Late in January 1946, having extended his homestay to more than a month, Norm returned north for the action section of his second rust-fighting season. With the arrival of February the plants began flowering, and he swarmed over the crossing-block's precisely arranged rows, cross-fertilizing each line with all the others, and doing it both ways.

Then he flew home to be an added comfort to Margaret.

Back in the City of Mexico he found the scientific staff augmented by the reticent lookalike who'd trailed him in grad school. Joseph Rupert had settled into the Hotel Geneve, but as friendship ripened Margaret offered the spare bedroom and Joe moved in with the Borlaugs. Jeanie still slept in a crib, so Joe got the second bedroom.

Though committed to Mexican agriculture, Rupert had come mainly for mental health. Three years earlier, just after earning his MS degree, he'd been drafted. Then, after a brief training as a combat medic, the Army had dispatched him to North Africa along with the new and naïve forces led by an obscure and somewhat suspect general named Dwight David Eisenhower. During the botched Battle of Kasserine Pass the shy agronomist had tended GIs extracted from Sherman tanks shattered by Rommel's high-penetration artillery shells. The sight also shattered Joe, and Stakman had arranged the posting to Mexico in hopes his student would grow scar tissue over the impressions of broken, burned and disemboweled bodies branded on his brain.

As friendship ripened Borlaug and Rupert became a mutual support group. For Joe there was no better therapy; for Norm their closeness supplied solace of equal import. The pair became brothers in all but surname, each helping the other get over psychological shock.

During that spring of 1946 two more Mexican students signed on. Both Teodoro Enciso [en-SEE-soh] and Alfredo Campos began as "weekend warriors," contributing Saturdays, school vacations, and other brief interludes their college advisors couldn't veto. Both approached their assignments with reluctance, loath to commit their inner-selves. Soon, though, they caught the Borlaug bug, ditched their egghead handlers, and sweated their hearts out amid the heat, flies, dirt and diseased plant tissues. They had found joy.

When it was time to head north to wrap up Research Round 2 Joe offered his services. Then Norm invited Teodoro Enciso, who possessed the priceless power of being able to converse with the locals.

Because harvesting the Foundation Foursome's five-acre final test would require a thrashing machine and also because he hoped to haul home hundreds of pounds of seed, Norm was allowed to borrow the boxy Ford pickup. George Harrar, however, demanded that he return it within one month. It was the only truck the program had.

By road, Sonora could be reached in two ways. One was dangerous, the other tedious. Norm chose the latter, which involved driving into Texas, crossing New Mexico and half of Arizona, and dropping down into the Yaqui Valley from the opposite side. If all went well, this 1500-mile circle route involving many miserable roads would take merely a week.

Anticipating trouble driving a Mexican truck into the United States he dropped by the Ministry of Agriculture and the American Embassy. Both assured him the border crossings would be quite uneventful. A special treaty allowed Mexican government vehicles free passage of U.S. territory for purposes of reentry.

Then, with spirits soaring, Norm, Joe and Enciso loaded the Ford pickup with all they'd need for the trip and the field trials. That included four extra tires; a 60-gallon drum brimming with gasoline (for the many stretches lacking gas stations); two small thrashing machines; 200 paper bags (for small seed samples); and 50 gunnysacks (for the hoped-for huge harvest).

Margaret brought little Jeanie downtown to send the strange expedition off in style. Norm kissed them both, waved cheerily from behind the wheel, and maneuvered the tiny truck out of Viena 26 and onto the boulevard leading north.

After three excruciating days squeezed onto the short bench seat of that cramped contrivance, the three agronomic adventurers reached the border. It was four o'clock in the afternoon, and they were desperate to cross into El Paso for a bath, a beer and a bed. But after glancing at the dusty pickup whose doors were painted with symbolic silver eagles, the border guard threw a tantrum. "Well, this is a real complicated procedure, seeing that there's a Mexican government vehicle," he snapped. "No use even talking about it now. Come back in the morning."

An hour later he closed the gate to America, forcing the three to snooze the night away in the open air on the dusty pile of gunnysacks behind the cab.

Next morning Norm referred to the treaty, to which impertinence the official instantly demanded full duty be paid. Norm noted that the equipment had no commercial value and in two days would be back in Mexico.

But the customs officer wasn't about to let a cross-border criminal sneak in two thrashing machines and four tires for personal financial gain! After much of the day had disappeared in successive rounds of verbal fencing, the federal functionary advanced a compromise: Citizen Borlaug would be permitted free entry if he allowed his personal paraphernalia to be separately shipped to Arizona by a bonded trucking company.

By now Norm was mad enough to commit mayhem. Harrar's restrictions meant he had no funds for such an emergency. Worse, the seasons had him trapped; he should already be in Sonora starting the harvest. So he grumpily handed over personal dollars, unloaded the equipment for the trucking company and headed west for Arizona with Joe and Enciso in an empty pickup.

At Nogales, Arizona's main gateway to Mexico, things got worse. When asked about the thrashers, tires and sacks the border authorities laughed. The bonded warehouse had nothing remotely like that.

Now the normally self-effacing scientist discarded all sense of decorum, not to say decency. Overcome by rage, he shared his view of the U.S. Customs Service with everyone within earshot.

An official then scurried to a phone and scurried back. So sorry, the trucker had made a mistake. But don't worry: the equipment was quite safe . . . in Los Angeles!

For almost two days Norm, Joe and Enciso slouched around the Arizona side of Nogales. Then when their equipment arrived they scuttled into Mexico thankful to be back where things worked and people could be trusted.

Driving hard they hit Sonora's capital, Hermosillo, about midnight. Pressing on southward they ran out of roadbed around 3 am and for 200 more miles trailed tire tracks that weaved between mesquite and cactus; hoping they were heading toward the Yaqui Valley, jouncing through dry arroyos and slithering through wet ones — all in pitchy gloom with not even a compass for counsel.

Dawn was breaking when Cajeme showed itself. The sight proved a happy one. The red orb rising over the spiky shoulders of the Sierra Madre provided a glorious backdrop to the panorama in which row upon row of wheat was holding out against stem rust. These included the possible backups he was herding forward, and the crossing-block survivors.

Most significant of all, though, was the five-acre test. Here were the makings of a rust-resistant generation. He decided to select the best individual plants and subject their seeds to a final performance check. Assuming they ace their final test, they'll become his instruments for keeping the disease from devastating Mexico's massive wheat fields.

During April and the first half of May the three companions drove themselves demonically. Making the thousands of field measurements, entering the data, and crunching the numbers to confirm the winners took two weeks. Collecting and thrashing the superior seeds took a further fortnight. Winnowing, drying and packing those seeds into the gunnysacks and paper bags absorbed yet another two weeks.

By the middle of May they'd logged the data into notebooks, labeled the sacks and paper bags, and loaded the truck. The winning seeds were about to undertake another step in their journey through time and space and chance.

When the moment to head south arrived, the little green government truck was piled high with botanical booty, not to mention spare tires and the 60-gallon gasoline drum. Borlaug then realized that entering the U.S. carrying all that cargo could bring untold grief. So he chose to entrust their fate, not to mention nerve endings, to the other route – the shorter one of greater danger.

This direct southward passage started out uneventfully. They dropped down the state of Sonora and entered long, thin, dusty Sinaloa. Paralleling the Pacific shore, they then entered Nayarit, a small state where roads went to die. In this trackless stretch maps were mere moonshine; wiggling through the wild scrub was best done by guess and by golly.

Cutting southeastwards through uncharted wilderness, they plunged blindly across a lookalike landscape hoping to hit Mexico's second largest city, Guadalajara. River crossings were the worst hazards. These were unavoidable since a surprising number of sturdy streams tumble across Nayarit, rushing from the sharp spine of the Sierra Madre to the sea. In 1946 most flowed free from any hint of a bridge.

On discovering a river in your windshield you turned and headed along the bank in search of help. Ferries were common enough, most comprising a couple of rowboats lashed side-by-side with planks laid over top. You paid the owner, drove up onto the planks, and let a cluster of kids on the far shore tug you over on a rope.

When nothing so safe or satisfactory was possible you sought a spot on the near bank where the most tire tracks met the murk. The key was to aim for the muddy scars on the far bank and hope nothing, least of all a hole, lay in wait underwater. Sadly, destiny did not always deliver on a driver's prayers, and during the rainy season river crossings were so perilous it was pointless entering this state on wheels.

That year, however, the rains overslept, and the intrepid trio bested Nayarit's most energetic waters. With neither nerves nor spirits unduly frayed, they navigated the isolated waste and struck the sprawling metropolis of Guadalajara dead center.

Getting home to Mexico City was a relief, and he'd certainly earned a rest. But it was already the third week of May; Central Mexico's wheat-sowing window would close *in a week*. Thus, after visiting the downtown office and sketching out the latest discoveries for George Harrar, Norm headed for Chapingo and began preparing 10 whole acres that would host his third bout with stem rust.

In his fear of the fungus, Norm was almost alone. Neither Americans nor Canadians remembered or cared to remember the malicious microbe that drains wheat's will to live. With Stakman's Newthatch, they and the world were enjoying wheat's golden age. Since 1935 there'd been no rust outbreak.

Norm thus confronted the red menace alone, in obscurity, and in Mexico. That summer in the irrigated fields around the Tarpaper Shack he concentrated on this single issue. To his team he said:

> If we split our effort up into splinter projects we'll never get anywhere. We can't wander off on sideshows; we must do one thing first, **beat stem rust!**

One evening in August 1946 he returned to the apartment from the fields at Chapingo to find Margaret more troubled than she'd been since Scotty's death a year before. She was again pregnant.

Although that news should have brought a glow of happiness, the older heartbreak had yet to heal. The couple considered the possibilities and consequences. Both expressed complete confidence, but their words carried neither conviction nor comfort. In truth their minds had fallen prey to private panic. Throughout the soul-shaking months ahead the horror of history repeating itself hid in their hearts like some persistent poltergeist.

That October flocks of hungry birds began descending on the Chapingo fields. Sparrow-like migrants seasonally use Mexican airspace as they swing back and forth between the Americas. And Norm's grain-ripe fields offered fine dining for all. Unless he acted fast he'd have no seed to reap and no science to report.

But what to do? Hungry birds are almost uncontrollable. There was just one answer: "Joe," he said, "we need bird boys."

That was easily arranged. The foreman now overseeing the fieldwork offered to recruit three youngsters from his village. They'd be there at dawn, he said, but only if they got five pesos a week *paid in advance*. Otherwise, their parents would find a better employer.

Norm handed over 15 pesos.

Next morning the bird patrol was on the job. In ragged shirts and frayed cotton pants, their heads hidden within sombreros barely topping the plants, three little scamps darted hither and yon on shoeless feet, tossing clods, cracking whips, bad mouthing in Spanish so the birds would understand the enormity of their crimes.

Borlaug shouted a greeting, and the boys approached slowly — then one stepped boldly forward. His face was square, his frame solid, his back straight. "Mi nombre," he said, "es Reyes Vega."

Placing his hand on the skinny flat shoulder, Norm replied in Spanish.

"Reyes Vega, you and your brothers do a good job. Come every morning and every evening, okay?"

"Okay, Señor."

The youngster was smart, but his parents seemed not to care. A couple of years earlier they'd sent him out to find work; five pesos a week trumped any hopes of higher education a kid might entertain.

As the boy disappeared down the path, shyly peeking over a shoulder, the glint of his gaze flashed back to the onlookers.

"Did you see those bright eyes, Norm?" Rupert asked.

"Yes, Joe," Borlaug replied, "He'll do well, that one."

When the Day of Judgment arrived in October 1946 Norm surveyed the outcome of his preliminary trial. The four types still stood tall, having yet again survived the stem-rust spore showers and this time having also survived the heat of Central Mexico's summer. Those four had aced this final exam.

The two that had come from Edgar McFadden both derived from Hope, the variety the Texas professor had created almost twenty years earlier by blending genes from modern wheat with those of emmer, the wheat that fed the ancients. Their rust-resistance thus derived from the species that probably provided the bread for The Last Supper.

After checking each individual plant in those plots, Norm saved seeds only from the 209th and 211th plants he came across. There were 200 seeds of each. Those became the varieties he called Frontera and Supremo.

The other two plants that aced their final came from Stakman's packets. Kenya Red and Kenya White derived from seeds a former-student had donated years before. Gerald Burton had saved the seeds from destruction by a fire that razed the experiment station in Kenya, the East African country where he lived. Kenya Red and Kenya White were identical except for the color of the skin on their seeds. Their special rust-resistance probably derived from pasta wheat but no one knows for certain because the records were lost to the flames.

Within a month Norm headed back north. This is where he began the practice of sowing test plots along the route to Sonora. Driving 300 miles north in the program's first post-war vehicle – a brand-new, wooden-sided Chevy station wagon – he and Joe Rupert established small plantings in the Bajío. Then they headed 300 miles further north and sowed similar plots in La Laguna, a newly developed irrigation district near Torreón. Finally, they ventured on yet another 300 miles into the heart of Coahuila, where they hoped to learn how their marquee foursome will perform under conditions approximating those across the border in Texas.

On reaching Coahuila's colorful capital of Saltillo, Norm and Joe visited a local agricultural college and asked where they might establish a trial. To their delight, an agronomy professor assigned two students to escort them to the perfect place.

In the outcome, the place would fall a little short of perfection:

At seven the next morning the four of us set out, heading southwards, back the way Joe and I had come the day before. An hour or so later, the students directed us to turn west into a remote highland. After maybe an hour's climb we came to a mountainside farm. The students introduced us to the owner, who pointed out a small field we could borrow for the trial. The plot clung to the south side of a very beautiful but also very deep valley. Despite its steepness, it seemed ideal for our needs.

The four of us prepared a patch about the size of a tennis court using hoes. After a while we noticed puffs of cloud crowning the hills at the head of the valley to the west. There, rain was falling; we paid no heed . . . it was miles away.

A couple of hours later Joe noticed that the nearby gully bottoms were brimming. Then things got serious. The little stream we'd crossed when driving into the field had surged over its banks. There was no way out—we were trapped.

The sky soon opened up on us too. October being still the dry season we were unprepared, and there was no possible shelter on that exposed slope. The four of us huddled together inside the station wagon. We were wet as sponges and had no way to dry off. Having put in a hard day's labor we were all famished but had no food. There was no heat either, and at that altitude the night air was cold.

We stretched out in the back of the vehicle. Even with my sleeping bag thrown over top we shivered, praying for daylight and clear skies while the deluge drummed on the metal over our heads.

Next morning, thank God, the rain stopped; but the floodwaters stayed high until late afternoon. By then all of us were thoroughly out of sorts. As I drove away no one was in a talking mood.

Back in Saltillo I rented a hotel room where we could clean up. Having hit the showers all four of us dashed for the dining room. Then to my surprise, as we crossed the lobby one of the students ducked over to the hotel piano and began playing and singing Mexican ballads. He was a muscular young man who'd already impressed me by his hard work. Now he showed the talent to lift our spirits. The tunes he coaxed from that battered old instrument were magical. With the assistance of a little tequila, the frustrations eased and for a while even the hurt of hunger subsided.

Taken all round, this young man impressed me so much that, a year later when he graduated from the Antonio Narro School of Agriculture, I offered him a job.

Thus it was that Ignacio Narvaez [nar-VY-es] manipulated a battered old bar piano to acquire a full-time position on the scientific staff.

Beyond changing Narvaez' life, this episode also changed Norm's. Never again would he leave town without stocking his vehicle with three sleeping bags, a 12-gauge shotgun, a fishing rod, a camp stove, and a cache of emergency rations comprising: 1) cans of meat, peas and peaches; 2) bags of dried beans and rice; and 3) a packet of ground coffee.

1. Norm was born in the upstairs room of this humble farmhouse, seen here as it was at the time. On the left can be seen the remains of the original Borlaug log cabin.

2. From the age of 7 Norm lived in this house, which his father built in 1921. Both houses and his one-room school are maintained by the Norman Borlaug Heritage Foundation.

3. Norm Boy, age 8 and his older cousin Vilmar (Sina Borlaug's brother) are clad in their standard work attire. Norm displays the cheeky smile and special charm that endeared all comers

4. At home during his high school days Norm still shows his charm, but in this era life was dissolving as the Great Depression hit. He spent those summers working in the fields, but this must have been a special occasion as he's sporting a tie, a watch and white shoes – things he'd hate to be seen with later in life.

5. Norm graduates with his BS degree in forestry, December 18, 1937. He and Margaret had been married almost 3 months. The Saude newspaper reported:

> Norman has maintained a "B" average for the whole four years of his college education. He was elected to two Honorary Scholastic Fraternities, Xi Sigma Pi, National Forestry Fraternity, of which he was president in 1936 and Alpha Zeta, National Agriculture and Forestry Fraternity. He was a member of the University wrestling team for three years and won his three "M's".

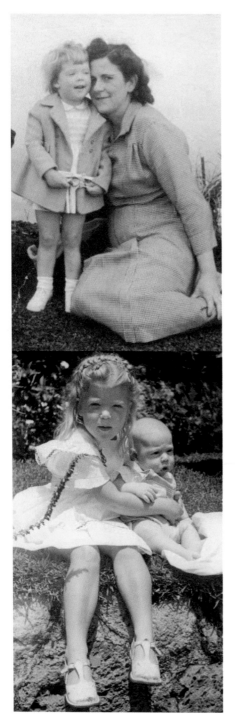

6. Jeanie and Margaret, 1945 shortly after their arrival in Mexico. This was when Margaret was coping with the horror of having a child succumbing in confinement far away in Delaware.

7. Jeanie [4 years] and Billie [4 months], Mexico City, summer 1947.

8. Cuernavaca, Mexico 1956. Jeanie remembers those days: "Bill and I were excited to see Dad when he lived at home, but even then he would leave at 5am and return around 8pm, so we really did not have much time with him. However, the time we did have was always quality time. He was genuinely interested in our activities and events. Dad took off six weeks every second summer to tour the U.S. and visit family and friends. Those were great vacations, and we had wonderful times — going to many baseball games and eating at a lot of Dairy Queens (he loved their ice cream). It was great for the family."

9. Coach Borlaug. Piloting young people to extraordinary attainment was as iconic a feature of his life as was his hunger fighting. During his days he helped thousands liberate themselves from locked down lives through science and through sport.

10. Mexico's first Little League season. Inaugurated by Norm and his colleague John Niederhauser (both seen here, with Bill Borlaug between them).

11. The champion Pony League team, 1961. Bill Borlaug is in the center of the front row.

12. Mexican wheat farming before Borlaug. In 1944 wheat was grown in thin stands and harvested by hand. The plants were mixtures, which made the grain hard to sell, mill and bake.

13. Mexican wheat farming after Borlaug. By the 1950s the wheat fields were densely packed with uniform plants. Norm is seen here with a Sonora farmer. Maybe this is Roberto Maurer's field – the one about which Norm said: "I really didn't know it was going to turn out this good!"

14. Norm is driving Aureliano Campoy's small combine at the Yaqui Valley Experiment station in about 1948. They are loading the truck with the bags of wheat. The man on the truck might be Campoy; the others probably include Enciso and Campos.

15. By 1956 Mexico harvested far too much wheat to be handled in sacks, and shifted to bulk handling. This is thought to be Norm's first student, José Guevara.

16. Farmer Demonstration day at the Yaqui Valley Experiment Station, probably April 1949.

17. Norm's support staff included Mexican boys, most of them scarcely literate, who began by scaring off hordes of sparrows and subsequently became cross-pollinators of wheat. Many of the gene matches that eventually fed the world were made by them.

18. Sonora, around 1970. Norm retains the movie-star aura but would be shocked to learn that fame lies in his future.

19. Norm is shown with the Wheat Apostles, probably the 1964 group. They are standing in a plot of Sonora 64, one of the first two dwarf whe released. The standard sized plants are in the plots all around

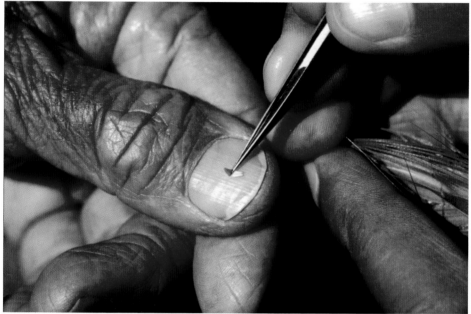

20. When cross-pollinating wheat the first step involves removing all the plant's own pollen sacs. As shown here, those are very small, which makes the process tedious and challenging.

21. A wheat-breeder's ultimate product is seedheads packed with plump grains that make great bread. To produce those shown here Norm and his team made more than 8000 cross-pollinations. This is one of the four dwarf wheats that will contribute to feeding the world.

22. When Norm went to Sonora in 1944 the town had a sleepy look. Its dirt streets (including the main drag shown here) and false-front buildings made it seem like a wild-west movie mockup.

23. By 1960 Obregón City was a showcase with wide paved streets, parks and playgrounds. Around the city were huge grain elevators as well as factories producing cookies, bread, flour tortillas and beer. In 1968 the main street was officially named Calle Dr. Norman E. Borlaug.

24. Pakistani Success, March 1968: From left, Borlaug, Oddvar Aresvik, E.C. Stakman, Minister Khuda Bakhsh Bucha, Ignacio Narvaez and a visiting stem-rust expert from the U.S.

25. Indian success, March 1968. Starting at fourth from left, you see the technical team that turned India from perennial famine to food surplus: Borlaug, Glenn Anderson, and M.S. Swaminathan.

26. Indian wheat farming before Borlaug. In 1963 wheat was grown in thin stands and harvested by hand. The plants were subject to stem rust disease. The yield ceiling was 800lb an acre and the highest annual production was 12 million tons (in 1964).

27. Indian wheat farming after Borlaug. By 1968, the wheat fields were densely packed with uniform plants and the yield ceiling had risen to 6000lb (3 tons) an acre. Nowadays India's wheat production is over 80 million tons.

28. Ludhiana, capital of India's Punjab. In 1968 food was everywhere and there was nowhere to store the surplus. When the monsoon rains threatened ruin the schools became store houses.

29. Wheat Apostles in Pakistan in April 1969. They represented countries around the world. They'd helped perfect the dwarf wheats and introduced Borlaug's seeds and his spirit to their nations.

30. In April 1968 Rollie Henkes, who lived not far from Saude, Iowa, traveled to Sonora to interview Norm. That August this photograph showing Norm standing amid dwarf wheat that barely rises above his knees adorned the cover of *World Farming* magazine. It was among the first public endorsements of the transformation that was coming out of the Mexican desert.

31. Norm and Margaret photographed in Texas in 1983. Because of Norm's never-ending absences Margaret was the rock of the family. She put up with the loneliness and did all the chores he hated, such as paying bills and keeping the bank accounts straight. Without that, the tale of these pages would not have occurred. Starting in the 1980s Norm spent the fall quarter at Texas A&M University, where he could interact with students and be with Margaret and their grandchildren.

1947-1948

Near Death

I n November 1946, Borlaug and Rupert began the opening stanza of the 1947 cycle. For three weeks they sowed large fields, which they hoped would produce 2 tons of Frontera, Supremo and the Kenyas.

Following that, they sowed hundreds of rows of the descendants of the cross-pollinations Norm had made back in the summer of 1945. Those unique gene mixes were sorting themselves out, and Norm hoped some might eventually produce his next breakout varieties.

At the Yaqui Valley Experiment Station neither the work nor the living was any easier. Nights in the rundown loft were shared with the weevil infested grain, not to mention the rats, mice, mosquitoes and snakes. Norm still marvels that his friend didn't rebel:

> Thank God Joe could take it. If he hadn't been through combat in the North African desert, I'm sure he'd have left. Who could blame him?

Conditions were so terrible Norm himself might have quit had not Aureliano Campoy once again stepped forward. Though he initially kept his distance, the farmer neighbor was awed by the strange goings on across the street. Norm and Joe often noticed him peering from his front porch as if puzzled by the unfathomable ways of gringos. However, during this winter season the shyness eased, and he began appearing several times a week:

> Campoy didn't have enough to occupy his time. He often came over to talk with us. He'd always show up after church on Sundays, when we were the only ones foolish enough to be out working!

Cathy Jones, whose property adjoined Campoy's, adopted Norm and Joe like a broody hen with orphan chicks. Saturday mornings they were required to join her trek to town for supplies. Sunday nights their presence was demanded for coffee, which always morphed into a meal. She did their washing and mending when common decency made those necessary. She listened to their talk and nodded approval of all their plans and opinions.

Having grown up in Connecticut Mrs Jones and her husband Cappy had come to Sonora as teenage newlyweds more than 40 years before. They'd survived the Mexican Revolution, one of the most violent on record. Even after Cappy died in 1931 Widow Jones stayed on, choosing Cajeme over Connecticut as the place to raise her two daughters.

Before Norm arrived, both daughters had moved stateside and Mrs Jones inhabited her cozy cottage alone. Perhaps solitude was what induced her to care for the curious creatures slumming in the disgusting dump across the street. Whatever the reason, her help was welcomed:

> I couldn't have survived without Mrs Jones. I was cooking my own food, sleeping in a grungy hayloft, seldom getting a bath. She provided comfort and a touch of home. Those kept me sane and made the Sonora work possible.
> Above all, though, Mrs Jones made me speak Spanish. On week nights she'd invite me over and then *force* me to brush up my grammar. By then I knew many words but couldn't make meaningful conversation. She was sure hard to please, and drilled me so relentlessly I at last learned to communicate.

During that Christmas, when Norm had gone home for family time Margaret's pregnancy was progressing. But he yet again abandoned her in her time of need. The wheat plant's growth cycle waited for no man; in Sonora by late January the flowers were swelling, and he had but three weeks to complete hundreds of cross-pollinations before the flowers faded and died.

Following those madcap action days early in February '47, he could and should have hastened home to be with Margaret. However, he tempted feminine wrath and remained an extra month in Sonora.

Though none then realized it, the pattern of existence had been set. For half of each year she would mind the store while he lived like a monk in this fleapit proper folks fled.

She remained forever sanguine about his schedule. This particular time, however, he strained her legendary tolerance by arriving home in mid-March, less than two weeks before she entered the maternity home in Lomas de Chapultepec.

Their third child was born March 29. It was a boy, and the sight of his firm back and fully formed body dispelled the fears that for months had flitted behind their smiles.

They chose to name him "William Gibson."

In no time he became "Billy."

Within days of the birth, Norm headed off once more. The sun had hastened north, and the Judgment Days were nigh. On the hot flat floor of the Sonoran Desert that April he paced the research fields, ruthlessly ripping out every specimen even marginally falling short of expectations. He worked with immediacy, making split-second decisions and never entertaining doubts. Only an infinitesimal number of the plants under study got tagged and had their seeds saved. The vast majority ended up as flour tortillas.

In the cohort he was herding forward he found that fate had handed him three surprises. The first involved Mentana, the variety Mexico had dumped because it succumbed to stem rust. In his first cross-pollination efforts Norm had included this variety as a gene donor. Now, four seasons onward, descendants of crosses between Mentana and Kenya were producing progeny undaunted by desert heat *or stem rust*.

The second surprise involved the other reputed loser, Marroqui. This supposed wimp now proved a whopper. Years went by before this riddle unraveled. Turns out, the predecessor's field staff had failed to realize (or at least report) that half the man's Marroqui crop had been eaten by the birds.

The third surprise was the discovery that wheats with Marroqui genes ripened two weeks early. That speedy maturity would become the first feature Borlaug built into the world's wheat crop.

All these advances were thanks to the Mentana and Marroqui seedheads he'd saved solely because he'd had nothing else to show for his first foray into Sonora.

Late that April he hauled Sonora's winning seed as well as the two tons of Frontera, Supremo and the two Kenyas back to Central Mexico. Never before had he handled seed by the ton and, because Chapingo lacked the land and machinery, he had no way to multiply it further. Mexico's farmers needed at least 5000 tons of seed wheat, and getting that much seemed quite impossible.

At the Chapingo home base visitors nowadays seemed to pop up from nowhere, curious about the emerald succulence bejeweling the weedy wastes. Thus it came as no surprise that one day in May when he was preparing nursery plots Norm looked up to see a small, round American staring at him.

The man was clearly agitated. His legs were firmly planted, feet apart, and he rocked from side to side as if unable to remain at rest. After the briefest of introductions Richard Spurlock poured out a tale of woe. "They destroyed my cows last week," he said, choking over the words. "I'm stuck here for four years with nothing to do!"

Norm instantly understood the meaning behind this cryptic comment. Back in December foot and mouth disease had broken out, and almost before anyone realized it, a quarter-million square miles spanning Mexico's middle were either infected or likely so.

This contagion that infects cloven-hoofed creatures was nearly impossible to control in 1947. An airborne virus, it could not be detected until the feet broke apart and the tongue tissues separated leaving lame, sick, salivating and very sorry looking livestock, a third of whom would die leaving the rest to infect their brethren. Slaughtering every susceptible animal was the only secure solution.

This is the strange phenomenon lurking behind the distressed stockman's plea in the spring of 1947. Spurlock managed a modern dairy farm in Toluca, a high-altitude valley on the far side of Mexico City. Despite every appearance of good health, his prize cows had been shot. With most of his contract still ahead, he needed something to do. "I've heard you know about wheat," he said as he rocked back and forth that morning at Chapingo. "I've raised grass and alfalfa but never a food crop. Can you get me started?"

Without a second thought Norm placed in this stranger's charge the multiplication of the seed he'd just trucked down from Sonora. Following the first rains in early May, he loaded up a pickup and drove the gunnysacks up the hill and onto the Toluca Valley, a couple of hours and a couple of cultures away to the west.

Known as El Cerrillo, the farm was owned by a wealthy Connecticut family and had land, peons, storage barns, and equipment. Indeed, it possessed a Massey Harris tractor together with plows, disks, harrows and a grain drill. They'd been bought to produce alfalfa and hay for the cows the government sharpshooter had subsequently shot. These shiny new Canadian-built implements made their mark with the first-ever major multiplication of Borlaug wheats, the 2 tons of Frontera,

Supremo, Kenya White and Kenya Red. It was the first-ever hundred-acre planting of Borlaug seed.

When the plants began flowering in July the action season had arrived. Norm entered the Tarpaper Shack and pulled a pair of fine-nosed tweezers from his pack and tied them about his neck with a length of twine. Then he stuffed his shirt pockets with paper tubes, paperclips, pens, and notebook, not to mention a hooked knife with a razor-sharp blade. Next he grabbed his canvas-bottomed stool and marched into the crowded ranks of crop plants for a twelve-hour session of cross-pollination.

As this was his fourth season, the process had become routine. It nonetheless taxed the brain and the body. You see, wheat crams its male and female flowers together for their mutual satisfaction. Anyone wishing to mate wheat must first violate the plant chosen as the bride by removing every male part at the precise moment when those tiny appendages have formed but have yet to develop pollen. The fact that this occurs *before* the flower opens means that the breeder must cut the top off each tiny floret merely to access its male parts. That is why Norm toted a canvas-bottomed stool. When castrating wheat 12 hours a day you cannot stand.

Even the subsequent step — providing the pollen from the plant chosen as the groom — presented problems because once opened to Mexico's broiling sky, pollen stays viable less than 5 minutes. This is why Norm's crossing blocks were arranged so precisely. During those hectic hours he had almost no time for wiping the brow, let alone walking between plants.

One day that July the head bird boy, Reyes Vega, wandered by and asked what Borlaug was doing to the wheat flower. Ever the solicitous coach, Norm demonstrated the cumbrous and complex initial steps: slicing open the florets, pulling out the pollen sacs, and hiding the feminized remnant within a paper tube to shield it from passing pollen.

When the boy asked if he could try it, the request seemed shocking. Since its nineteenth-century beginnings cereal breeding had been performed by eminent academics. Norm, however, quickly indulged the lad. And almost from the start, the school dropout picked up the procedure as if born to it. Indeed, before 1947's three-week flowering season was over he'd become as adept as a modern microsurgeon. By then the world's most unlikely wheat-breeder, a village kid without formal learning or technical preparation, was wielding the knife, tweezers, envelopes, pens, paper tubes, and notebooks with aplomb and operating on the intricate wheat flower parts with speed, skill, precision, and what amounted to saucy ease.

Norm and Joe were in a buoyant mood as they approached Judgment Day in October 1947. Never had they felt closer or more energized. Back in May they'd tiptoed into unmapped chromosomal country; now they could see that by herding forward the progeny from his 1945 cross-pollinations they'd uncovered four descendants that were looking good. This new quartet had been fashioned by combining Newthatch, Marroqui, Mentana and Kenya, and they offered major advances in yield and quality.

With all that motivating their minds Norm and Joe were in high feather when, late one Thursday afternoon they dropped by the office in Viena 26 to file the field notes and grab their mail before heading home. But as the secretary handed over their piles of letters she let slip six fateful words: "Doctor Harrar wants to see you."

I dropped the mail on the corner of the secretary's desk and followed Joe into the director's office. George was behind his desk as usual. But I was surprised to see Stakman lounging on the sofa along the right-hand wall, pipe gripped between his teeth and tobacco tin tight in his hand. Although retired from the University of Minnesota, he came down a couple of times a year to see how we were getting on.

After we'd exchanged greetings, George dropped his bombshell with his standard suddenness. "Funds are running short," he said, "so we want you to abandon the Yaqui Valley. Sorry Norm, but you've got to do this. Sonora is too isolated; it's costing too much. From now on, focus your work on the Bajío."

In a long life containing many shocks this was maybe my greatest. His words fell heavy as an axe. We were being instructed to ignore the very place that was the key to getting the country fed. To think we'd not be going back was almost unbearable.

At that point, sad to relate, I began losing self-control. "You gave me the responsibility to make Mexico self-sufficient in wheat." The words came out far too loud for that tiny office. "Now you're tying one arm behind my back, and ensuring I can't succeed. The Bajío can't meet the country's needs. Only Sonora can do that. In the Bajío there's not enough water or land, and the holdings are too small."

Then I completely lost my composure. "If this is a firm decision," I yelled down at Harrar behind his desk, "you'd better find someone else because I'm leaving!"

A second thought occurred: "I'll stay until you find a replacement. If Joe takes over the program I'll leave tomorrow." And I swung on my heels and headed for the door.

Before I got halfway I noticed Joe beside me: "That goes for me too!" he shouted over his shoulder.

And we stalked out side-by-side.

But the story then took another twist:

Back in the secretary's office I grabbed my pile of letters and then flung them down in disgust. What was the use of checking the mail?

Then in the spread of scattered envelopes Aureliano Campoy's return address stared up. Intrigued, I opened the envelope to find a blind carbon copy of a letter the old farmer had laboriously typed out in English: "Dr. Harrar," it began, "I want to congratulate the Rockefeller Foundation. For the first time in the history of Mexico someone is helping the farmers. I admire what you're doing, and it will have a big effect here in Sonora."

But the kicker came at the end: "Why don't you help your own staff? Why don't you give them the things they need? Borlaug and Rupert are living and working under terrible conditions. Why is that? Why do you treat your people so badly?"

Pinned to my copy was a handwritten note: "It is time somebody was helping you," it said.

I handed the missive to Joe. I was convinced that I'd just let our friend down by quitting. "Hell," I said, "this is the worst possible time for a letter like this!" and stalked out of the building feeling worse than ever.

In truth, we should have gone straight home. Instead we went to a cantina and drowned our sorrows. I've seldom been intoxicated but this was one unforgettable time. Midnight was long gone before we got back to the apartment. Margaret was so angry we'd skipped her dinner and were obviously the worse for wear she wouldn't let us in.

She and I got into a shouting match through the front door.

It was like some comic-opera farce.

It was also the final straw: my career was over; my marriage too.

Impartial observers might not believe the farce's final act: the aggrieved party behind the locked door actually relented. Despite every provocation, she admitted the worthless miscreants.

Nonetheless, next morning both lowlifes scuttled away before dawn, too wretched in mind and body to endure more feminine fury. They planned to devote their last day on the job to a proper wrap-up. Before abandoning all hope for helping the hungry they wanted to see just how far they'd gotten. Moreover, they'd leave behind the top seed and a tidy record for anyone who might follow.

First, though, they needed to retrieve the field notebooks. As they entered Viena 26 a voice emerged from Harrar's office, and Borlaug received yet another shock: Stakman was sitting on the sofa, puffing the pipe and holding the tobacco tin tight as before. This was truly historic since it was 6:30 and, as far as Norm knew, no one had ever seen Stak at work before 10:00.

The crafty professor looked straight through his protégé. "You're acting like a child!" he said in the tones that reduced students to rag dolls.

Norm was by now past the point where the faraway look and stiletto voice were effective. "What the hell do you mean?" he yelled. "Dutch is making it impossible to solve Mexico's wheat problem. It's that simple!"

Stakman now glared just as he did at exceptionally wayward undergrads, but could see that he was getting nowhere. "Calm yourself, calm yourself," he said at last. "You and Harrar are too much alike . . . ornery as hell. Let me see what I can do."

That Friday, Joe and Norm were depressed even while recording yields of over a ton an acre! Afterwards, the disconsolate duo returned to Viena 26 to pick up their final mail, surrender their notebooks and conclude their careers.

Pinned to the mail slot, was a note instructing them to report to the director's office.

On entering the august office, the pair found both Harrar and Stakman waiting. The moment was taut with tension. A breathless silence hung between them all. Norm was sure he was about to be fired!

Then George Harrar delivered an even greater shock: "Forget what I said, Norm. Go on working in Sonora. We'll find some way to support you."

This was unnerving because Harrar never recanted a professional decision. Stakman's personal influence must have helped. But the clincher would have been the letter from the Sonora farmer who, while himself living hardscrabble, was reaching out to better the lot of the strangers who'd come to improve Sonora farming. That would have touched Harrar's humanitarian heart.

Having completed the work at Chapingo, Norm drove to Toluca to help Spurlock harvest the hundred acres. His hopes, however, were rebuffed when a rain swollen cloudbank rolled in from the wide Pacific. After waiting a few days for the land to dry he tried again but as if on cue the clouds rolled back. Subsequently, this action-and-reaction repeated itself until the bottom dropped out of Spurlock's fields. No machine could move across 40 acres that had become little more than marsh.

Water is a fickle friend to wheat farmers. In the seed-sowing season there's no greater ally; in the seed-harvesting season time no greater foe. Dampened grain attracts mold and may even sprout before leaving the parent plant. Either way, the crop is rendered worthless.

For that reason the seed multiplication operation that would empower Mexico's wheat farmers now teetered on the brink of disaster. And with the forecast predicting more storms marching forward from the South Seas, Norm was about to lose several seasons' work, if not his senses. You see, he'd committed all the available seed to this multiplication.

In desperation, he grabbed Joe Rupert and hauled him out to Toluca. Slaving like the serfs of old, the lookalikes sickled hundreds of thousands of plants, using loose stalks to bind them into the bundles that old timers called sheaves. Spurlock provided peons for the even bigger task of hauling all those sheaves through the marshy mud to shelter.

Finally, having endured a week slogging in soupy slop — hair sodden, clothes filthy and boots like mud footballs — the group could admire thousands of bundles safely stacked in the big barn. Later, Spurlock's workers methodically turned the sheaves to ensure the heads dried without molding or sprouting.

Beyond being fantastic this exploit yielded 2800lb an acre — more than four times that year's Mexican average. Despite Mother Nature opposition, they'd reaped 50 tons of grain by hand.

"You know what this means, Dick?" Borlaug gushed. "We're on our way! Another planting will give us 5000 tons. Next year maybe we'll have all the seed the farmers need!"

By then it was November 1947, and before leaving for the trip north and Round 6 Norm and Joe packed the seed of the summer's winning plants. They also packed 200lb of Kenya Red and Kenya White, which they planned to multiply specifically for Sonora farmers to sow.

Given the size of the load George Harrar had relented and released *two* pickup trucks. One was the old green Ford with the government eagles decorating the doors; the other a brand new long-body Chevrolet with a screened-in top. Both had been released with a strict stipulation that they *be returned immediately*.

When the convoy left Mexico City Norm drove the smaller vehicle, with Oscar Nery Sosa, a Guatemalan student, as his passenger. Joe followed in the new Chevy, accompanied by Teodoro Enciso and Alfredo Campos. Norm's truck carried the Kenya seed as well as a kerosene fueled camp stove and the cache of emergency food; Joe's toted a small tractor as well as miscellaneous supplies and equipment.

For this trip Norm had decided to cut across the Sierra Madre Occidental on a new road linking the states of Chihuahua and Sinaloa. This was a big risk because that route through the mountain massif that people refer to as the Devil's Backbone had yet to be formally opened.

The mid-November morning was bright and clear, and the three-day 800-mile run to the city of Chihuahua proved uneventful. After a night in a downtown (and downscale) hotel they headed out on the main road west. Then, toward noon, just as they began bending up the mountain barrier's eastern wall the sky turned leaden.

Though mid-November was still the dry season, the midday sky hung low and dark cloud-strands dangled like bangs from heaven's brow. Then, just as the quaint convoy entered the giant gash through the ramparts of the Mexican Rockies, the sooty sky loosed a deluge. Water cascaded down the cliff, skittered across the roadbed and fell into the void next to the passenger-side wheels.

Still they pressed forward, and the newly cut section of road proved to be a single lane carved from the perpendicular rock comprising the south wall of the Barranca del Cobre, Mexico's famed Copper Canyon that size-wise puts the Grand Canyon to shame.

Peering through the waltzing wipers Borlaug saw the dirt surface turning greasy. Still he kept on until on rounding a blind bend he had to brake suddenly to avoid hitting the back of a large truck that loomed out of the murk before his bumper. He and Enciso sloshed forward to discover that ahead of the truck the canyon wall had collapsed.

Norm then sloshed back around the blind bend, hoping to find a way out of the impasse; but as he approached there came a rumble, and the ground commenced shaking as an avalanche of rock and earth collapsed the ledge they'd just traversed.

In the nick of time a pickup truck had pulled in behind Joe's. Its driver proved to be the engineer in charge of the road construction. In trying to secure this area his workers had struck columnar rock. Indeed, the hard outcropping had proven so recalcitrant Mexico had appealed for help to the Soviet Union. Moscow, in turn, had dispatched a renowned specialist to oversee the placement of the explosives. He was right there in the engineer's pickup. Moreover, the bulky truck in Norm's windshield carried the dynamite.

To Norm the Russian's presence seemed a blessing. Mexicans would move mountains to rescue anyone who might know Premier Stalin.

Thankfully as evening descended the rain let up, and Norm set up his camp stove and retrieved the emergency rations. Those few cans of meat, peas, peaches and coffee as well as bags of dried beans and rice provided the sole sustenance for eight souls wedged on that ledge.

He recalled the scene with a sideways laugh:

> Neither Joe nor I minded doing the cooking and sharing our food but the Soviet engineer was perhaps the most offensive individual I've ever met — and I've certainly met my share. Somehow Joe's former tour of duty in North Africa came out, and even while eating our food the Russian sneered about Rommel whipping the whole U.S. Army. He made the point not once but endlessly. Amazingly, Joe stayed cool, calm and civil. To this day I can't believe he didn't tip that guy over the edge!

On the second afternoon the food ran out. Soon thereafter, however, the clank of a bulldozer was heard echoing off the rock walls up ahead. An hour later the machine itself emerged into view, pushing tons of liquefied spoil off the ledge.

The operator next hooked a chain to the front end of the big truck, told Borlaug to attach his towrope to the back end, and began hauling both vehicles over the still-oozing surface. This was scary, since either the big truck or the little pickup might fishtail over the lip. Alternatively, the dynamite might do the job.

But the outcome proved ordinary. The bulldozer pulled them through the danger zone and the convoy cautiously descended the long and winding road down the Sierra Madre western wall. With heartfelt elation the little party crossed Sinaloa's flooded flats to reach the town of Los Mochis as night fell.

After renting rooms in a cheap hotel, Norm and Joe retired to the bar to try to rebuild their shattered spirits. Settling back into the comforts of a highball, they observed the communist engineer saunter in and look around. They kept their heads down, and under his breath Joe expressed a rather coarse comment explaining just where the man from Moscow might go. The unwelcome presence, however, sauntered over and sat down, acting with seeming genuine friendship. Following a Cuba Libre, conversation blossomed and all three got on like old comrades in arms. Now that it was behind them, the wall of death seemed like a lark.

Although the peril was past, the problems persisted. Rain had washed out the highway to Sonora. Borlaug then made a crucial decision: He and Joe hustled Enciso and Campos to the train station, unpacked the seed and small tractor and arranged for those and the two young Mexicans to take the next train to Sonora. Before he left, Norm told them to get everything out to the old experiment station and *plant the damn seed!*

Norm, Joe and the young Guatemalan trainee then headed toward Mexico City via the direct descent down the coast. They were duty bound to return the pickups to George Harrar, but this time the route of greater danger would show no pity.

The difficulty began when they reached the Santiago River. Rain from the Sierra Madre cloudburst was barreling out of nearby Lake Chapala in a heaving, hurrying, bubbling brown tide. Indeed, the river seemed big enough to be draining half the nation, which in a sense it was since Lake Chapala is like an inland sea and the Santiago is its major outlet.

The sight was terrifying, but not so terrifying to overcome Norm's sense of responsibility:

> At the river crossing a couple of women were washing clothes by the water's edge. They told us a truck had gone across earlier. The other bank was just 150 yards away, and we could see a road-worker camp. I decided to go ahead despite the oncoming darkness and the swollen torrent.
>
> After removing the fan belt to stop the blades throwing water over the wiring, I attached a piece of rubber hose to the exhaust pipe and tied it so that the end stood up like a snorkel. Those were common procedures when driving in Mexico in the 1940s.
>
> Then, following the imprint of the previous tire tracks, I drove that little pickup down into the flow. The view ahead was not comforting; the river writhed between its banks and the current seemed to have raised the middle. And right there, in the highest part of this surging chocolate tide, the engine stalled.

At first I wasn't concerned but the engine refused to start and water was spurting in through cracks around the door. Oscar was clearly scared and as the cab began filling he let on that he couldn't swim. I had to do something. So I yanked off my boots, yelled I was going to get help, climbed out the window, and started walking toward the road-building camp.

Although the water was only waist deep, the bottom was stony and sharp and cut my feet as I pushed against the current to keep upright. Then, all of a sudden, one foot slipped, and I went tumbling into the deeps below the crossing. In that powerful tide there was no chance of swimming. The turbulence sent me rolling and tossing into the dark depths. I could feel consciousness passing away. It seemed like the end.

Luckily for me, instinct stayed sharp, and on sensing the clutch of the current slackening I kicked my way to the surface. The river had curved, and the water churning around the bend was depositing me toward the inner side, which happened to be the far bank.

Hope rushed back, and willing my body to move I struggled into the backwash and dragged myself out onto a rocky shoal. I'd made it across. I was sodden, gasping like whooping cough, my whole body shaking from shock.

There was no time for musing about myself . . . Oscar needed help. Somehow I managed to stumble the 200 yards to the road-building camp. To my horror, the crew was standing around staring at the truck stranded in mid-river . . . awaiting the inevitable. Water had filled the cab and Oscar was standing on top pleading for help. Yet despite his cries, no one was doing anything.

Even I was out of ideas. Then I noticed the Caterpillar grader. I strode to the man who appeared to be the foreman and told him to start it up. He said it was out of fuel. When I pointed to a tanker trailer nearby he explained that only the engineer had a key, and he'd gone off to the next village for the Saturday night movie. Then he shrugged; nothing could be done.

Grabbing a stick, I stuck it in the grader's tank. It was empty all right but dregs of diesel remained. The sight of that brown stain on the tip of the stick won over the foreman, and he started the grader and drove it to the water.

Luckily, it was fitted with a winch wound with steel cable. I grabbed the sturdy hook on the end and waded out along the ford to stretch that lifeline out to our little truck. Five of the road crew came behind, holding up the cable as it unwound. We were all very scared; darkness was descending, the speeding water was ripping at our bodies, our hold on the cable was precarious. Also my legs weren't too steady and the sharp stones were again cutting my feet.

On reaching the pickup I found that there was no place to attach the cable. The current had scoured out so much soil from beneath the tires the front bumper was resting on the bottom.

But something had to be done, so ducking under the bubbling tide, I scraped away rocks and gravel, and managed to loop the hook under the bumper and back onto the cable. Then I waved to the grader driver on the shore. As the cable took the strain I felt sure our boxy green pickup would flip over and toss Oscar into the deeps downstream but with all six of us hanging onto the upper side, it slowly slid forward, grinding on the rocks.

The moment when it emerged in the shallows and slid up the bank was memorable. The old Ford looked like some sea creature being yanked from its natural habitat. Brown fluids spurted from every pore.

By then, night had fallen and getting the second pickup across was impossible. Next morning, however, the waters had receded enough for Joe to drive over. Even so we couldn't proceed. Getting the drowned government vehicle back in running order took all day. To our amazement, the crankcase was empty. Even now, that seems hard to believe; the water must have pushed out the oil.

In the upshot the adventure turned out okay. Nonetheless, we dared not mention the incident to George Harrar. It took about a year to pluck up the courage to show him Joe's photograph of the scene — just the top half of the precious pickup sticking above the raging waters and the young student who'd come from Guatemala to learn how to be a scientist standing on top in terror for his very life!

On arrival at the apartment Norm was in bad shape. Margaret demanded he seek help, but after a long soak in the bath he retired to bed. When he awoke 10 hours later she called the neighborhood doctor, who dressed the cut and swollen feet and ordered a week of bed rest. "Impossible," Norm retorted. "The season is already passing and our whole program depends on that seed in Sonora."

Within 48 hours he'd landed at Cajeme airfield. His heart was racing as he was driven toward the unprepossessing experiment station in the arid emptiness. But when the vehicle turned in through the concrete pillars worry turned to wonder as he admired the rows of dense seedlings emerging from the damp earth beside the half-mile driveway.

Teodoro Enciso and Alfredo Campos had worked their hearts out. They'd saved the season; the program remained on track.

Campos soon thereafter returned to complete his college degree. When the fields began flowering in February 1948 Norm and Enciso worked as if the weight of the world rested on their shoulders. During that wheat-mating period each strove to complete every cross possible with four hands, two heads and twelve hours of midwinter daylight.

Among the hundreds of crosses, a dozen or so involved pollinating Kenya Red with Frontera and Supremo and vice versa. For this, there was no apparent practical need; he was just double-charging the chromosomes with Kenya- *and* Hope- type resistances.

Late that April, he set about organizing a Farmer Field Day. Back in November he'd laid out pairs of small plots. Now, anyone could casually stroll along the path slicing across the Yaqui Valley Experiment Station and see the best seed to plant and the best way to plant it. Among other things the side-by-side plantings showcased the importance of controlling weeds, watering at the right time, and sowing on the right date with the right spacing and at the right depth. The differences were, for the most part, dramatic. Properly sown and properly supervised, top performers such as Kenya Red produced twice as much as any Sonora farmer had ever achieved. Trouble was, no farmer wanted them:

> In the spring of 1948 I attempted to drum up interest in our first Demonstration Day. I visited radio stations, newspapers and government offices. I paid for advertisements and put up flyers in town and along the roads. In big letters the flyers said: FARMERS FIELD DAY — FREE BEER AND BARBECUE.
>
> Still, not a single soul would commit to coming. Then on the street in Cajeme I chanced to meet Reza Rivera, an economist working for the Banco de Mexico. "Leave it to me," he said, "and don't worry . . . you'll have an audience."
>
> When the Saturday arrived, Enciso and I were ready. We'd rehearsed our talks and printed a pile of handouts. We had small bags of seed to hand out as gifts. Aureliano Campoy had found a flatbed truck from which I could address a throng. Mrs Jones had supplied trestles and tabletops for the beer and barbecue.
>
> Our problem was a lack of audience. Through the morning Teodoro and I sat on the back of Campoy's borrowed truck, waiting for the crowd to arrive. Above all, we wanted the big farmers whose word carried weight in the community.
>
> By midday the attendance had built to 25. Accountants, secretaries and clerks from Reza Rivera's office made up 20. Five more were farmers. One of those was our neighbor Aureliano Campoy, who already knew everything. Three more had come for the beer. Only one person out of the whole audience genuinely wanted to learn.
>
> Putting aside our disappointment, Enciso and I showed off the new wheats and how they should be grown. We didn't do too well. And it was not just my poor Spanish; a couple of farmers

loudly challenged every statement I made.

I replied with equal frankness and considered I'd put across a good case. But their harsh words, which mainly reflected ignorance and prejudice against Americans, undermined the audience's confidence. At the end when I called for questions no one spoke up. Not one of the 25 wanted any of the seed packages, either . . . they just wanted the beer and barbecue.

During that fiasco Norm had noticed a young man standing silent but attentive in the background. This was the single participant who'd come to learn about wheat. Once the others were engaged with the beer and barbecue the farmer sidled up and introduced himself.

Roberto Maurer was of medium height and modest manner. Aged in his late twenties, he was handsome in an understated way, with serious dark eyes and the romantic sagging mustache Mexicans equated with manliness. His manner was courteous, his attitude reticent, and his English flowed in slow, pleasant, modulated tones, each word loosed with care. Borlaug liked him at once.

"I've never really learned how to grow wheat well," Maurer explained. "Will you come out and show me what to do?"

Norm was happy to comply:

A week later, I took a morning off from the end-of-season chores and dashed off to the Maurer's place. These were the days before herbicides took the heartbreak and back-break out of weed control, and the Maurer fields were strangled.

"Roberto," I said. "Never plant wheat without first preparing the land. The soil around here contains too many weed seeds. You must irrigate and get those to germinate. Then you cultivate. Only after that do you sow wheat. Next year we'll take 50 acres and do that. And I'll also share our best seeds and all we've learned."

Although it was time to head south, Norm decided to hand out free samples of the four still-unnamed breakout varieties he'd been herding along since the first cross-pollination session back in 1945. During this winter he'd bulked up two of those (still unnamed) lines, and produced enough seed to plant 60 acres of each.

Doing the rounds, he called on the biggest Sonora wheat growers, offering the seed as a gift. Not one evinced any interest. Even his friends Campoy and Fierros turned his gift down:

They made no bones about it. Their indifference was clear. Each said something like: "Thanks but I've already got the best seed."

May of 1948 saw the start of Norm's seventh season of relentless research. Yet as he approached that summer's genetic jousting at Chapingo his superiors regarded him with distrust, not to say dismay. He'd caused a lot of aggravation and had not produced any reduction in Mexican hunger.

As to that, Norm was unconcerned; he was fixated on creating enough Foundation Foursome seed to fill the national need. Within two days at Toluca he and Spurlock established the planting big enough to yield 5000 tons of Frontera, Supremo, Kenya Red and Kenya White seed wheat.

Then, at Spurlock's suggestion, they took a sack of Supremo and a sack of fertilizer and called on an impoverished farm a tad past the village of San Juan del Río. The gifts seemed to delight the farmer. Holding out the sacks containing the keys to a fine future, Norm told the farmer to apply fertilizer to the planting site, which at the time simulated scorched earth. With his arm outstretched to receive the gift, the man froze. "Señor," he said, looking terrified and almost shaking with fear, "that is *venemo*! It will poison me . . . and my family."

That was an unshakeable superstition and neither Borlaug nor Spurlock could be bothered arguing the point. Taking back the prospect of prosperity, they drove farther along to a larger landowner named Carlos Rodríguez. Having passed over the seed sack, Spurlock hauled the bag of fertilizer from his pickup, mimicked the act of broadcasting it by hand, and placed the bag at the man's feet so there'd be less chance of a refusal. Though the farmer seemed dumbstruck at the risk he was being conned into taking, he made no move. The two Americans left him standing rigid by his field, the bags of seed and fertilizer side-by-side beside his shoes; a look of perplexity plastering his face like a mask.

Driving back to the city, Borlaug worried aloud. "We're on the right track, Dick. But we're never going to get seed out to farmers this way."

Reyes Vega now enjoyed the professionals' complete trust. The boy who'd formerly chased birds for five pesos a week had proved a star wheat breeder. He was now emasculating and pollinating twice as fast as Norm, who prided himself on his blinding speed.

And that was far from his last contribution. In a single day Vega revolutionized the whole procedure. This makeover began when he pointed to the minute horseshoe-shaped structures that became apparent when wheat flowers were cut open. "What are those things?"

he asked. Norm explained that they were the glumes, and they had to be pulled out one by one to expose the separate pollen sacs beneath.

Reyes Vega then slipped his imagination into top gear. Clipping the glumes off with small scissors he opened the whole interior to view, and saw that all the pollen sacs could be pulled out in a single motion.

To Norm this mass-deflowering was an amazing spectacle and a big boost to his efforts:

> Reyes Vega's discovery saved us man-years of effort. Before, we'd picked out each of the male parts one by one with tweezers; now, we yanked them out together.

Later the former bird-boy with the bright eyes and deft digits soon found yet another shortcut. Taking a flower head from the plant selected as the pollen source, he clipped off the glumes, and then stuck the stem in the ground. Under the sun's severe gaze all the pollen sacs blossomed within five minutes.

The head bursting into a bright yellow ball and shedding pollen like a Roman candle was more than a treat to see. Now when researchers spun the yellow-crowned heads between their fingers, they deluged the stamens with masses of pollen. This saved time, boosted the success rate, and vastly increased the number of cross-pollinations per flowering season. Elsewhere, wheat breeders might cross a few hundred flower heads in those three weeks. But thanks to an illiterate kid's insight, the group in Mexico hereafter made thousands twice a year.

By Judgment Day in October 1948 it was clear that the four finalists being herded forward from the 1945 cross-pollinations had aced their tests. These fresh new brooms matured a couple of weeks early. They produced over a ton of grain an acre. And they resisted stem-rust.

In 1948 Norm released them into the mainstream of mankind as: Kentana 48 (from the Kenya-Mentana cross) and Yaqui 48, Nazas 48, Chapingo 48 (all from Marroqui-Newthatch crosses).

These, his first made-from-scratch wheats, became the Follow-Up Foursome. He hoped this quartet would become the breakout varieties that would make Mexico's wheat crop healthy and productive.

1949-1953
All Fall Down

When Norm returned to Sonora in November 1948 he first recovered the seed he'd tried to give away back in April. Grabbing those sacks, which contained what were now called Kentana 48 and Yaqui 48, he set out to confront his reluctant friends. This time, Aureliano Campoy and Rafael Fierros accepted the gifts with good grace. During his six-month absence, they'd independently decided to at least be polite. Norm also visited Roberto Maurer and also got him started on the specially treated 50 acre patch.

Nonetheless, all three farmers seemed reluctant to accept the gift. Stem rust had burdened wheat with a reputation so evil no gringo could open Sonoran minds, let alone hearts.

To loosen the mental logjam he needed the endorsement of Rodolfo Calles [KY-es]. Mexicans in those days looked to a patriarch for guidance. Calles was the Yaqui Valley *patrón* because his father had been Mexico's president and he'd been Sonora's governor. Indeed he was the dotty governor who almost two decades back had plopped the Yaqui Valley Experiment Station out in the middle of nowhere as a vehicle for driving Sonora up and out of dust and destitution.

Now, however, the place had him strangely spooked. Norm invited Calles to tour the research plots and offered the latest seeds. It was all in vain: the invitation was declined, the offer refused. Both rejections were made with grace but left Norm gritting his teeth in frustration. He had no way to break through the mental logjam.

As the winter season progressed, Norm's friends Campoy and Fierros became notably distressed. The Kentana 48 and Yaqui 48 in their fields looked mediocre. It was now plain they'd been duped by this foreigner

127

who, like all the rest, talked a good line.

Indeed, Borlaug's plants *were* underwhelming to the eye. Yaqui 48's seedheads were short and hairless. Their homely appearance was, however, deceiving since their 200 flowers each produced three grains instead of the normal two. Put another way, an acre of Yaqui 48 produced *half as much again* as anyone hereabouts had ever seen.

Though Kentana 48 looked more impressive, with long seed hairs (awns) and long seedheads, it too projected a plain-Jane aura.

Yet for all the outward manifestations of mistrust, something strange was bestirring the Yaqui Valley mindset. That became apparent in April 1949 when, despite the absence of flyers, advertising, barbecue or beer, almost 200 farmers showed up for the second Farmer Field Day. Moreover, most were keen to capitalize on the experience. And this time they treated him with respect and asked thoughtful questions.

Speaking from the bed of a pickup truck, Norm launched into his spiel. As before, he'd laid out plantings arranged in pairs. Some exposed the qualities of plant lines he was breeding. Others showed how farmers could wheedle high performance from current varieties. A few disclosed his very latest discovery: that the land hereabouts was malnourished.

To illustrate this last issue he'd laid out side-by-side squares and treated them with different fertilizers in differing amounts and at different points during wheat's growing cycle. The squares demonstrated that nitrogenous fertilizer applied in the right amount at the right moment produced 60 percent more grain.

Other plant foods showed no effect. The Yaqui Valley, he declared, needed nothing more than 40lb of nitrogen to make *each acre* deliver almost 500lb more grain.

Actually, he used metric units and, thanks to Mrs Jones, his Spanish now spun out in smooth sentences, so he expected a vigorous response. For a few pesos worth of plant food he'd virtually promised each of them a *60 percent* raise. Having finished a flourish, he asked: "Are there any questions?"

No one responded. All 200 faces gazed upward in silence. He figured he must have bombed or maybe mistakenly employed a Spanish word so vulgar they'd been left stunned.

Jorge Parada and Eduardo Vargas — two of the rural leaders he most hoped to win over — stood in the front, deadpan like the rest . . . not even scowling. Then Parada stepped forward and seemed to speak for all when he said: "Doctor Borlaug, I'd prefer not to say this because you might misunderstand." The Spanish was formal, the diction exquisite, the wording polite. "We appreciate your work on breeding wheats and we see that it could become very helpful. But the soil in this valley *needs no fertilizer*. Yes, you're getting an effect; we can see that. However, this experiment station has been mismanaged for years; the land here is the poorest around. Any good farmer will tell you that you'll get no response *on his place*."

"I'm sorry," Borlaug replied in Spanish. "This is what we've found, and I'm so convinced nitrogen will generate greater production that next fall I'm going to hire an agronomist and send him out to establish fertilizer trials on different farms."

Jorge Parada immediately spoke up. "Well, I want to participate," he said. "Use my place for one of your tests."

A week or so later, Norm took a morning off to visit Roberto Maurer. The specially treated 50-acres proved stunning to the eye. The rest, however, remained a weedy wreck. "Why didn't you make me plant the whole farm like this?" Maurer said with a smile so plaintive it suggested resentment at his advisor's professional oversight. "Well," Borlaug said, letting out more of the truth than was good for his reputation, "I really didn't know it was going to turn out *this* good!"

B eing unable to face financial ruin, Aureliano Campoy left until last the field he'd so foolishly sacrificed to Borlaug's gifts. Finally, though, he had no choice and sent in his small combine harvester, which fed the grain into sacks that were carried aboard.

Then he got the biggest surprise of his long life: "A huge stream of grain was pouring out. I hadn't anticipated so much. I told the foreman to go back and bring more sacks. He returned with two or three and I took one look and said: 'Hell, go back and get twenty or thirty!'"

So much grain spilling from so small an area left Campoy dazed. Even though both varieties were comparable, Kentana 48 most touched his heart. Still befuddled, he drove across the valley to confer with Rafael Fierros. Upon arrival, though, he saw that his friend's crop had yet to be harvested, and the sight kept him from blurting out the news. For a time, he turned the talk to this and to that, and then he injected an innocent sounding question: "What are those wheats you've got there? They look pretty poor."

"Oh, they're just experimental things Borlaug gave me," Fierros said with an angry shrug: "Neither is any good."

That gave the visitor an idea: "Tell you what," he said, "You give me the harvest from your Kentana and I'll give you my Yaqui in return. That way, neither of us will have to handle *two* bad seeds."

That spring Norm had every reason for satisfaction. In his test plots Kentana 48 and Yaqui 48 yielded 2800lbs an acre. Compared to the 750lbs Mexico's finest growers typically achieved, these newcomers — given a boost from fertilizer — added a ton or more an acre. For the Yaqui Valley (which had a million acres) this leap in yield and income represented a tremendous opportunity. Moreover, the built-in rust resistance rendered the harvest more reliable.

Beyond all that, by the end of April he could see that in seed-multiplication plots the other two members of his Follow Up Foursome (Chapingo 48 and Nazas 48) were yielding amounts approaching *3600lbs an acre*. If they performed that well in the real world, Mexican farmers might approach 2 tons an acre.

Following the Sonora season Norm moved back to Central Mexico. He'd now completed 8 seasons of nonstop science and his May-October home-stays had turned into treats every family member anticipated. This is when they got their balance back.

None enjoyed these treats more than Margaret. Life for her was rough. Most days she faced not only a foreign language, a foreign neighborhood and foreign friends, but also a nearly foreign husband.

Obviously, she tolerated more than any wife should. Down the years, though, neither she nor the children expressed annoyance at the so-called head of the house's absence. "He's never been home a lot," she once told a reporter. "We just live with it."

The long absences disturbed Norm as well. Behind the disguise of dedication hid a homebody; he lived with a perpetual pang of guilt. He feared he was becoming something of a cipher to his children despite all attempts at breaking through their reserve — playing ball with Billy, for example, and talking with Jeanie in their secret code, Spanish.

Nonetheless, he couldn't resist slipping in a little work. Jeanie remembers summertime picnics taken in the wheatfields where she got the "thrill" of covering wheat flowers with long paper tubes. Blond and blossoming, this six-year-old functioned with an easy grace, coping effortlessly with the differences between the cultures. While attending school she'd discovered a natural ability for language and, to her father's amazement spoke Spanish with a flawless Mexico City accent.

By contrast, Billy was a trial. Now entering the "terrible twos," he was not only rambunctious but also subject to frightening bouts of asthma as well as allergies severe enough to trigger four-alarm responses. His father, the cool, calm composed scientist was an easy touch. Billy merely had to murmur in the night and he'd be by the bedside, wheezing too.

In September, with the harvest just a month ahead, Norm and Dick Spurlock toured the Central zone and found the nameless traditional wheats turning red. The air smelled like sour milk.

On the way home, the pair stopped by the place where a year earlier they'd left the bemused farmer standing rigid beside bags of seed and fertilizer. As they admired a handsome field of Supremo, Carlos Rodríguez appeared from behind his house. With a yell he raced down the dirt path. Falling on Borlaug, he embraced him in a bear hug, his eyes unashamedly gushing liquid joy. Sweetness seemed to spill from his lips, though the words flew too fast for Norm to fathom.

Other men then came running. They too embraced the scientist. Finally the womenfolk appeared, holding back but obviously thrilled.

"What's this about, Dick?" Borlaug asked. "They hardly know me!"

Spurlock explained that the farmer had harvested three times more than his little patch had ever provided. More to the point, though, his were the only healthy plants in the neighborhood. The Rodríguez family deemed it a gift from God and considered Borlaug the angel sent for their personal salvation.

"It is a simple thing," Spurlock replied. "They're saying thank you for having something to eat when the family would otherwise have been hungry!"

About this time a professor from Mexico City's National Polytechnic Institute approached George Harrar bearing a personal request. "One of our best students is being forced to quit," Pablo Hope [HOO-PAY] explained. "Her family is too poor. If you could provide her a part-time job she'd be able to complete her studies."

The scholarly supplicant noted that the student's father had fallen ill and couldn't work. As a consequence her mother had fallen behind in tuition payments. The student, he said, showed exceptional talent and tenacity but was being forced to abandon her studies to become a seamstress and help out the family.

To Harrar, such a request was irresistible. Evangelina Villegas was appointed Library Assistant, Part-Time. Slight of build and retiring of manner, Eva [EH-vah] seemed as shy and self-conscious as an elf. Indeed, she slipped into the group almost unnoticed.

Assigning Eva to the library was doubly dubious since almost all the books were American and she knew no English. This came clear one particular Saturday morning when Borlaug was checking the latest journals. Suddenly, Wellhausen dashed past the library door barking as he went: "Eva, please bring me the Who's Who!" Having no clue as to what he wanted or even what he'd said, she stood in the small book-lined chamber, frozen with fear. Noticing her paralysis, Norm pointed to the big red volume. She seemed immensely grateful.

Sad to say, while winning the farmers' trust, Norm was fast losing the foundation's. You see, the Big Apple had finally uncovered the disgraceful state of his paperwork.

To the prelates of paper in the New York skyscraper this employee lacked professionalism. He never planned ahead and never sent in proper reports of all he was doing. To pay someone who didn't know where he stood or where he was going was unacceptable. Worse still, they'd learned that this nettlesome novice insisted on wasting half the year a thousand miles from where the foundation was authorized to work.

In this special sense, Norm *was* deficient. He later told a reporter:

> I like to see action. I don't know how to deal with paperwork. Neglect of paper is my worst habit.

To his credit, though, George Harrar now ignored this appalling imperfection of placing the interests of the hungry above those of his handlers. He'd learned to accept that the more latitude Borlaug got the more he'd accomplish.

But those above Harrar in a New York skyscraper hadn't yet seen that light. Through the years in which Norm was fighting fungi and farmer indifference he received continual demands for written projections precise enough for checking from a distance of 3000 miles. He complied with only half a heart:

> I needed to be a scrambling quarterback, to dart and weave and grab each chance that showed up in front of me. I couldn't know in advance what would appear, let alone how I'd respond.

This sniping issued periodically from the shadows behind his back. From time to time consultants were dispatched. Typically pencil-pushers were selected as the inquisitors, and few returned positive reviews. A common conclusion: his work was "not up to the standards of research expected in a university."

I n Sonora in November 1949 the farmer friends who'd struck their strange bargain multiplied their new seed. Aureliano Campoy sowed Kentana 48; Rafael Fierros sowed Yaqui 48.

This took courage, since the community still resisted the gringo's seeds and recommendations. Across the vast Yaqui Valley no other farmer sowed the new wheats or used fertilizer.

Norm started his own 1950 cycle by sowing the summer season's winning seeds. This was his tenth nonstop season, and to outsiders, everything he'd attempted had proved unproductive. He had yet to produce any food for the hungry masses.

For his promised fertilizer tests Norm had hired a new graduate named Raúl Mercado to establish trials on five farms. Each trial covered five acres and was divided into two equal sections. One section was dusted with ammonium sulfate. Borlaug's seed was then evenly sown over both.

As the season progressed Norm several times toured the valley peeking at the fertilizer trials. By spring the five farm sites clearly show one side carrying much more grain. Indeed, when the harvest weights were submitted, ammonium sulfate had in four cases boosted production. On two, the fertilized side produced 60 percent more grain.

Jorge Parada, however, reported a lackluster response. Both sides of his field — an awkwardly shaped tract with an irrigation ditch angling across the middle — had yielded the same amount.

This was a setback because Jorge Parada was one of the farm leaders who set the standard for local wisdom. Having personally inspected the property, Norm sensed an error had occurred, so later when they crossed paths in town he raised the issue: "Something's wrong, Don

Jorge, my eye doesn't deceive me that much. Next season I'll provide more seed and fertilizer, and you try the test again."

Again Norm was left gritting his teeth in frustration. Could the mental logjam *never* be broken?

As the time for harvest approached, Norm advertised his third Farmer Field Day at the Yaqui Valley Experiment Station. Come that Sunday, 400 farmers showed up — twice as many as the previous year. Once again, they seemed eager to learn and asked positive questions.

Also during that busy April the farmer friends who'd struck their strange bargain both recorded exceptional harvests. Campoy now had several tons of Kentana 48 and Fierros had several tons of Yaqui 48.

Arriving back at home base in May 1950 Norm found that the Rockefeller Foundation group had increased with the addition of specialists in insect pests, potatoes and animal husbandry. Chapingo's 160 acres were no longer enough for everyone. He in particular needed more soil space. He was now sowing seeds by the millions.

Then when visiting Richard Spurlock in the high mountain valley of Toluca he discovered a farm for lease. The owner was friendly and fascinated enough to low-ball the annual rent, a concession that overcame Harrar's initial opposition to a rogue research operation 70 miles from the rest of the group.

Borlaug's new site, a practicing farm of the standard Mexican model, had only the shed the farmer had built to store his meager tools. Having been prepared with an ox and a wooden plow, the fields were far from fancy.

This crude farm in Toluca and the decrepit station in Sonora hereby became Norm's prime work sites. To professionals, this was final proof of his incompetence. Neither place had facilities for laboratory support or office support. Neither had any place to store equipment or seeds.

Worse still, the two sites were polar opposites: At 8,500 feet above sea level, Toluca was perhaps the world's highest wheat-breeding station. The Yaqui Valley, by contrast, was more than 1.6 miles lower. Being essentially at sea level, it was among the world's lowest wheat-breeding stations.

And beyond contrasting altitudes, Toluca and Sonora were separated by 10° of latitude. Moreover, their topography and soils conflicted:

Toluca was hilly with clay-loam; the Yaqui Valley was flat and sandy. Toluca depended on summer rains that came whenever nature chose; Sonora was served by the government canal, and could be watered whenever soils got thirsty. Even the seasons clashed. Toluca hosted Norm's summertime crop; Sonora hosted the wintertime crop.

To the wheat breeding profession his method of sequentially subjecting evolving gene combos to such disparate challenges was scandalous.

Around this time a government field station in the breadbasket area known as the Bajío set aside a section of land for Norm's use. This new site, located near the town of La Piedad, posed a practical problem: no one thereabouts knew how to care for, let alone breed, wheat plants.

This is when he devised a daring plan that was perhaps the most scandalous of all: he initiated a dozen of the largely unlettered bird boys into the arts of managing wheat research and of cross pollinations.

This group — most of them barely into their teens — developed an abiding reverence for the gringo who'd given them the chance to grab the golden ring and make something of themselves. He drove them by his own example and they responded by matching his maniacal zeal. And like Reyes Vega 200 miles away in Mexico City, these backwoods Bajío boys possessed cool hands.

Emasculating wheat flowers requires steady finger work, not just because wheat's male organs are tiny but also because each one sprays hundreds of pollen grains. Borlaug had to ensure that every last pollen sac got removed. To this end he first divided the boys into groups of five and engaged the groups in a simple game: Anytime anyone (including himself) finished removing the pollen sacs they initialed and dated the paper tube covering the emasculated flower. Three days later, when it came time to consummate the mating, a different group took over.

Wheat pollen hits the eye like Day-Glo, and when the paper tube was opened any sign of yellow radiance proved that the first group had failed in its duty. For that crime the members were required to buy the second crew Coca-Colas. "One of two things is going to happen," Borlaug explained: "You're going to learn to do it right or you're going to pay the price. Hopefully, you'll not be spending all your pay on soft drinks."

The boys quickly caught on. The daily Coca-Cola contest neatly balanced competitiveness with camaraderie and stimulated youthful juices. To them, though, the best part was the chance of a free drink after ten hour's toiling, broiling and building thirst.

In a surprisingly short time these under-schooled novices mastered processes previously performed by over-schooled professors. Indeed, they crossbred wheat with more will and skill than probably any scientist before (and maybe since).

By now, these and other grade-school dropouts had become an integral part of the research operation, and an education fund was established. Operated by the poorly paid scientists, rather than their rich employer, this was an unofficial and unsung recognition of the unlettered youths who were sustaining their success.

Eva Villegas became the fund's treasurer. In the year since being lost in the library the barrio waif had come far. More mature than her 26 years, she now spoke halting English and, while continuing to take courses for her BS degree in biochemistry, she'd worked herself into a position on the research staff. The talents and tenacity the Polytechnic professor had foretold were emerging.

Indeed, the grit behind the girlish appearance and reserved manner now revealed itself as the education fund's treasurer. Eva knew what a peso meant to an impoverished kid and never hesitated to hit up her seniors. Whenever the fund's monies ran low she'd buttonhole the illustrious PhDs. "Come on, come on," she'd prod, "put some pesos in."

Thanks to Eva the bird boys got the schooling their parents had denied.

That fall of 1950 chilling news arrived from Minnesota and Manitoba: in scattered locations across the Great Plains and Prairie Provinces a new stem-rust race had taken up residence.

Stakman's revelations rendered this fact visible. Of all the 300 rust races, a variant of the 15th he'd identified was the most obscure. It derived from a single sick plant mailed in from New York State in 1938. Stem-rust 15B merited interest only because it killed *every* wheat in Stakman's rust-race test.

The chilling missive Borlaug received from his northern colleagues in October 1950 explained that rust-race 15B had suddenly spread. A year earlier Stakman's mail had brought a single diseased stem carrying 15B (again from New York State). Now at least one in every four of the fat envelopes contained that race.

Though Norm was far away, he knew that the great rivers of high-altitude winds were about to deliver 15B rust to Mexico. And his plants were as vulnerable as those above the border.

The other great issue on his mind was the wheat plant's spindly stem. He'd now made possible grain loads heavy enough that the fall and spring winds were blowing the fields down. Farmers were seeing their fields bending to kiss the dirt. Complaints were mounting. Criticism of the gringo outsider was mounting too. Plants on the ground were a dead loss.

Shrinking the crop seemed the only answer; shorter stems would be less likely to bend. Having never heard of a dwarf wheat, Norm dashed off a letter to the U.S. Department of Agriculture asking for a few seeds of every sample in the World Wheat Collection. This was a big ask. The World Wheat Collection had seeds of 30,000 different plants. Surely among all those there must be one with a short strong stem.

On the way north to Sonora Norm spent a week at La Piedad sowing a 10-acre plot that would multiply Yaqui 48 seed for later distribution to farmers across Central Mexico.

Moving on to Sonora, he found the desert air rife with change. For one thing, Campoy and Fierros were being besieged by neighbors desperate to buy Kentana 48 or Yaqui 48. As the first farmers to peddle his seed to their peers, they set a terrific precedent:

> In the beginning Campoy and Fierros had resisted taking the seed. Then they were turned off by the look of the plants. But after they'd harvested their fields I'll be damned if they didn't pull off the best bargain I've ever seen. Both made a killing!

This season Norm tested the vast World Wheat Collection. Sadly, by April 1951 his hope of finding a shorty had been dashed. Although a smattering of small specimens had appeared, even those pint-sized possibilities fell over when fertilized.

With the winter crop maturing, he dropped by the Parada place to check on the second run of the valley-wide fertilizer trial. The planting occupied the same cockeyed field. Although a few weeks short of maturity, the fertilized side again seemed to be carrying twice as much as the rest.

Nonetheless, some weeks later when Jorge Parada submitted his final figures both sides had produced the same amount. No change.

More than frustrating, this was maddening.

On his way south when he stopped off in La Piedad his routine was rudely disrupted. While inspecting the 10-acre Yaqui 48 multiplication he spied a few plants bearing more grain than any wheat in Mexico had ever been seen to yield.

The patch was only tiny and it was hiding in a far corner where few people ever ventured. The sight, however, proved so surreal Norm became like one possessed. What could be the cause?

Wellhausen also happened to be on hand, harvesting corn trials. Suddenly he found himself yanked to the back of the station. "Just have a look at that, Ed!" Borlaug yelled. "What do you make of it?"

The calm corn breeder was intrigued, then suspicious. He strode back to the station office and marched in on the field manager. "Just tell us," he demanded, "exactly what you did when you fertilized Dr. Borlaug's wheat during the growing season."

Extracting the truth took time. Having disregarded the order to refill the tractor's fertilizer bin *at scattered locations*, the man was scared. He'd always stopped at that corner. Spillage had accumulated, and the scientists estimated that those few square feet had received at least twice the prescribed dose.

The outcome proved historic: Clearly, the nutrient overdose had done the plants a power of good! It exposed an easy way to boost Mexico's production above anything Norm had imagined. Yaqui 48 had a much higher yield ceiling than even its maker knew.

B y May 1951 Norm had put in 12 seasons of relentless research. What's truly amazing is that those years of manic activity rested on the faith that eventually someone would step forward and produce enough seed for the nation's farmers to sow. Mexico itself had no way to do that: Neither government nor private enterprise was about to waste time on such a hopeless crop as wheat.

For a while there seemed no possibility of our parable proceeding. Then Richard Spurlock and an improbable pair of tractor traders stepped forward. They knew nothing about growing wheat but with Borlaug's help not only produced all the seed for Central Mexico, they got friends, neighbors, acquaintances, and clients by the hundreds to sow the seeds.

These efforts were facilitated by the Mexican farmers' discovery that the gringo's seeds provided a ticket out of poverty. Those who sowed them could double their output and double their income. And as that news began trickling outwards, more and more took the plunge.

Accordingly, in that summer of 1951 Central Mexico's wheat crop began expanding as if pumped by a physical force. Finally Norm was having an effect on hunger.

While dealing with official duties in Central Mexico, his mind continued to be haunted by the mystery of the on-farm fertilizer trial. His new wheats possessed that magical magnetism of moneymaking, and in Sonora nitrogen elicited the most production and the most pesos. Why then had Jorge Parada failed?

Then in May Parada himself showed up in Chapingo. The Rockefeller Foundation had replaced the Tarpaper Shack with a modern field station complete with office block and laboratories.

On seeing this farmer standing on his office doorstep Norm felt confused. The man was a thousand miles from his roots, and his first words only heightened the confusion: "Dr. Borlaug," he said, "I owe you a great apology."

"What for, Don Jorge?"

"My foreman assured me that both sides of that field were the same size. But after writing you that second note I went out and checked for myself." He paused, looking distinctly uncomfortable: "The truth is that the unfertilized side is almost twice as big as the fertilized one. So, what you've been saying all along is absolutely true."

Then he added another signal shock: "My mistake is especially embarrassing because I've just come from the Shell Company . . . I've signed an agreement . . . I'm now the Yaqui Valley distributor for ammonia and urea!"

That summer of 1951 proved warm, damp, and ideal for fungi. As the season progressed, red, yellow and orange spots began dotting Norm's plantings in Toluca. The occurrences were small, scattered, and seemingly minor but their significance was immense: this fungal race was feasting on the Borlaug-built beauties that had captured the loyalty of millions of farmers, if not of the whole country.

Thus did stem rust send him reeling back all the way to the starting line. Across this already hungry land 15B was on the loose; the force controlling food production was once again the fungus with the fingers of mass destruction. Any return of warm damp weather would likely see 15B stem rust fell Mexican wheat like a scythe. Nationwide.

All his efforts had come to naught.

Although in his own fields Norm had seen his varieties starting to collapse, Mexico's overall output in 1952 jumped from 400,000 to 750,000 tons. The national yield, which had averaged 750 pounds an acre, soared to 1000. In addition, more farmers were growing more wheat, lifting the wheat acreage from 1.25 to 1.8 million.

Mexico's food supply now relied on the four wheats he'd first recommended. But Frontera, Supremo and more were vulnerable to 15B stem rust; and by the time their stalks were blackened and bent, it would be too late. Farm families would face ruin, and he'd be blamed.

He had no option but to start again, back where he began in 1945. Thirteen seasons of dedication meant nothing now. And he had perhaps two years to redo all that work before stem rust would take charge.

His response can be judged from the fact that during that summer of 1952 his nurseries contained almost 70,000 distinct wheat lines. And his quest for genetic advances against 15B stem rust that year included a staggering 6,000 individual cross-pollinations. Nothing on such a scale had before been attempted.

For this fresh campaign, his major prospects lay with 60,000 different wheat types from his own collection as well as 6000 more from the U.S. Department of Agriculture.

During 1952 an unusual possibility suddenly popped up among the myriad advanced progeny in the research fields. This singular plant matured fast, yielded well and possessed the red-tinted grains Mexican millers preferred. Above all, it seemed to be immune to 15B stem rust.

Norm and the boy wheat-breeders had blended the original at La Piedad. In time, he named it Lerma 52, after the Rio Lerma, a snaky river that ambled past the research station. Although raising hopes for immunity to 15B stem rust, this rangy powerhouse had a singular fault: its grain produced bad bread.

For this reason Norm that summer began a parallel campaign aimed at ensuring all his varieties made good eating. To open this second front he sowed plots of both Lerma 52 and Newthatch, Stakman's star-studded creation whose flour raised bakers to rapture. In July he cross-pollinated their flowers; by October he knew that that first backcross had produced a few specimens whose grain produced fair loaves. One stood out above the rest, however, and he hoped its 200 seeds might eventually get him to the promised land of a 15B-resistant wheat that produced good bread.

In March, 1952 Norm happened to visit Argentina, where yet another stem-rust race was devastating the wheat crop. His traveling companion, Burton Bayles, was a U.S. Department of Agriculture wheat breeder. One evening while relaxing over a cocktail in Buenos Aires, Norm asked him if there were any true dwarf wheats. To his amazement Bayles replied that a few years earlier a USDA coworker had stumbled upon some short-stalked wheats that didn't fall over when fertilized.

This revelation sent Norm's soul soaring. Unfortunately for him, though, they were the wrong kind of wheat for Mexico. They'd been found a world away, in Japan. And they were performing poorly in trials in the U.S. Nonetheless, he wrote to Orville Vogel in Washington State asking if a few seeds might be shared with a colleague in Mexico.

It was also in 1952 that the Rockefeller Foundation suddenly decided to replicate the Mexican operation. The first clonal copy of the Agricultural Program would be erected near Cali in Colombia.

Given this expansion, the foundation brass needed help at headquarters, and only one person fit the job description. Thus it was that George Harrar got plucked out of Mexico and made Director of Agricultural Sciences in the foundation's New York HQ.

In October 1952, the results of Norm's fifteenth bout with the fungus were visible in the giant planting of wheat types from his own collection as well as from the U.S. Department of Agriculture. This gargantuan survey of a total of 66,000 wheat types produced six survivors. Only those could withstand the 15B rain of terror. Amazingly, all six were from his own stable: Kentana 48, Lerma 52, Kenya Red, Kenya White and two half-perfected lines, later named Chapingo 52 and Chapingo 53.

Those hardy half-dozen had one common ingredient: the Kenya-type resistance from the seeds that Gerald Burton had rescued from immolation and bequeathed as a gift to his former professor, Stakman.

On arriving back north for 1953's opening season Norm sensed a transformation in Sonoran society. That November several farmers planted Kentana 48 and Yaqui 48 for personal profit. Given the Valley's vastness these plantings contributed little. Yet their significance was immense: They were the first Borlaug-bred wheats to contribute food to the world.

To Norm personally, this waypoint was inconsequential. He knew that in reality 15B stem rust was a step ahead of him. To stave off disaster he needed to recommend safe replacements for Frontera, Supremo and Yaqui 48.

Thus during the early days of 1953, with signature audacity, he set out to quash the very varieties he'd developed through eight years of endless toil. He distributed alerts and issued radio announcements. In the upcoming season no current variety should be sown. A new scourge had its sights set on every one.

Wheat farmers must shift to Kentana 48. Now!

In the U.S. and Canada, the 15B threat was immense. Wheat was both nations' staple. Americans, for instance, annually consumed 15 billion pounds of breadstuffs and derived 40 percent of their calories just from this one crop. Although in 1953 the silos and food stores still held goodly stocks of grain and flour, 15B meant that might be the last.

Such situations are nowadays splashed across the national news, morning, noon and night. But those were woefully backward days before scientists sought to become headline heroes. As a result, during this crisis wheat breeders never dreamed of going public, let alone leveraging popular concern into personal publicity or a plethora of research dollars. To the contrary, they felt a dulling sense of duty, nay shame that those condition had arisen on their watch.

In hopes of discovering a miracle means for breaking the fungal stranglehold, North America's wheat breeders and plant pathologists convened a council of war in Winnipeg during January 1953. Among the 40 attendees were Harrar, Stakman and Borlaug.

From the outset morale verged on morbid. And as the deliberations proceeded the mood plunged. The USDA's chief cereal pathologist got caught in the downdraft. "By god, Norm," Herman Rodenheiser said during a quiet moment on the first afternoon, his face pallid and stricken: "I think we're running out of genes . . . there's no resistance for this thing, anywhere!"

"Rody" Rodenheiser, however, had been peering into his own mind and as the discussions waffled onward without end he proposed collecting every wheat that carried any smidgen of stem-rust resistance and growing them side-by-side in different parts of North America using a uniform protocol. This would be an all-volunteer exercise; local wheat scientists would sow the seed, maintain the plots, record the results, harvest the healthiest specimens, and return those seeds to the central organizers for consolidation into a new pool for a subsequent round of plantings the following year.

This selfless collaboration would, he explained, expose and concentrate 15B-resisting genes. Moreover, seeds of the surviving plants would be in the hands of American and Canadian wheat breeders who could seize the chance to apply their own talents. He called his conception the "International Stem Rust Nursery."

During the Winnipeg council of war Norm casually informed Rodenheiser that he'd gladly grow their special seeds during the winter, thereby squeezing in an extra round of nurseries while northern soils were snowbound. As long as the seeds reached Mexico City before November, he'd carry them north to Sonora, sow them in separate plots, and maintain the plants alongside his own. In April the separate groups could send staff members to harvest and record the results and haul home any surviving seeds in time for the northern planting.

The idea met with general approval and George Harrar allowed Norm to add it to his duties. This new venture, however, could neither be publicized nor formally incorporated into the program, whose agreement with the government strictly limited its help to Mexican interests.

Throughout most of 1953 Norm's plea that Mexican farmers switch to Kentana 48 hung in the balance. No one would commit to change when their fields looked so great. In the upshot, though, the farmers did make the break. They had come to trust the word of a gringo.

The seed Campoy, Spurlock and the tractor dealers multiplied of their own accord proved vital. With it, Kentana 48 moved from understudy to center stage. And in Mexico's wheat fields it would in time prove a star performer, both in grain production and in disease protection. Thanks to the rapid adoption of Kentana 48, the fickle 15B fungus attained only a minor presence in Mexico.

That year of '53 also delivered a family concern. Now six years old, Billy was in worsening health. The asthma and allergies had become chronic and severe. Something needed to be done.

One night, Margaret suggested the possibility of physical exercise. Thinking back to his own boyhood, Norm agreed. Athletics might help. Next day, he mentioned the matter to John Niederhauser.

Intrigued, this breezy good humored colleague, whose specialty was potatoes, loved the idea. With six rambunctious sons Niederhauser needed ways to keep overly healthy boys from falling into mischief. Almost casually, he suggested Little League, a new but increasingly popular sport he'd heard about back in his home state of California.

The two scientists wrote a note to Little League headquarters in Williamsport, Pennsylvania asking about starting a Mexican program.

Also during the summer of 1953 Norm received a slim envelope from Pullman, Washington. Enclosed were 60 seeds of the original Japanese dwarf wheat called Norin 10 as well as 20 seeds from crosses Orville Vogel had made between Norin 10 and three of his standard-height varieties.

Norm added the envelope to the other items he'd haul north for the next Sonora season.

1954-1959

The Quiet Revolution

A fter Norm arrived in Sonora in November 1953 he established the now-standard operations for 1954's opening stanza. Then he opened the envelopes containing the 80 seeds Vogel had posted from Pullman. Those seeds derived from ten wheats created by a Japanese wheat breeder who'd named them Norin. None had ever been put to practical use, but in 1949 an American agronomist helping Japan recover from World War II had spotted the tiny plants in a remote research station and sent seeds back to the U.S. Department of Agriculture. The plants, he wrote, are "so damn short, they're pretty much underground!"

In 1950 a hundred Norin seeds had reached Orville Vogel at Washington State University. In the three years since, he'd grown them out and also cross-pollinated some with his own varieties.

The Norins were winter wheats — a type that is planted in fall and is preprogramed to hibernate under snow pack. Norm of course needed "summer wheats" — the kind that is planted in spring and never sees snow. Back in Argentina, Bayles had urged that he chill Vogel's seed for six weeks in a refrigerator to overcome that need to hibernate. But at the old Yaqui Valley Experiment Station Norm took most of the seed from Vogel's envelope and sowed them directly, like the rest.

Norm was in Sonora during that spring of 1954 when word arrived that in Mexico City the agriculture minister was firing all the staff members whom Norm had trained.

The minister, a former army general named Gilberto Flores Muñoz, was renowned for ending careers with single-word telegrams. Now he'd decided to rid the nation of the traitors who'd worked with Borlaug.

He'd been told they were secretly working for the glory of gringos.

Norm was appalled:

> They were good people whose sole "crime" was their association with me. One was Benjamín Ortega, who'd been among my first and most capable students. He'd risen to become director of agricultural development for much of Mexico's northern region and was among the country's most capable scientific administrators. One day at his office in Torreón he received a telegram:
>
> > *Cesado* [dismissed].
> > Flores Muñoz.
>
> Benjamín was devastated, as were we. . . . He himself went to Mexico City and confronted the general — a very brave move in those days when government was a scientist's only possible employer. To his credit, the minister saw the injustice. A second telegram followed:
>
> > *Reinstalar* [reinstated].
> > Flores Muñoz.

Still and all, the situation remained worrisome. No one knew who the excitable executive would strike next. Or when. Or how. Rumor had it that Borlaug himself was slated for deportation.

One Sunday afternoon in Sonora, Aureliano Campoy strolled over to the field at the old station. "How's everything going?" he asked.

"Jeez," Norm blurted, "the Minister of Agriculture wants to shut us down and I'm to be thrown out of the country!"

Those words sparked an explosion. "To hell with that," the old farmer yelled. "My nephew is the head of the Ejidal [peasant-farmer] Bank in Cajeme. He knows Flores Muñoz; he served on his staff once. I'll go see him."

Then Campoy added a second thought: "You better go see Don Rodolfo."

By this time Rodolfo Calles was testing a field of Kentana 48 and was developing a solid, if still suspicious, regard for the crazy wheat man who'd come amongst them. Borlaug caught him at home: "If this problem isn't solved our work will be stopped," he declared. "We'll get a telegram from Flores Muñoz and I'll be gone — for good."

Calles said he'd look into the matter, and next day telephoned back. The situation was even worse than Norm knew: *All the Rockefeller personnel* were to be deported. The order was even then sitting on the minister's desk. "We've got to stop this right away," he said. "I'm going to Mexico [City] tomorrow."

Next day, the former governor, Roberto Maurer and a representative of the peasant-farmer organization flew to the capital, where they found General Flores to be smooth, soft-spoken, even friendly. He admitted he was about to banish the Rockefeller Foundation. His decision was based on evidence his staff had submitted.

Sending for three of his aides, the general ordered them to state their charges. The federal functionaries recited a list of corn, wheat, and bean varieties the Americans claimed as their own creations but that had been bred on Mexican research stations by Mexicans. The list included several wheats.

Having been forewarned of this claim, Roberto Maurer passed the general a page detailing the pedigrees of these particular wheats, all of which Borlaug had made from scratch. Both Maurer and Rodolfo Calles had signed the statement as witnesses to its accuracy.

Flores Muñoz scanned the page, looked at the signatures, and passed it to his underlings, conveying his question by raised eyebrows. The answer came in the form of embarrassed, even fearful, downcast gazes.

With an imperious wave of his hand, the general dismissed them, and shook hands with the Sonora supplicants: "They will be dealt with in a most proper fashion, señors," he said. "But you were lucky. You were just in time." He tapped the document on his desk. "Once I'd signed this, I'd have fought you to the end before changing my mind."

In January when Norm returned to Sonora following the Christmas break, he found that the plants from Vogel's seeds were stuck in the seedling stage. They were awaiting the winter that never comes in Sonora. By the time they began exposing stems and flowers, the regular-sized wheats were long past flowering. By ignoring their need to hibernate Norm had squandered Vogel's priceless gift. It would prove his most shameful blunder.

By then, though, this line of research seemed hardly worth worrying about. Vogel's plants had proven hopelessly susceptible to stem rust, leaf rust, and stripe rust. Most were pocked with so many red outbreaks they appeared to have contracted whole-body acne. Eventually, all succumbed without producing a single viable seed.

Norm abandoned hope of developing dwarf summer wheat.

I n 1954 Little League was barely a decade old and purely American. Nevertheless, executives at Little League headquarters jumped at the chance to go international. Norm and John Niederhauser received the requisite authorization together with advice on establishing a league, arranging venues and maintaining match rosters. By year's end they had the enterprise in operation.

Aztec Little League had four teams. Most players came from American families. Games were held on the American School's well-worn diamond during a season stretching from March through June. Norm and Niederhauser each coached a team and recruited a couple of friends to coach the other two teams. Norm's squad was named the Aguilas (Eagles). Billy played catcher and pitcher.

Although both scientists were happy with this sideline, they kept it quiet from their colleagues. For that they had three good reasons: 1) both feared George Harrar would conclude they were goofing off; 2) boys' baseball seemed unlikely to have any future in a land of such deprivation; and 3) the standard of play was terrible, the scores astronomical, the fielding inept.

That same year, Norm and Ed Wellhausen chatted several times about the difficulties of working at the Yaqui Valley Experiment Station. Clearly, the Sonora end of the wheat program could no longer operate way out in the wilderness with machinery borrowed from neighbors.

Then during a visit to New York, Wellhausen asked for funds to build a replacement experiment station. George Harrar turned the request down with such asperity that Wellhausen wished he'd never brought such an outrageous possibility to the world's richest charity.

A s the calendar clicked over into 1955 Norm had the Sonora operations running full tilt. That April Rodolfo Calles finally faced down his fears and asked to visit the old station. Norm was of course delighted, and with the plants then nearing maturity he suggested an immediate visit. The former governor who'd poured his youthful dreams into establishing this weathered old research palace got to see the whole operation, including up close and personal looks at the rust-resistant types, the improved-bread types, the "new bulls" observation area, and the various demonstration plots.

To the former governor all this seemed like the realization of his 20-year-old dream. "Now I'm convinced that this is serious business," he said as they ended the tour. "How can we rehabilitate this place? What can we do to make it better for you?"

For such a magnificent offer Norm had no ready answer. He did, however, later mention the conversation to Wellhausen.

First thing next morning Ed telephoned Calles. "Don Rodolfo," he said, "there's not much point in rehabilitating the old station. Dr. Borlaug cannot work effectively out there. There's not enough land. Also it's hard to keep staff, seeing there's no clean water for drinking, no schools for children, no market for groceries, and the access road is terrible. Don Rodolfo, it would be better to move the whole operation to a more convenient location and start again."

"If Dr. Borlaug wants a new station," Calles replied, "just tell us how much land he needs and where he wants it."

Wellhausen explained that about 100 hectares (250 acres) was required. It should be on a paved road, and close to town . . . hopefully, within ten kilometers (six miles).

"We'll get that for you," the ex-governor declared. "You'll have it in ten days!"

Rodolfo Calles began working the phone and quickly located a farm that was on the market. Next he did the rounds of local farm-machinery dealers, grain merchants, bankers, farmer cooperatives and the rest. By drawing on a lifetime's accumulation of local goodwill, the Yaqui Valley *patrón* collected enough pledges to both purchase the land and provide a modern research facility.

Thus it was that grateful constituents joined to provide the gringo the work site his rich employer had so recently and so dismissively denied. Together, they bought 250 acres of flat, irrigated, fertile land on the east side of the main south road and made it available for wheat research. It was six miles from town. And the commitment was indeed signed in ten days.

In Mexico City during the Christmas 1955 break, Borlaug and Niederhauser approached local offices of four U.S. corporations, asking each to sponsor a separate Aztec Little League team. With so flawed a first season they faced a hard sell. But as pitchmen this pair was perfect. The big-hearted, affable, unhurried, ever-cheerful Niederhauser projected the friendly funnyman. Borlaug acted the straight man; solid, stable, but fundamentally likeable behind his seriousness.

This one-two punch pushed aside reluctance — perhaps even reason.

Support came notably from Sears Roebuck, Colgate-Palmolive and Proctor & Gamble. The funds would arrive before the playing season opened in the spring.

That April, Americans and Canadians wended their way to the sands of Sonora. This was the second year of Rodenheiser's International Stem Rust Nursery, and for the second time several dozen wheat scientists took advantage of Borlaug's offer to squeeze in an extra round of rust research while their own fields were frozen.

Their impressions of the old experiment station have gone unrecorded but surely weren't complimentary. Although now spruced up, the facilities still projected a depressing aura.

During a rugged week in this dun-colored void the visitors harvested their breeding lines, saved the seeds from the best, and rushed for the airport to haul their precious progeny home in time for spring sowing in locales from Arizona to Alberta to Arkansas.

Some also carried home seed samples of Borlaug's leading lines, including the 15B-resistant Kentana 48. This is the first means by which Borlaug's gene gems began lifting North America's food supply.

Beyond helping American and Canadian wheats resist rust-race 15B, this collaboration first exposed Borlaug's work to outside scrutiny. Before, he'd been an unknown recluse toiling in a foreign desert. Now, the shades had parted and the profession realized that this guy was someone to watch. Norm explains:

> During the International Stem Rust Nursery, outsiders got to see our wheats and our shuttle breeding. It was pretty much the first time we were taken seriously.

No wonder. To outsiders the Mexican plants and the shuttle breeding procedure certainly seemed suspect, even seditious, yet wheat was prospering mightily in Sonora. This was when the experts began questioning the textbooks' claims and wheat-breeding's basic beliefs. And in time, all would learn that by breeding wheat at disparate locations Borlaug was producing varieties that were adapted to an amazing array of climates and conditions.

That summer of 1955 Norm was focusing on the fight against 15B. Kentana 48's continued immunity was a consolation. Then as the season moved toward its end he heard that a Toluca farmer had seen some diseased stems.

Norm went out to inspect the damage and, with sinking heart, noticed that the red dabs were disfiguring Kentana 48.

In time, he'd learn that the cause was stem-rust race 139. Though this rare strain had been known for 20 years in the U.S. and northern Mexico, it had never caused serious damage. The occurrences were small, sporadic, strictly localized. Besides, Race 139 lacked the power to penetrate Yaqui 48, so out of all the 300 different rust forms it was among the blessed few Norm had never needed to care about.

However, the sight on that particular Toluca farm was frightening. Obviously, Race 139 could unlock the Kenya-type resistance. And, given Kentana 48's soaring popularity, there was nothing to stop the fungus going forth to multiply across Mexico's burgeoning million-acre wheat lands.

At that point he faced the following perplexity:

- Kentana 48's Kenya-type defense resisted Race 15B but remained susceptible to Race 139;
- Yaqui 48's Hope- and Newthatch defenses resisted Race 139 but remained susceptible to Race 15B.

This is where the manic effort six years earlier paid off. During those trying months, when he and Enciso had worked alone as if the weight of the world was upon their backs, a few days had been devoted to crossing Kentana 48 with Yaqui 48. For good measure, they'd crossed several hundred specimens both ways, with half each variety's plants acting as female and the other half as male.

In the five years since then he'd herded the crossbred progeny forward. During those ten seasons he'd saved and replanted seed from only the finest few plants. Now his five best were released to farmers in the areas infected by both Race 139 and 15B. This Fab Five (Chapingo 52, Mexe 52, Chapingo 53, Bajío 53 and Bonza 55) possessed the genetic capacity to repel two fungal foes never known in Mexico at the time of their conception. That alone was a sort of miracle.

Cash for the boys' baseball league arrived just in time for the spring season's opening. It was very welcome because interest had suddenly soared and Little League was verging on becoming a social phenomenon. Saturday mornings, whole clans showed up to cheer and sing and dance with delight following passages of good play. It gave a special lift to those whom life was to be endured, not enjoyed.

Almost two years had passed since Norm abandoned hope of developing dwarf wheats. Still nothing useful had showed up. But during the summer of 1955 he suddenly recalled Vogel's envelope, which was languishing on a shelf at Chapingo. On an impulse, he checked again and found eight seeds he'd retained as a possible reserve.

Rather nonchalantly, he added the tattered envelope to the pile to be hauled north in November.

When he returned to Sonora that November everything had changed. During his absence the Sonora operations had quit the old Yaqui Valley Experiment Station and moved to the brand new facility the grateful locals had built. The Northeast Agricultural Research Center was the perfect place to make progress. It would become world renowned under its Spanish acronym: CIANO [see-AH-noh].

Among CIANO's inaugural operations was the nurturing of the eight seeds of the Norin-based dwarfs forgotten these two years and more in an old torn envelope. Norm had already followed Burt Bayles' advice, Before coming north he'd moistened the grains on a bed of cotton and condemned them to six weeks confinement in the cooler.

Those seeds no longer expected winter, and he planted them in eight separate pots hidden deep inside the building designed as a plant-protection laboratory. There, encased within walls, ceiling and concrete floor, the seedlings were beyond the reach of stem rust spores.

Although they were quite safe deep in that dungeon, he surrounded them in muslin shrouds to intercept any sneaky spore that might perchance float down the corridor.

Upon his return after the Christmas break in January 1956 he found the eight plants had progressed past the seedling stage. Both indoor and outdoor specimens were at the same stage of life, but the eight under grow lights deep inside the building were only half the height of the masses of standard plants living outside under the Sonora sun.

In February, the indoor and outdoor plants began to flower. The time for action had arrived. Norm and two colleagues prepared the putative brides growing outside the building. For that honor he'd grown small blocks of eight of Mexico's finest — including Kentana 48, Yaqui 48, Lerma 52, and Chapingo 52 and 53. After their male organs had been excised, the remnants were quickly enclosed within paper tubes clamped shut with paperclips.

Three days later the scientists entered the inner sanctum, removed the muslin shroud from one dwarf plant, snipped off the flower head and carried it gently outside. Following the Reyes Vega innovation they cut the glumes, and propped the precious flower stalk in the soil for five minutes of sunning. Then they showered its pollen over the chosen mate's expectant stigmas.

Following that, they mated the remaining seven Japanese brother wheats with their seven arranged Mexican brides.

That April Borlaug's work received its first formal international recognition when wheat professionals held their second stem rust conference in Sonora, over a thousand miles from Minnesota, Manitoba and the other areas being mauled by the 15B strain.

The participants surely resented traveling to so remote a location. But the place they found in the middle of the Mexican wilderness proved so surprising they could barely believe their eyes. In this ultra-modern facility wheat research and farm practice operated on a continuum, with results moving outward to farmers and practical needs feeding seamlessly back to researchers. At CIANO trust was the operating ethos. This was no science center . . . it was a service center. Its directors and financial backers were the district's dirt farmers. And its star scientist was a kid from Iowa corn country.

That spring, the 1956 Aztec League leapt to 14 teams. Over half the players were Mexican; and not coincidentally, the quality of play soared.

Though most of the Aguilas now came from a spirit-crushing slum near the American School, Norm treated each as if he were a born champion. "There's no damn messing around here," he yelled in Spanish. "Give the best God gave you, or don't bother competing!"

Later he wondered whether subjecting disadvantaged youths to Coach Bart's physical and psychological treatment was right. But the boys responded. On the baseball diamond they got their first taste of talent, and it was terrific. A surprising number developed into fine athletes. That season, the Aguilas went *18 games without lo*ss.

B y year's end Borlaug's battle with the fungus had been won. The combination of Hope- and Kenya resistances had stem rust on the run. It had taken 11 years, involving 22 seasons of toil. He now released the Fab Five (Chapingo 52, Mexe 52, Chapingo 53, Bajío 53 and Bonza 55), and those fast maturing, supremely healthy, standard-height plants collectively lifted Mexico's wheat yields 83 percent to an average of 1370lbs an acre.

With each acre producing too much wheat to handle by sack, Mexico switched to bulk handling. Combines harvested the fields and pumped grain by the ton into trucks that hauled it to grain elevators. From those concrete towers, freight cars railed the raw grain to customers throughout the country. A massive new rural industry was taking shape.

The 1956 harvest proved sufficient to provide all the flour needed to fulfill Mexico's burgeoning hunger for bread, flour tortillas, rolls, cookies and crackers. Grain merchants now trooped to places like Torreón and Toluca rather than Texas. And the farmers were paid promptly, properly and respectfully.

As the new year of 1957 got underway, Mexico's wheat farmers turned into fertilizer fanatics. Soon thousands of acres of Borlaug-creations were groaning under more grain than their slender stems could bear. The plants looked spectacular but as harvest time neared the seedheads got heavy, breezes blew harder, and whole fields bent over to gracefully kiss the ground.

No matter what means of persuasion Borlaug tried, farmers in ever-increasing numbers willfully and wantonly broadcast more fertilizer than his recommended 80lb an acre.

Given that these human propensities were unstoppable, he faced even greater pressures as he began the third round of his contest with the Japanese genes that shortened stems and held up heavy grain loads.

Those cranky DNA segments were proving wily adversaries. Although he'd gotten them corralled and had plants with short stout stalks none was useful because:

- The male flowers were mostly sterile;
- The heads refused to hold the seed — scattering it over the ground;
- The leaves and stems were susceptible to rust spores;
- The grain's soft texture made it hard to mill; and

- The grain's weak gluten produced bad bread.

Herding all these genetic traits was not unlike herding cats. In that era when genes couldn't be detected or injected his only tool was the flower's male element. By sprinkling pollen grains like genetic grenades he could, in principle, jolt good genes into prominence. However, pollen (like most males) also carries bad genes. From here on, purging bad genes from his crossbred beauties dominated his days.

Supporting him in these efforts were support staffers who accompanied what had become a wheat-research expeditionary force with annual voyages up and down the country. The technical crew was led by Reyes Vega, who at the ripe old age of 20 still indulged in wheat breeding but now acted mainly as "Master Technician." The title was contrived but good management had become as vital as good science, and Vega had proved himself a master. Norm explains:

> Reyes Vega deserved the honor. We turned the logistical support over to him. He organized all the field operations and kept track of the details. Along with several other field boys who later also became Master Technicians, he played a helluva role. They relieved us of mountains of work. And they did it better than we ever could. Without them, we scientists wouldn't have gotten very far.

Mexican Civil Service paychecks were based on academic laurels rather than anything so lowbrow as competence. But, exerting his maverick streak, Borlaug elevated the technicians to pay levels comparable to an Ingeniero Agronomo (agricultural engineer). In other words, he treated bird-chaser graduates like college graduates.

By this time, the boys, once trapped in lowly lives, had coalesced into the world's most accomplished wheat-breeding assemblage. Their liquid-motion fingers manipulated pollen and plants on a grand scale. Their metamorphosis touched him more deeply than it touched others:

> Those guys were truly impressive. I'd always been an advocate of youth. "Give the young fellows a chance" was a comment I repeated to colleagues and counterparts. But in this case words were not up to the task. In their own research all the professionals I knew refused to elevate rank amateurs to positions that traditionally demanded degrees of higher learning.

In May 1957 the expeditionary force wrapped up in Sonora and moved back to Central Mexico. By the fall of that year, the panorama painted by the fourth-generation dwarf wheats appeared as abstract as ever, evidencing the sobering fact that, despite two years of unremitting toil, no advance had been achieved.

The momentum in Mexican wheat development had died. The dwarfs were a disaster. There seemed no way to navigate around the labyrinthine barriers heredity had erected against anyone shrinking spring wheat several sizes.

I n 1957, to everyone's surprise, all Mexico embraced youth baseball. To handle the sudden press of boys clamoring to pitch or bat or catch fly balls on Saturday mornings, John Niederhauser helped set up three more Mexico City leagues — Maya, Toltec and Metropolitan. Then he helped arrange a citywide championship. Other cities established their own. Even a national championship was underway.

Without knowing, the two plant pathologists had tapped into a deeply hidden talent pool. In 1957 the Aguilas won 10 more contests without a loss and topped the Aztec League. They'd melded into a committed, almost instinctive, group:

Those little guys were mean . . . I tell you, they were tough!

In fact the whole country's pre-teen talent was getting terrific. The team from Monterrey in northern Mexico that year won state, regional and national championships, and then took off for Williamsport to test themselves against the best of the rest.

That August, Norm couldn't forsake his fields to follow the first foreign team to compete in the Little League World Series. John Niederhauser, however, got himself to central Pennsylvania and was on hand to witness the ultimate triumph: Monterrey, Mexico 4; La Mesa, California 0. It was the Little League championship's only perfect game.

B y now Norm and his research squad had forged a bond akin to that of troops sharing a life-or-death struggle – one demanding that every member contribute feats of skill and endurance.

Australian biographer Lennard Bickel, writing shortly after these events, summed up Ignacio Narvaez's recollection: "[I]n all his years with Borlaug he'd never seen his teacher concentrate with such intensity on a single variety. He watched Borlaug's mood change as he studied the dwarfs — now angry, now delighted, now frustrated but always, always patient. Month after month Narvaez saw Borlaug shaking a problem to pieces like a terrier with a knotted rag, worrying and tossing it back and forth, never letting it go."

But despite the outward evidence that wheat genes had him outclassed, Norm never doubted eventual success. Moreover he wouldn't settle for just shrinking the plant. His historic fusion of tall summer wheats from Mexico and short winter wheats from Japan had exposed several astonishing new qualities. For one thing, he had plants whose spikelets carried six grains — three times the normal number and twice as many as even Yaqui 48. This alone would uplift productivity *two or three times*.

For another, he had plants that sprouted six or more stalks rather than the usual one or two. As each stalk produced its own seedhead, this offered another way to pack extra productivity into every acre.

And beyond all that he had plants that resisted the prevalent races of leaf rust, the fungus infecting leaves rather than stems.

Collectively, this was an incredibly powerful genetic mobilization, and he decided to rebuild the wheat chromosome incorporating *all of them together*. His goal now is super wheats with:

- Short, stiff stalks;
- Six seeds per spikelet;
- Six stems per plant;
- Resistance to leaf rust;
- Resistance to 15B- and 139 stem rust;
- High yield;
- Adaptability to many latitudes and climates;
- Speedy maturity;
- Grain that makes great bread.

Even for someone not operating alone in the Mexican wilds this was an incredible challenge. He hadn't yet made the first trait practical and now he'll attempt to bring out *eight* more rare qualities, several of which the crop had never before expressed. Moreover he had to do it all by feeling his way through the blindfold blackness of that era before gene sequencing was possible.

In September 1958, right after the research plots had been harvested, a hurricane swept in from the Pacific Ocean submerging western Mexico under a relentless combination of swirling winds and falling sky. Among other things, storm water surged down the

Sierra Madre massif in cataracts far surpassing what the rivers could dispose of.

Water piled up until the plains resembled lakes. The Lerma — Mexico's longest river, which normally ambled quietly past the La Piedad experiment station — spread sideways to drown the fields and invade the research facilities. At first, things only looked bad. Then the swollen surge lapped the storehouse containing the seed just acquired from the hundreds of experimental dwarf-wheat lines.

Perhaps it is well that Norm was not present; there's no telling what risks he'd have run to save those seeds. As it was, the station's head mechanic (José Flores) a soldier (José García), an agriculturist (Abel Arredondo) and his field assistant (Abel Melgosa) improvised a raft out of empty oil drums and old wooden planks. The four scrambled aboard to cross the watery maelstrom and rescue the seed.

That afternoon, the wind and current happened to be working in violent opposition. On the return trip the raft, heavily laden with seed, proved too unwieldy and too unstable to withstand the choppy torrent.

In the middle of the flow it capsized.

The seed disappeared beneath the raging whitewater.

Abel Arredondo and his colleague Abel Melgosa drowned.

Though the seed loss set the program back, Norm had planted duplicates at the other facilities. Moreover, little of what he was doing to tame the dwarf wheat seemed to be going anywhere.

Despite fourteen years of unbroken dedication, he was as active and spirited as those around him, few of whom had reached half his age. Day after tedious day he struggled alongside the field-hands, doing the same tedious tasks, sporting the same dusty khakis, cursing the same mosquitoes, tugging at the same kind of sweat-stained baseball cap to thwart the angry sun.

Seeing only the lack of progress, his peers dismissed him: Borlaug was beaten. Borlaug was merely playing for pride. Borlaug couldn't face reality. It was so sad. He was the only one who didn't know this was the endgame.

About this time one of Europe's prominent wheat breeders dropped by. On seeing how much was being attempted and how little was being accomplished James MacKey was appalled. Taking Norm aside, he grabbed him by the arm and spoke with great earnestness. "Stop wasting your career," he pleaded. "This is a hopeless mission!"

Actually, though, Norm believed victory was within reach. Season after season he'd make thousands more cross-pollinations, plant the resulting seeds, and study the progeny for years, retaining seed of only the odd plant that approximated the visions in his mind.

By the fall of 1959 he'd put the dwarfs through nine development cycles and introduced a range of genes that should have produced grain in quantities beyond any ever seen. No dwarf wheat was ready for the big time. However, one line seemed farmer-ready. It stayed upright when fertilized and it could produce twice the normal grain yield. But its grain was hard to mill and its flour made bad bread. Those were critical limitations, but possibly correctable with further breeding.

By 1959, the Farmer Field days had turned into fiestas. To a surprising extent this was due to radio. Small, cheap, portable transistor sets were showing up, and in rural Mexico they had a special appeal. CIANO's weekly radio broadcast attracted loyal listeners among wheat farmers. After hearing about the demonstration day, many came to see whether the rhetoric on the dial matched the reality in the dirt.

The Yaqui Valley had by then been transformed. Rodolfo Calles' vision had proven out. Agriculture had indeed lifted the state up out of dust and destitution. Sure, the plants were tall and subject to falling on their faces, but this former Wild West wasteland was generating more than half Mexico's wheat grain.

The sleepy town that 14 years earlier had resembled a stage-set for a matinee movie had morphed into a vibrant metropolis with 100,000 inhabitants. That former backwater without even a graveled road now had wide, paved, well-lit streets. The dusty main drag had become a wide avenue.

Cajeme was no longer swathed in insignificance or hopelessness. The burgeoning wheat harvests had attracted food processors. Around the town clusters of grain elevators stabbed the sky. Nearby were massive flourmills. Grupo Bimbo had built a huge new factory baking bread and cookies for much of Mexico. A Corona brewery was turning Borlaug-built grain into liquid gold — much of it for thirsty Americans.

And along with the dust of the past, Cajeme had shaken off its name. It was now known as "Ciudad Obregón" after Álvaro Obregón, the local garbanzo farmer who by force and fair judgment had risen to be presidente in 1920 only to be assassinated for his success in bringing

Mexico's violent ten-year revolution to a close.

In addition to streetlights, Obregón City had sidewalks and storm-water drains, not to mention parks, playgrounds and other public amenities. And just beyond the city limits, a few miles down the highway past CIANO, an airport capable of handling jets — the new-fangled planes that somehow had found a way to fly without propellers — was being built.

Urban planning set this place apart. And behind that planning lay a commanding emotion: civic pride. This was a successful city, and its citizens were more than satisfied . . . they were gratified. The place that once was raw now exuded raw power, and most people understood that it was the power of a wheat seed.

That same power even transcended the state line. In Sinaloa, Coahuila, Durango, Michoacán, and a dozen more states attitudes toward wheat had reversed, and with more farmers growing more than ever the national production was soaring at a rate that would soon top 5 million tons — *a fourteen-fold rise since Borlaug arrived.*

This heady leap rested not only on the seeds but also on their management. Farmers these days applied fertilizer, weed control, and irrigation water at just the right times for greatest production. And the plants responded with profits.

Already dubbed the Quiet Wheat Revolution, this makeover was touted as Mexico's best and only bloodless insurrection. Of note was the fact that it arose in the countryside and stemmed from local enterprise. Of note, too, was the fact that everyone benefited: poor and not-so-poor, urban and rural, here and across the land. Millions of Mexicans were by then enjoying the cheap flour tortilla that was soaring in popularity.

As 1959 came to a close Norm had put in 28 seasons since the summer of 1945. In other words, he'd spent a third of his life struggling to make Mexican wheat healthy, productive and good to eat. And now he'd moved his adopted nation to higher ground; local farmers produce all the wheat their nation needs.

Moreover by 1959, the other parts of the Mexican Agricultural Program were showing success. Wellhausen had Mexico's corn production soaring toward 6 million tons, three times what it had been when he arrived in 1943. John Niederhauser, the colleague who'd helped start Little League, had turned potato from a specialty into a staple grown by thousands of Mexico's small farmers. And sorghum, beans, and other crops were progressing as well.

Furthermore, that year the Rockefeller Foundation awarded the last of its planned 250 agriculture fellowships. Most had sent young Mexicans to study in the United States, Canada or Europe. Nine out of ten had returned home with good academic records, and at least three had ascended to positions of national influence.

From formerly having a mere handful of agriculturists with a Masters and none with a PhD, Mexico now had around a hundred MS graduates in the agricultural sciences and several dozen with doctorates. One of those was Ignacio Narvaez who'd recently returned from Purdue University in Indiana, bearing in his suitcase that most sacred of modern good-luck charms, a PhD. Another was Eva Villegas, to whom North Dakota State University had awarded a Ph.D. in Cereal Chemistry and Plant Breeding.

All in all, the agricultural science profession had indeed been created from scratch. Mexico's keen young students and technicians were taking over from the old guard, bringing positive attitudes, doing productive research, and injecting a hard driving spirit and the need for speed to keep their countrymen properly fed. This new generation of agriculturists was enlivening farmers, scientists and even politicians. Their oldest members were in their mid-twenties but they were introducing a new and aggressive approach to agronomy.

Thus, as the 1950s came to a close, Mexico's agricultural research was judged to have come of age. The country seemed capable of meeting its own agronomic needs. Thanks to George Harrar's foresight, John D. Rockefeller's funds, and Norman Borlaug and his colleagues the country was no longer hungry and had the capacity to carry on crop development without further help. The Mexican Agricultural Program was therefore closing.

In the eyes of the Rockefeller Foundation's Elect, Borlaug's thorny little project that seemed to never end had accomplished its mission. Even George Harrar declared it was time for Norm to go. The scientific responsibilities would be transferred to an agency the Mexican government has constituted to carry the operations onward.

Norm was given a month to step aside. Strangely, he didn't demur. This rebuff was, after all, also an honor: he'd been hired to do a job, and now he'd done it.

Nonetheless, he was far from happy. Could he in good conscience forsake the vast research enterprise he'd nurtured for fifteen years? Was it right to abandon the ongoing experiments in the Yaqui Valley? In Toluca? La Piedad? Other places? Could he turn his back on all the young technicians who counted on him for labor and leadership, if not for life? Could they find paychecks of another sort?

And what would happen to the partially perfected dwarf wheat lines? It was wrenching to see the summer sun bathing the gilt heads of those ugly ducklings' knowing they might grow into swans.

He'd lifted the crop that supplies a third of Planet Earth's food but he'd lifted it but a single step, and he had almost a dozen more wondrous steps in train.

His life's trajectory hereby reached yet another turning point. Regardless of his capabilities or the fact that his motor still ran in top gear, his contract was terminated.

Should there be any future battles, they'd have to be in some different theater of conflict. But where would that be? The dwarfs' seductive possibilities for helping the hungry had drawn him in so deep he'd neglected his own needs. And his family's.

He had no job to go to. And being let go was truly terrifying to any Great Depression survivor.

In three months he'll turn 46, and before then he must somehow scare up a new line of work.

PART III

The Far Side
[Asia]

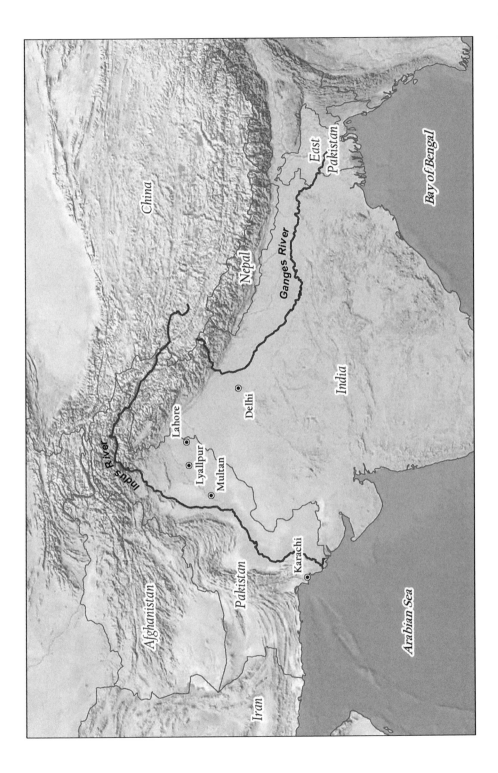

1960-1962
Deliverance

While closing down the Mexican Agricultural Program in 1960 the Rockefeller Foundation – in a surprise move – awarded Wellhausen a new contract. Ed was to launch a project to uplift corn production in the nations below Mexico. Most surprising of all, he'd run it from his current office, which was outside the target area.

That fluky notion required the funds to be housed in a Mexico City bank, which in turn allowed some dollars to be side-slipped to the local agriculture ministry. Those misdirected Central-American corn-research funds were for Borlaug to wind up his work before heading off into the sunset.

To take better advantage of modern agriculture the Mexican government had created the Institute of Agricultural Research. When the agriculture minister asked who should take Norm's place Norm replied: "Nacho should run the wheat program. He can do it as well as me."

Ignacio Narvaez, the kid who 13 years earlier had saved Borlaug's sanity after a cold night trapped on a mountain thus got elevated to Mexican Wheat Czar while Norm sought out a new job.

Finding work proved difficult until, out of the blue, United Fruit asked him to tackle Panama Disease, a fungus threatening the banana crop. The threat was so great that the company would double his salary to $18,000!

For that wealth he'd merely have to accomplish the impossible. Having neither flowers to fertilize nor seeds to sow, banana plants cannot be bred.

Buoyed by that challenge, Norm agreed to take the job. Margaret approved as well. She and the children – Jeanie (now 17) and Bill (13) – would move to Honduras to help him build a better banana.

Norm had but one proviso: he wanted to bring along two young Mexican technicians familiar with his plant-breeding methods.

Although that would more speedily thwart the fungus that imperiled the company's, not to mention tropical America's, economic survival, the executives (of the corporate entity today known as Chiquita) fretted over the additional cost.

And that mindless temporizing over a trivial expense allowed just enough time for another wondrous intercession.

S ince his graduate school days, when he'd shared flax-research findings with Norm, Al Moseman had joined the Rockefeller Foundation and risen into the upper echelons of administration. He now was the only foundation leader who wanted to keep Borlaug on the payroll.

His was a lonely and seemingly hopeless struggle and after several rebuffs, Moseman concluded that his only chance was to play for time and pray for a miracle that might allow Norm to remain on staff.

Then in January 1960 he learned that the UN Food and Agricultural Organization (FAO) was preparing to send a team of specialists to survey wheat and barley research across North Africa, the Middle East and South Asia. Hustling down the corridor to George Harrar's office, Moseman urged that the foundation designate Norm as its representative. It would be a just reward for all his contributions.

Norm was unaware that his friend was plotting on his behalf. He'd by then retreated from Sonora to be with the family and enjoy their last Christmas and New Year celebration in Mexico.

Then Harrar phoned from New York: If Norm would like to join the United Nations team, the foundation would cover his expenses for the two-month trip. It was an offer Norm couldn't resist.

In February 1960 Norm first stepped into the outer darkness beyond the Americas. Traveling under the sky-blue UN flag, he and three other specialists assessed FAO-funded research in 14 hot and hungry countries between Morocco and India. In each country they quizzed farmers, endured tedious technical talks from stuffy senior scientists, and inspected mediocre wheat and barley research operations.

Norm could see that the governments were fixated on industrial development and paid agriculture little heed. Yet these 14 nations were said to have "earth's hungriest, saddest, poorest, most desperate people."

Wheat was their staple, and several — Libya and Tunisia, for example — featured great looking research fields of what he recognized as Kentana 48, Yaqui 50 and Lerma Rojo 54.

How his own babies had crossed the Atlantic he didn't know, but they were the finest on this side too. Mexicans were using them to lift their national food supply, but here the authorities remained indifferent. When he urged they multiply the seed and supply it to their farmers they brushed him off with endless excuses. He found it disgusting:

> They had the answer to their nations' most fundamental problem before their eyes, yet they refused to act. I couldn't believe it. Despite the plants' obvious power to lift production of their main staple, the senior scientists insisted on doing more study. "Something might go wrong," they said.
> Truth is, they were getting paid to act but were afraid to.

This overt intellectual cowardice convinced him that the system was rotten at the top. The mass millions in 14 nations would go on being hungry, sad, poor and desperate because their leaders lacked courage, vision or any appreciation for the need for speed.

Finally the panel returned to FAO headquarters in the heart of Rome, where each member was obliged to pen a personal response. Norm now faced a problem. Recommending that 14 countries dismiss their scientific elites would accomplish nothing. He needed a positive alternative. His mind, though, refused to answer the call:

> For several days I was gripped by mental paralysis. Then one afternoon, in desperation I walked across the square to St. Peter's and sat leaning against a wall, lost in thought.
> Half of humanity was going to bed hungry. Their governments gave agriculture low priority. The senior scientists were so ineffectual they ignored the obvious answers before their eyes.
> How could all that be changed? What would alter the priorities? How could new vigor and new varieties be introduced?
> Then as I sat there in the dim light, images of Mexico's keen young students and technicians came to mind. Their enthusiasm had enlivened farmers, scientists and even politicians. All those had taken heart, and Mexico was being transformed.

Hastening back to the office FAO had provided, he pulled out a pen and began scribbling:

> I propose the first order of priority should be the rapid, intensive, and practical training of a corps of dedicated young agronomists from each country willing to take part. The FAO can select the candidates and screen them for the best human material available. If there are countries that have no people with university training, then we should take the best possible and give them this training. I further recommend that, with the

agreement of the Rockefeller Foundation and the Mexican government, these young men be sent, for roughly a year, to the establishments in Mexico where so many young agronomists have already been trained in the new aggressive approach to modern agronomy.

As an aside he suggested that he himself might oversee training the new hunger-fighting cadet corps. And as a final addendum he recommended that *every year* the 14 countries between Morocco and India be provided samples of the latest and best seed from Mexico's wheat research plots.

Then, having handed in his barely readable scribble for typing, he headed homeward for one final fling with wheat before heading for Honduras and the challenge of remaking a fruit crop that couldn't be remade.

N orm reached Sonora just in time for the 1960 Farmer Field Day, the fourteenth since the one in 1947 when a single farmer came to imbibe facts rather than free beer.

Anticipating 3000 participants, Nacho Narvaez had planned the April 7 event with military precision. Tractors would drag trailers laden with a hundred or so farmers sitting on benches through the fields.

Nine displays exposing the best plants and best practices had been laid out. The tenth display would let the farmers see the new dwarf wheat bearing twice the normal grain load.

In this, the new director is pushing his luck. The plants looked great but were not ready for the big time; their grain was soft in the center, making it hard to mill, and their flour made bad bread. Norm remembers warning Narvaez: "When they see those, Nacho, you're going to have a real picnic on your hands."

Accordingly, at the dwarf-wheat station Narvaez posted his most pugnacious lieutenant, Alfredo García. Others were assigned as backup guards. "Let no one off the trailers," Narvaez charged. "The farmers can listen. They can look. *But none must touch!*"

When the time came Borlaug stood back, taking photographs. As the first convoy reached that station the tractor driver stopped too soon, and García strode forward to demand he bring all four trailers within easy earshot. Just then, though, the occupants spotted the new plants, arose as one, leapt from their trailers, and plunged into the plot.

Even on calm days García was a keg of powder. Now he screamed curses and tried shoving the farmers away. But the press of a hundred sturdy bodies merely propelled him back onto his own precious plants.

Restoring order took ten tense minutes. When the trailers were finally reoccupied and rushed on to the next station García remained doubled over – pained, panting, furious. He'd said not a word about the half-height wheats. He'd recovered not a single seedhead.

Secretly Borlaug was pleased. Elsewhere, stealing seed might be considered a crime; here it signified a food-production revolution. And that, after all, was his goal.

Sadly, the seed in the hundred farmers whose pockets sprouted wheat like the Straw Man's would make millers mad and bakers blanch.

L eaving the next research round in Narvaez's hands, Norm seized his first chance in 16 years to help another country: Argentina.

This raised yet another ruckus at HQ. Harrar feared that American wheat growers might regard Borlaug's effort as aiding and abetting the enemy. In return for tax breaks U.S. foundations pledge to never damage the national interest. By helping a wheat-exporting rival Borlaug might jeopardize the foundation's financial future.

Despite the risk Harrar eventually relented – asking only that Borlaug keep a very low profile in Buenos Aires. Norm was forever grateful:

Argentina was the only well-fed country I ever worked in. And those six months were well worth it. In time, our efforts helped wheat production soar, and not only there. Later, the dwarf wheats helped also Brazil, Paraguay, Chile and several more Latin nations that would have suffered hunger without them.

His six-month sideline also generated a favorite story:

One night in late November I returned from a long day at Castelar [an agricultural research facility] and read in the local newspaper that fifteen U.S. governors had arrived in Buenos Aires. Argentine Airlines was inaugurating a direct flight to New York and had flown in the governors as part of the celebration.

Two of the names I recognized, and as I headed out to work the next morning I dropped by the Hotel Grande and handed the clerk two of my business cards to pass on.

About 6:30 that night I returned to my very modest hotel, and was surprised to see a huge black Cadillac limousine standing out front. I was even more surprised when the driver spoke up as I passed by. At first he was deferential but his expression turned anxious when he saw my sweat-stained khakis. He instructed me to change quickly; I was already late for the governors' reception.

I sure felt out of place in the Hotel Grande's ballroom, surrounded by chandeliers, plush carpet and fancy wallpaper. I also felt uncomfortable among all the dignitaries, socialites from

Argentine high society, U.S. embassy staff and, of course, the governors and their wives.

Moving down the receiving line I met the first of my friends, the Minnesota governor. We instantly recognized each other from the University of Minnesota Athletic Department, where in the 1930s I'd been a wrestler and he a football player.

"What the hell are you doing down here?" Orville Freeman asked. So I explained I was helping Argentina grow more food. His manner abruptly changed, and in a sideways whisper he said, "Norm, we've got to talk. Let's get together later."

A couple of times during the evening Orville spirited me away into a corner, but someone always interrupted for some perfunctory introduction. Nonetheless, from his few questions I got a sense of what was in the wind. Just a couple of weeks before, Kennedy had won the presidential election. Orville's queries, which were all about the state of world agriculture, convinced me that my old friend would soon be moving to Washington D.C. To a colleague the next morning I blurted out: "I just met the next Secretary of Agriculture!"

Somewhat further down the governors' receiving line I found the other friend. He too asked: "What the hell are you doing down here?" And after I explained, he said: "Norm, how on earth did we get to a point like this?"

As he said those words he gazed around that ornate ballroom with all the dignitaries and functionaries bustling about and sensitive to his every whim, and was overtaken by emotion. Two big tears rolled down his cheeks. And he pulled out a handkerchief.

Seeing his distress, an embassy matron bustled over. "Governor," she said, "are you ill?"

"No," he replied, " . . . just some cigarette smoke in my eye."

He was my old high school football comrade Robert E. Smylie. I remembered back to the night after high school graduation. I'd spent it in the tiny loft over the Smylie's gas station. Bob had then had a miserable life, sleeping alone in that loft and hand-pumping gas for truckers through the night.

We'd not seen each other since that time, but he'd undergone an incredible journey. First he'd moved to Idaho to live with a maiden aunt. Then he'd worked his way out of crushing poverty, put himself through law school, and entered Idaho politics.

When we met in Argentina he was already into a second term as governor and would later be elected once more. He ended up the state's most respected citizen, and people refer to him fondly as "the Grand Old Man of Idaho politics."

My old friend Bob Smylie had amounted to something after all!

Upon his return to Mexico a surprise awaited. During Norm's time-out in Argentina his proposed hunger-fighting cadet corps had been organized. The Rockefeller Foundation had found the funds. The Mexican government had provided the visas for foreign students to come and learn to grow wheat the Mexican way. And the UN Food and Agriculture Organization had chosen candidates from eight of the world's hungriest, saddest, poorest and most desperate countries.

At the airport just down the road from CIANO in February 1961 earnest-looking young men arrived from Afghanistan, Egypt, Libya, Iran, Iraq, Pakistan, Syria and Turkey. Two others, Norm's personal selections, arrived from Argentina.

All brought bags, brief cases and bewilderment. Instead of a grand adventure, they'd gotten dumped into a more isolated spot than the ones they'd left. Why on earth had the UN picked such a backwater?

The bewilderment quickly faded. Within days the newcomers had toured the Yaqui Valley's fields and spent face-time with friendly English-speaking farmers such as Roberto Maurer, Rafael Fierros and Rodolfo Calles. And within weeks they witnessed combines harvesting vast fields and disgorging grain into seemingly endless lines of trucks.

It was all very impressive. And at each stop Borlaug pounded home his belief that they were about to acquire the knowledge, the skills and the seeds to make their own countries look like this. They would be Wheat Apostles.

Next the trainees were made to manage trial plots and field operations. Their guide, Reyes Vega, gave orders with verve and authority. He demanded that every task be performed flawlessly. His students never knew that just 15 years before he'd been an illiterate kid chasing birds for 5 pesos a week.

In this new enterprise this ex-bird-boy was a full partner. Privately, Norm told the students: 'If you want to know how to run a big breeding program, follow Reyes Vega and talk to him. You'll learn more that way than from me or any other scientist.'"

In April, Norm took over, having the trainees toil beside him harvesting the myriad plantings, measuring the yields, and selecting the seeds for the next round of research. For many, this was their introduction to manual labor. However, with the scientist beside them toiling harder than anyone, they complied without complaint. This man they'd never heard of wove a kind of spell. In its shadow they forgot themselves, the heat, the dust, and the flies. Out there in the Sonoran Desert they absorbed his style. And they found the joy he found in the struggle to feed hungry humankind.

Personally undaunted by demotion, Norm remained fired with the mission to make the world's top food crop carry its full weight. He and Narvaez were collaborating to continue advancing the dwarf wheat and they'd co-opted the foreign trainees as a new work force.

Husky, slim and as energetic as any of his youthful Mexican superiors, Norm slipped in among the lower ranks reporting to those former students half his age. Norm himself had just turned 47, and some of his charisma was a charade:

> I still could hold my own with youngsters who were in their prime and physically tough. That helped me be effective, but I never told them how I felt at night back in the hotel room.

The group next moved indoors to analyze the data, write up the findings, and thrash and clean the winning seed. They put most of the product aside for the next research round, but they also packed samples for the special project Norm had urged on the UN Food and Agriculture Organization. Those seed packets would go to 14 countries and put earth's hungriest, saddest, poorest, most desperate people on the front edge of wheat's wave of progress.

Next the group made up packets for the Department of Agriculture in Washington. Herman Rodenheiser would mail those out for testing against stem-rust. For the first time some would go to locations beyond the U.S. and Canada – Argentina and India, for example.

In May the trainees were conducted south to Central Mexico and in the high plateau near Toluca taught how to begin a new research round. Backs bent, brows dripping and shoes caked in dust, they leveled the land with small tractors, laid out experimental plots, sowed seeds, and applied fertilizer and irrigation water.

Then in July they learned the art of cross-pollination, helping make the thousands of crosses for Round 33 in Borlaug's sixteen-year waltz with wheat.

In Mexico City late in July he staged a simple farewell ceremony. Then the graduates flew home toting suitcases stuffed with seeds of his best experimental lines, including the partially perfected dwarfs.

Despite geographical, linguistic and cultural differences, the formerly bewildered youths had melded into a confident, capable, competent hunger fighting corps. They returned home committed to making Afghanistan, Argentina, Egypt, Libya, Iran, Iraq, Pakistan, Syria and Turkey *just like Mexico.*

During their time in Sonora Norm and Narvaez had spotted patches of downsized wheat. Some farmers had spent the summer multiplying their few hundred heisted seeds and now in November were sowing a second increase. Norm advised instant action:

> Nacho, you'd better move fast. With those bad grains, no one's going to buy the harvest. And when the farmers find that out, we'll all catch hell.

Narvaez thus faced his first professional crisis. In Mexico City he notified the milling industry's representative that a radical new generation of wheat was coming on line — one that would boost national production. Sadly, however, the seed had prematurely escaped the experiment station. Farmers were even then sowing it on a sizable scale. Those farmers expected to get a fair price for their grain. Few, however, knew that it had poor milling qualities. And if the millers rejected the harvest, Mexico's wheat lands would erupt and the national uplift would be delayed.

The miller's rep seemed mortified but after a few days of consultations he returned: "If these varieties will increase yield as much as you believe," he said, "we'd be traitors to reject them. We'll get over the difficulty. We say . . . release the new dwarf wheats!"

Although several advanced lines had escaped during the field day, the main vagabonds were a pair of plants that were head-high to a three-year-old (3 foot 7 inches). In experiments they yielded around 2.5 tons an acre, or roughly twice Borlaug's previous best and five times more than Mexico's best when he'd arrived on the scene. Most importantly, these two could be heavily fertilized without falling over under the resulting weight of grain.

Narvaez immediately initiated the tedious process of planting and replanting ever-increasing numbers of seeds until there would be enough for farmers' needs. Among themselves, however, the scientists found this utterly galling. They'd dedicated five years to making the crop carry its designated load, only to deliver deeply flawed types.

While Norm labored in distant obscurity his own family lived in the second-floor apartment in Mexico City. Margaret had now spent 16 years there, running the family mostly alone. During those years Norm had been around only between May and November. And even then he left before dawn and got home after dark.

The adjustment was hard; Margaret longed to be able to visit the outer world as her husband did. The two had been married 24 years and never had a honeymoon. Norm solemnly promised he'd rectify that . . . just as soon as he can fit it in.

For author Lennard Bickel she recalled: "I had to take the good with the bad, being married to a great man — though perhaps I say that out of blind love. I am not a scientifically minded person, but I knew he needed a home, a place to come to where he would always be comfortable and happy."

That spirit made possible everything that was to transpire. "My Mom provided the stability in our home," Jeanie explains. "With Daddy away so much, she did the banking and the shopping, paid the bills and managed all the family affairs. Had she not been such a strong person, either Bill or I would have been a mess or my Dad couldn't have done all he did."

Bill spent that summer of 1961 playing baseball for his father, the coach. "Little League was the epicenter of our family," he recalls. "During summer months we had practices on Tuesdays and Thursdays and games on Saturdays. Dad found the time to make them all."

By now 15,000 Mexico City boys were enjoying Little League. Bill Borlaug, however, had graduated to Pony League, which included kids aged from about 14 to 17. Games were played at the American High School and Norm still coached with joy, flair and success. That very year his team, the Toltecas, won the Pony League Championship. Half a century onward one of the players, Gordon (Russ) Sutton, recollected:

"In the early 1960s, I moved to Mexico City with my mother and two brothers. My father had passed away when I was twelve and my mother thought his pension would go much farther living in Mexico.

"We moved to a small house in Mexico City and the first thing my Mom did was enroll us three boys in baseball.

"I was lucky enough to end up on the Toltecas. Norman Borlaug was our coach and he coached us all the way to a league championship.

"What I remember most about Coach Borlaug was that he was a kind and giving man with a great work ethic. My mother did not have a car or much money and for years Coach Borlaug would pick me up every day and take me to baseball practice. At the end of practice or a game, he would drop me off at home. During the ride, win or lose, he would give me advice about baseball and his philosophy of life in general. I cherished those rides and all the wisdom he had to offer.

"When I couldn't afford a baseball glove, he gave me one. It was used, but it had a great pocket and I am sure, at one time, it belonged to his son, Bill.

"Once in a while, he bought my brothers and me cokes and hot dogs. Because we were poor, I am sure he helped my mom out with any fees that had to be paid for the privilege of playing baseball.

"While driving to practice, I always noticed in the far back area of his Chevy station wagon were bags and bags of small, green plants. Little did I know that I was riding with the man who was in the process of feeding the world."

With the coming of 1962 Norm could survey the verdant Yaqui Valley and see his creations making a difference. By putting down roots, thousands of wheat farmers were building up wealth. Many were building California-style ranch houses, including air conditioning. Most were sending their kids to school. All had bought a truck and a tractor. Some were starting businesses. One had built a motel just off the town's main street, calling it the Costa de Oro [Gold Coast], presumably referring to the Yaqui Valley's million acres of golden fields.

In February 1962 the second batch of trainees arrived in Sonora from Cyprus, Egypt, Ethiopia, Iran, Iraq, Jordan, Libya, Pakistan, Syria, Saudi Arabia and Turkey. In addition, Norm had invited ten South Americans and a bevy of Mexicans.

From dawn to dusk during those springtime days the wheat plots at CIANO echoed the cheerful chatter of this multinational work force measuring and recording the vital details distinguishing thousands of wheat gems from the masses of wheat garbage.

That April a big friendly Canadian came to harvest the research plots for his countrymen. This was Glenn Anderson's second visit to this hard-to-find hideaway. Back in 1961, he'd impressed Norm by voluntarily staying over and helping teach the trainees long after his counterparts had gathered their seeds and suitcases and scurried for home. This time Norm took Anderson fishing along the irrigation canal and plumbed the strength of his convictions:

> Glenn's drive to excel was impressive. He was impatient with mediocrity, lethargy, sloppy science, the status quo, and bureaucracy. I tucked all that away in the memory bank.
> I also provided him seed from our latest and best dwarf lines. They were not quite ready for use, but I figured Canadians would appreciate their short stiff straw. That was a unique factor and a basic advance of great commercial value. I figured that a nation that runs on wheat would be very excited.

Just before sending the International Stem Rust Nursery samples to Rody Rodenheiser in Washington Norm added five envelopes containing experimental dwarf lines. The 200 or so seeds in each envelope had been gathered from plants so pitiful he should have been ashamed to let anyone see them.

By that fall grain from the imperfect dwarfs filched from the 1960 Farmer Field Day was trickling into commerce. By then, farmers had bulked up seed and begun selling it to their neighbors, who were planting production fields.

Narvaez now named the pair Pitic [PIT-EEK] and Penjamo [pen-HAH-moe]. It was a big moment: Pitic 62 and Penjamo 62 were the world's first commercial dwarf summer wheats.

Borlaug by now was frantically cross-pollinating in hopes of developing replacements. With the millers in mind, he was hardening the grain's center; for the bakers he was strengthening the gluten. This was a hit-or-miss process, and he depended on Eva Villegas's laboratory skills. During the harvest season, he hauled in hundreds of seed packets for testing. Eva then milled them into flour and baked the flour into little loaves. She had veto power over his progress. If the tests came out bad Norm had to abandon that plant, regardless of its value for farmers.

No longer the elfin figure, Eva has in the intervening decade earned an MS from Kansas State and a doctorate from North Dakota State. Ranking among Latin America's most respected biochemists, she now traveled the world lecturing on cereal chemistry in Spanish or English.

But her main effort was the mission to make dwarf-wheat grain make great bread. The dilemma in 1961 was that thousands of crossings had shown that the gene that shrank the stem was genetically linked with another that weakened the stretchy protein that makes bread rise.

One day in the fall of '62 Eva happened to be beside her laboratory at Chapingo when Norm pranced down the path waving four seed packets. Her filing cabinet bulged with analyses made on the contents of similar packets he'd brought her from Toluca. But this time his manner seemed different. Instead of professional calmness, he radiated enthusiasm as he shouted: "Eva, aqui tenemos los mejores toros!" [Eva, here we have the best of the bulls!]

Norm, commonly described his genetic lines as if he were breeding cattle, but she understood that this was the golden moment when his gambit with dwarfing genes might be about to pay off.

It's hard to credit the level of effort he'd invested. The quest for a practical dwarf wheat had taken six years and more than 8000 cross-pollinations. The particular seeds in the packets he was waving in the air came from progeny of the 8156th — a figure indicating their rarity and his resolution. From the 60 or so plants emerging from that 8156th gene blend he'd isolated four special standouts.

Plants grown from these seeds feature every trait he'd ever sought. They can break the 3 ton per-acre-yield barrier. They are immune to stem rust. They were about waist high. They were adapted to conditions as diverse as Toluca's moist sky-high mountainside and Sonora's bottom-dwelling desert. Moreover they produced multiple stems, each stem produced its own head of seed, and each seedhead produced almost twice the normal number of grains.

No wonder Norm pranced down the path that day at Chapingo. The seeds in these four packets represented his greatest masterpieces. They could open horizons higher and wider than any known.

But could they make good bread?

Everything rests on Eva's analysis.

N orm could by now exert influence in nine countries where Wheat Apostles were pre-positioned. With them, he shared the latest seeds and latest insights. Nonetheless, the most perilous country in the most populous continent remained beyond reach. India, you see, refused to send trainees. It needed no help from Mexico!

The connection came about inadvertently after Rodenheiser mailed out the thimbles of seed for the 1962 International Stem-Rust Nursery and a few grams of Borlaug's five embarrassingly bad experimental dwarfs reached New Delhi.

India was the most perilous country on the most populous continent. There, people production outstripped food production annually by 5 percent. Many of the 400 million Indians would be struggling with outraged stomachs had not America been dispensing edibles for almost a decade.

But by 1960 India's case of congenital hunger seemed incurable. More than half the vast land area was under cultivation and most of that was overused. There were no more forests to cut, swamps to drain or deserts to water. Crops could barely carry their current loads. Food reserves were nonexistent. The treasury was bare, ruling out purchases on the open market. And every month brought a million more mouths. Experts had declared that 10 million Indians would starve.

Only American generosity kept India from mass starvation. The federal program known as Public Law 480 supported a steady stream of ships stretching from the U.S. to the far side of the world. Millions of tons of wheat, corn and sorghum were hauled across thousands of miles of ocean, unloaded through crowded ports and rushed inland over hundreds of miles of congested roads and railways to tens of thousands of relief centers serving millions of desperate Indians.

The New Delhi government operated a vast food delivery system that unloaded U.S. grain in a dozen ports and spread it throughout the sprawling nation of over a million square miles. There, more than 50,000 "Fair Price Shops" passed out sacks of grain to more than 100 million poor people who would otherwise go hungry.

This giant operation – history's largest famine relief – had been a huge success. After almost a decade, however, it was spawning unintended consequences that could quickly turn it into a failure.

For one thing, millions of the poor were forced to fast when, as commonly happened, a ship got delayed at sea and the Fair Price Shops stayed shut. For another, Indian farmers had stopped striving to grow extra food. To them, Fair Price Shops were far from fair. As a consequence the food supply was sagging just as the need was soaring.

India was a country of farmers, but its government accorded them little respect and few resources. Its socialist leadership rejected any notion of competition, market forces or profits.

Although India was a democracy its legislators were beholden to an all-powerful policy body, the Planning Commission. Following the Soviet Union, it issued five-year plans the emphasized Stalinist dreams over starvation concerns. Thanks to those dreams national policy emphasized industrial development, armaments, nuclear weapons and international eminence. The Planning commission was so powerful that even cabinet ministers could not override its demands.

By 1962 food shortages had undermined confidence in the country's leadership. With fear of hunger in their thoughts, millions were growing resentful; insecurity had become a national trait.

Contributing to the unease were the testy relations with Pakistan, which then straddled India on both sides. Apart from borders, the two nations shared little beyond dependence on wheat and the monsoon.

One of the world's most intense regular weather events, the monsoon delivered up to 90 percent of a year's rainfall. The rains normally arrived in June and lasted four months. They fed the farms, which in turn fed the people, who in turn fed the economy and fueled progress.

Sadly, though, the world's most intense regular weather event was not all that regular. Some years it delivered the blessed liquid perfectly. Some years it delivered floods that sweep away crops and communities. And some years it failed, leaving plants and people stricken and starving.

This is how things stood that October day when the few grams of seed of Borlaug's embarrassingly bad experimental dwarfs reached India's capital of New Delhi.

No one knew the dozen or so seeds in each of Borlaug's five packets were anything special. Indeed, when they were sown the resulting plants looked like living horrors.

The one who saw past the exterior facade was Momkombu Sambasivan Swaminathan [swah-mee-NAH-than]. A scientist at the Indian Agricultural Research Institute in New Delhi, he was intrigued by the smallness, the stem strength and the immunity to stem rust, which was then plaguing all of India's local wheats. Peering intently at the 50 or so plants through his rather thick spectacles he saw great possibilities.

Swaminathan immediately wrote a letter inviting Borlaug to visit India's wheat lands and give his advice.

In Mexico City late in the year Eva Villegas made her pronouncement: the special short-straw strains – the four selections from the 8156th cross-pollination carrying Norm's highest hopes – *were indeed great bread makers!*

Given this endorsement, Norm urged that the seed be bulked up and supplied to farmers *fast*. But the Agriculture Ministry worried about a stem rust variant that possessed the power to infect two of these four. That rust race occurred only in the southern and more humid sections of Mexico but the authorities insisted on holding back the two wheats until they could be safely sown countrywide.

Norm was furious that those two should be held back. Knowing it would cause trouble, he urged their release in Sonora and other northern, drier, wheat-growing areas where they were safe to grow. But what could he do? The Agriculture Ministry had the jurisdiction, and it refused to release the two super 8156 siblings, which were actually the best plants of all.

1963

Pivot Point

As 1963 opened Norm was absorbed in his Sonora duties. His wheat progeny were all around. His days of disorder were behind. He was leading the quiet life of a teacher and researcher.

Though he should have taken time out for satisfaction, he was looking toward the next horizon. He was advancing the 8156 dwarf generation. He was managing plantings as a gift to snowbound colleagues in Canada and the U.S. He was maintaining myriad observation plots for interest, for insight and for inspiration. He was shrinking pasta [durum] wheat and triticale, which are quite separate but complementary cereal species. And beyond all those he was performing his real responsibilities: training the Wheat Apostles, who this year came from Argentina, Cyprus, Egypt, Ethiopia, Iran, Iraq, Jordan, Pakistan, Syria, and Turkey.

Then Swaminathan's letter arrived from New Delhi.

By March Norm was winging eastward on his second trip beyond the Americas. Following a brief session with Swaminathan in New Delhi, he headed out for a month's immersion in India's wheat lands.

The timing was terrific; the Ganges Plain was abuzz with preparations for the harvest. But this trek stirred the blood. Rural India looked like rural Mexico had when he'd arrived almost 20 years before. Misery was manifest. Grain was harvested by sickle and manhandled in sacks that weighed up to one quintal (112lb). Yields were typically 7 quintals an acre, which pinned millions of families on poverty's edge.

He saw that Indian society had lost its moorings and was adrift. Experts had declared that 10 million Indians were about to starve. Norm could see that low yield was the cause. Absent high-performing crops, four out of ten rural Indians lived on less than 10 cents a day. Absent cash, they had to fashion lives out of nothing, and dwelt in mud-walled huts without sanitation or running water. Absent electricity, they cooked over smoky open fires fueled with sundried cow dung. Absent public transportation, they lived marooned. Absent schools or a teacher, they could not improve their children's prospects, let alone their own.

These sights were especially upsetting because Norm had just left the Yaqui Valley, which shares latitude, climate and conditions with India's northern plains that produced most of its wheat. Sonora's farmers were preparing for the harvest too, but come April they'd harvest over 3 tons (50 quintals) an acre, which was far too much for sickles and sacks. For six years they'd been using combine harvesters, heavy trucks and bulk handling.

Norm's dilemma was how best to bring a similar makeover to India. One thing was certain: India's system for agricultural advancement was rotten at the top. At stop after stop he suffered through seemingly endless recantations of research that could never lift hunger's haunting shadow from the land. Most of the researchers were engaged in what he scornfully called "chasing academic butterflies." A prime example was the widespread irradiation of seeds to induce mutations.

To him it was a crime to waste time when people were hungry. The only thing worse was the excuses:

> When I asked about the need to modernize agriculture, both scientists and administrators typically replied, "Poverty is the farmers' lot; they are used to it."
> I was informed that the farmers were proud of their lowly status, and was assured that they wanted no change. After my own experiences in Iowa and Mexico I didn't believe a word of it.

Not even India's scientists were confident of science. Doubt dominated all discussions about the food supply and the future. Worse still, the society was turning against science.

But, given the pervasive pessimism, paralysis and smug acceptance of a food production system stuck in the ancient past, introducing an alternative would be difficult. National policy was crushing the soul out of its own farming community:

> I came out of that tour certain that whatever we provided, the farmers could never make a change by themselves. Before a wheat revolution could get off the ground issues reaching all the way to the top of the government had to be settled.

He also saw that, though not a hopeful place, rural India was far from hopeless. Many technical possibilities had not been tried. He decided to spark some optimism. In addressing a group of administrators and scientists in the city of Kanpur, he made four predictions:

- In a few years India will double or triple wheat production;
- Demand for fertilizer will skyrocket;
- Cultivation practices will change beyond recognition; and
- The country will have difficulty handling the harvest!

They all thought him quite mad.

Only in one farming region did he sense the possibility of opening a door to the wider future: Punjab [puhn-JARB], a broad, flat and fertile expanse extending across the headwaters of the great rivers Indus and Ganges.

Punjabi farmers reminded Norm of those in the Yaqui Valley. They seemed a scrappy lot, shrinking neither from a stranger nor a silly question. Above all, they seemed committed to bettering themselves.

He also found that driving spirit among a small cadre of scientists. Some were located at universities in and near the Punjab. Others were at the Indian Agricultural Research Institute in New Delhi.

The day before he headed homeward, Norm was guest of honor at a luncheon at the Indian Agricultural Research Institute. Present in that small room in the library were a dozen motivated visionaries – friendly, competent, optimistic, eager to hear his views. These particular specialists saw their country's food and agriculture needs in strategic terms and understood the need for speed. This small group included Swaminathan, who headed the IARI's division of genetics, and B.P. Pal, who directed IARI's graduate school.

High expectation enlivened the proceedings. Norm began by elaborating on the people he'd met during his month's immersion:

> *The agricultural researchers.* They are not contributing enough; too many are merely holding down a job, striving for academic laurels or wasting their time on scientific sideshows.

> *The politicians.* They are treating the farmer unfairly by not properly rewarding his effort. That is self-defeating because the farmer's the guy who grows the food. You can't play fast and loose with his faith; he must know the score and feel confident about his future. He must also be adequately compensated for his labors.

The farmers. They are much more capable than anyone is crediting. They can achieve big advances. They're not conservative; they're not happy with their lot; they don't like their present situation. Give them a chance and they will respond and the food supply will strengthen out of sight.

As Norm ended his presentation Swaminathan raised the issue of the moment: "Now that you've seen all this," he asked, "do you think your wheats could do for India what they've done for Mexico?"

Silence descended. Borlaug sensed the group willing him to pull from his pocket the final solution to their country's flirtation with famine. But lives were at stake and he couldn't be certain his seeds would work on this side of the world:

They were hoping I'd declare our wheats capable of transplanting the whole Mexican experience into India. I could not give them this assurance. I wasn't at all sure. Caution was necessary.
"There are imponderables," I said; "we just don't know enough yet."

The spirit that had energized the room deflated like a balloon with a stickpin. But Borlaug was far from downcast:

I smiled at Swaminathan. "On my way home I can find out the things we need to know," I said. "Give me a few weeks and I'll write you a report answering the question."

Norm was thinking of three of the Wheat Apostles. Two were next door in Pakistan; one was in Egypt. All knew how to grow Mexican wheats and all had taken home samples of his best seed.

Pakistan's Wheat Apostles were Mansur Bajwa [1961] and Nur Chaudry [1962]. They worked at the main agricultural research institute in the town then called Lyallpur. Norm anticipated slipping in quietly and seeing them in private. However, on reaching the Ayub Khan Research Institute he was greeted by its director, Anwar Hussain. On hand too was the Pakistan's Secretary of Agriculture – Malik Khuda Bakhsh Bucha had motored down the 70 miles from the city of Lahore. And in the courtyard behind the office complex was a gathering of civil servants, researchers, reporters, and scattered westerners. A special field day had been arranged in his honor.

It was the eve of his 50th birthday:

Following formal greetings and ritual cups of tea the throng trooped out behind the administration building to inspect the side-by-side rows of Mexican and Pakistani wheats.

Addressing the gathered host, the institute director turned the occasion into a tribute to his own work. He made a big hit. All the viewers were nodding; Pakistani plants were strong and productive. That was obvious.

Then Anwar Hussain turned toward the Mexican wheats. "These don't fit in Pakistan," he declared. "See how inferior they are."

Turning to me, he said almost apologetically: "Dr. Borlaug, your varieties aren't well adapted here." His sorrow seemed genuine . . . seeing I'd come so far to find disappointment.

But that was not how I saw things. "WHAT IN THE HELL IS GOING ON HERE?" I yelled loud enough so no one could miss the message. "You didn't plant them properly. They're too far apart. And you haven't fed these damn things . . . They haven't been properly fertilized. And no weeding has been done!"

That took the administrator aback; he'd probably never been challenged on his home turf – certainly not so bluntly nor before his boss or his country's press. However he replied respectfully but forcefully: "Dr. Borlaug, this is the way wheat *must* be grown in Pakistan. See how beautiful our own varieties are!"

By now I was losing my grip: "The agronomy is all wrong," I stammered. "You didn't fertilize enough. You planted them too deep and got a poor stand. Everything is wrong. No one can tell anything from these tests."

"Sir," the director said loudly and with finality, "THIS IS THE WAY YOU PLANT WHEAT IN PAKISTAN!"

During the following hours, which were devoted to showcasing the station's own successes, Norm insisted to whomever he could button-hole that there'd been a miscarriage of science, maybe justice. More than mishandled, his plants had been mangled:

Over and over I kept repeating my message. "Twenty years of targeted research lie behind these wheats. With them, Mexico went from hunger to self-sufficiency in 12 years. Pakistan can do the same thing. In fact, you can do it faster!"

But the words echoed hollow. Everyone could see that in Pakistan his plants were pitiful.

As the afternoon wore on, Norm noticed a small owlish man wearing thick-rimmed glasses standing in the background scribbling notes with a stubby pencil. It was not a happy sight. The man must surely be a reporter. Norm foresaw tomorrow's headline: PAKISTAN'S WHEAT SURPASSES MEXICO'S. The thought was depressing. Years would pass before so public a setback could be overcome.

Also standing in the background were his two young trainees. Both

Mansur Bajwa and Nur Chaudry were strangely silent, almost frozen. Something in their stance told the story:

> They'd clearly been marginalized. Trying to improve wheat in Pakistan was a lost cause. I gave up arguing and, after a miserable afternoon under the blistering sun, was hustled off to the institute's guesthouse for chicken curry served with all the pleasantries.
>
> During the meal the agriculture secretary, sitting beside me, was friendly and, despite the day's revelations, seemed far from discouraged. With him, I continued pressing the case. However, Malik Khuda Bakhsh Bucha made clear he was no scientist; indeed his grace and charm made him seem shallow and superficial. It was not encouraging. And at the end I couldn't tell if he believed me or his own eyes.

Rigid scheduling left no chance to talk privately with his young colleagues. But following the dinner, just as he was being hustled toward the exit, the two sidled over. "We've got something to show you in the morning," they said.

He explained he'd be leaving at ten; there'd be no time to meet.

"We'll come at dawn," they whispered.

As Borlaug fled the dining hall, the owlish scribe who'd been scribbling in the background extended a hand. "Haldore Hanson," he said.

Hanson was smallish, slim and serious. His strong, almost molded, face featured thick gray brows and a winning smile. As they ambled toward the institute guesthouse, Norm noticed he was carrying an enormous briefcase.

In Borlaug's room Hanson yanked a bottle from that briefcase, seized the carafe of boiled water, and soon was thrusting forward a liberally enlivened glass: "I wrote down all you said this afternoon," he explained. "I don't know much about agriculture but you seem to think your wheats can make a difference. Did I hear you right? Is a big lift in food production possible in Pakistan?"

Borlaug stared over the rim of his glass: "Basically, you heard correctly. That fruit is just waiting to be picked. Data from the plantings you saw today will show Mexican wheats to be inferior, but that's only because they were mishandled."

Hanson took another sip of scotch and peered intently and said, "We have some talking to do."

Rather than a reporter, Hanson was the local Ford Foundation program director. His institution had never run an agricultural development project. Yet because nine out of ten Pakistanis were farmers, he was keen to link his efforts to Borlaug's.

Hanson's main fear was that his bosses back in the Big Apple would argue that the Ford Foundation lacked the technical expertise. Norm told him not to worry:

> "We'll gladly work with you," I said. "Between the Rockefeller Foundation and the Mexican Institute of Agricultural Research we've got the technical staff, the seeds, the scientific know-how. We can provide these, and train more Pakistanis as well."
>
> Strictly speaking, I had no authority to commit the Rockefeller Foundation to a Pakistan program. But I'm sure glad I did.

On this, one of Norm's darkest of days, Hal Hanson's confidence shone as the single bright spot. That anyone might support plants whose inferiority had been made so plain came as a huge relief. The next day would, however, prove better:

> I tried desperately to sleep that night. My mind was in turmoil. I'd promised to send the Indians an answer, but what could I say? Here in Pakistan Mexican wheats looked awful. Should I tell Swaminathan that? Would he trust me or would he trust the research data that seemed so damning?
>
> At the moment when dawn was breaking a tapping on the window brought me out of a fitful doze. I slid back the curtain to see Bajwa and Chaudry standing in the gloom. Quickly I pulled on work clothes and boots. The three of us crossed the dewy lawns, wordlessly wending our way in single file down the tracks between experimental plots to an area beyond.
>
> It was all very mysterious until the two stepped aside and I could see four green plots, each roughly the dimension of a bowling lane. Although they carried no labels or nameplates, I immediately knew what they were.
>
> In the grainy light of a Punjab dawn those four Mexican varieties stood as strong and as heavy with seed as in the Yaqui Valley. This was perhaps the greatest sight of my career. It was so captivating I could have danced.
>
> Bajwa and Chaudry seemed delighted too. We shook hands; we laughed; we knelt and peered closely at those wonderful friends. We all knew they foreshadowed something great.
>
> For me this came as a revelation. The cobwebs of doubt were instantly swept away. Everything I'd dreamed of finding was there before me.

Not until later did Norm recall that it had been his 50th birthday, and concluded he couldn't have gotten a better present.

There remained, however, a riddle. And he remembered raising it with Bajwa and Chaudry:

Why didn't you grow the whole breeding nursery like this?
He wouldn't let us.
Who wouldn't let you?
The Director of Research!

This was an amazing revelation. Their foreign training officially suppressed, the pair had secretly kept aside some seeds, planted them where no one would notice, omitted all labels, and cared for the plants in the way they'd been told not to use. It was an act of immense courage; had they been caught, their careers would have ended.

At Egypt's main wheat breeding station at Giza Borlaug found not only his trainee El Ham Talaat [1961] but a repeat performance. As they stood almost in the shadow of the Sphinx, yet another pompous research director declared Mexican plants inferior.

The plots bore that out, but Norm could see that once more a Wheat Apostle had been marginalized by the superior charged with producing more food. The mismanaged Mexican plants had fallen far short of their potential.

At the very instant Norm was about to uncork a storm of protest he noticed Talaat's face:

The young man seemed agonized. I sensed that further revelations were to come, so I held my tongue. Sure enough, next day Talaat drove me 60 miles north to a small experiment station at Sakha in the Nile Delta. There, he'd grown several plots exactly as we did in Mexico. Those looked as beautiful as any I'd ever seen.

Relieved in mind and restored in spirit, Borlaug hurried homeward. He was on Pan Am's Flight 001, which flew westward around the world. As it droned over the Atlantic between Shannon and Gander he sat wide awake through the night. His stream of consciousness was a rushing torrent that kept repeating: This thing can go! It can really take off!

The return to Sonora coincided with the harvest. For a month the wicked winds had huffed and puffed but the dwarf wheats still held their heavy heads high.

Sadly, he had no time to savor the thrill. The coming days were spent teaching trainees to deal with the data pouring in from the research plots; showing them how to document breeding-nursery results; and helping them manhandle the harvest.

Nights that April were spent holed up in the Costa de Oro. Despite tired brain and tired muscles, sleep wouldn't come; Swaminathan and his colleagues in New Delhi needed his report. Each evening he retired for a hot bath followed by a pen-and-paper session with his mind and his new mission.

In the loneliness of that motel room he wrote about all he'd seen in the last six weeks. By contrast with Pakistan and India, Sonora seemed like paradise. On the back of a few high-performance plants, grain filled silos that reached high in the sky. That year's harvest would approach 2 million tons.

Two decades back, this area had mirrored the rural misery he'd just seen on the far side of the world. Obviously, India and Pakistan needn't go hungry; their farmers needn't remain impoverished.

His 20-page answer to Swaminathan's question opened with an explanation of what he'd learned since leaving New Delhi. Later pages expressed his confidence that India could double her wheat harvest *in eight years*. In part they said:

> The evidence at this time is circumstantial; but fragmentary as it is, there is the prospect of a spectacular breakthrough in grain production for India. The new Mexican varieties that I have seen growing incline me to say that they will do well in India and grow beautifully. But though such opportunities do exist, there are conditions that must be met with fact and action — and not with talk and probability. If the disease resistance holds up in its present spectrum — and we can check that quickly — and if the quantities of fertilizer and other vital necessities are made available, then there is a chance that something big could happen.

Then he threw in a caution:

> I must warn, however, that senior scientists and administrators must not hold this thing in check and must not restrict the ardor of the bright young scientists. If they do this, they will cause roadblocks and bottlenecks for which the poor will pay the price in continued hunger.

Finally, he damned the professionals:

> They are mostly chasing academic butterflies, and that is distracting them from what needs to be done to solve the hunger

problem.

Although happy with the language, Norm hated the look of his report. In their ignorance of English, CIANO's secretaries had liberally littered laughable misspellings throughout. What could he do about that? Too ham-fisted to handle a typewriter and wearied by dawn-to-dark days in hot dusty fields, he took the easy way out:

> In the end I mailed the crude manuscript to Ralph Cummings with a note: "Please get this edited and retyped before sending it on to Drs. B.P. Pal and M.S. Swaminathan."
> The Rockefeller Foundation office in New Delhi had English-speaking typists, and I felt sure someone there would soften my blunt language and drop my most offensive charges. In particular, I expected them to remove my hot and hasty comment about academic butterflies, which would anger Indian scientists no end.

In a similar letter accompanying a copy to Pakistan's secretary of agriculture, he apologized for the bad spelling and told Malik Khuda Bakhsh that his counterparts in India were likely to inject money and Mexican seeds into their programs. It was his first attempt to prick national pride and play each side off against the other so as to ratchet up food production in both.

With the Sonora harvest finally completed, he prepared duplicate sets of seeds containing small samples gathered from 225 of that season's best performing plants, including Pitic 62, Penjamo 62, and several of the still-developing 8156 dwarf generation. These last seeds were his discards. They'd been taken from plants he'd since abandoned for some fault or other.

Although the shipments weighed over half a ton he paid Pan Am to fly them to South Asia. That cost a fortune but assured the seeds would arrive before the December sowing deadline.

Borlaug hereby reached a supremely satisfying point of his life. He'd completed his responsibility to South Asia. Now he could return to his day job in Mexico. He was a teacher at last:

> I saw no need for further involvement. My active participation in Pakistan and India was over. Their scientists now had good seed. They could carry on by themselves.

That November Indian and Pakistani scientists sowed the half-ton seed lots Pan Am had delivered. These gifts were used to establish plots on experiment stations and in farmers' fields scattered throughout wheat lands on both sides of the India/Pakistan border.

Shortly thereafter, Haldore Hanson invited Norm back to inspect Pakistan's efforts. Having considered he'd already done his part and certain that another visit within the same year was wildly excessive, Norm went only reluctantly.

But events would vindicate Hanson's wile and wisdom. He had by then met most of the agricultural officials who needed to sign off on the issue of adopting Mexican wheats. And it was proving a tough sell. Mobilizing his journalist's flair and skill, he'd compressed Borlaug's technical notions into brief, hard-hitting prose. Knowing he needed to impact the minds of officials who knew no science, he pressed home Norm's ultimate conviction that the country *could double its wheat production in eight years*.

Now with Norm and his freshly retyped 20-page report on hand, Hanson contacted Malik Khuda Bakhsh. Intrigued, the genial agriculture secretary invited both to afternoon tea.

The two showed up at his home on the outskirts of Lahore anticipating a quiet chat but instead found the large villa stuffed with officials from universities and government, experts from extension services, and administrators from several food-related agencies.

This was disconcerting:

> We hadn't expected speaking to a professional audience and had to rapidly rearrange our presentations, making them much more precise and official sounding.
>
> Hal opened the proceedings with a step-by-step exposition exposing the issues holding back Pakistan's wheat production. He did it brilliantly.
>
> Then I explained how Mexico was being transformed, adding that during the previous years five young Pakistani scientists had been trained and could transform this country in exactly the same way. I told about Bajwa and Chaudry's results at Lyallpur that I'd seen back in March. And I explained what the four plots signified for Pakistan's future.
>
> Finally I summed up by reiterating my belief that Pakistan could double its wheat production *in eight years*.

The audience heard out these foreign foundations' representatives in total silence, and the lack of applause or appreciation made clear that the room was redolent with rejection. Norm was dismayed:

> Even as Hal and I were driven away we knew that opposition was breaking out.

Across the border in India, Swaminathan had moved quickly after Borlaug's report and the half ton of seed arrived on Pan Am. Dividing the seed into 14 equal lots, he distributed those to agricultural institutions across his country's wheat-growing areas in time for the November planting season.

Mexican wheats thus got their first scientific measurements in farming areas on the planet's hungriest half. Swaminathan required the recipients to follow strict research protocols. Next April everyone would know with scientific certitude just how Mexican wheats would perform in South Asia.

At the same time Swaminathan divided into three equal lots the small samples gathered from 225 of Borlaug's best performers. He kept one lot for himself and sent the others to agricultural universities in the wheat-growing area.

Those samples were for purposes of inspection. They would be planted in 225 tiny plots – each labeled with the Borlaug's coding number.

They of course included seed from some of Borlaug's still-developing 8156 dwarf generation. No one expected anything to develop from them. They were, after all, his discards.

1964-1965

Breaking Bread

Norm was given no time to savor success. In February 1964 Pakistan requested he formally present the case for Mexican wheats to its National Action Planning Committee, the authority empowered with pyramiding Pakistan's food production.

Norm resented traveling so far so soon, and the trip proved a horror. Before his flight could leave New York several feet of snow buried the runways. A taxi inched him through the frozen streets of Queens, but no rooms were left at any inn. On returning to Kennedy International Airport – newly named by a nation shell-shocked by the assassination just two months back – he whiled the night away, sleepless on a bench.

Next day, he boarded Pan Am's Flight 002 that flew eastward around the world. Despite a vexing inability to sleep on planes, he remained unworried because following the long passage to Pakistan he'd have 24 hours to rest up. However when the Boeing 707 reached Karachi at 4 am, the Ford Foundation driver passed over a note: "Go to KLM Halfway House," it said, "take a shower and be back at the airport at 7 for a flight at 7:30." Turns out, the meeting had been moved up a day; it would be later that very same morning. And it would be in Lahore, which was still 600 miles away!

On reaching the Department of Agriculture in Lahore he'd suffered more than 48 hours without sleep, and was mortified to find a formidable assortment of dignitaries sitting silent and straight-backed around one side of a polished table in a formal chamber.

This unwelcoming committee included the deputy agriculture minister, three research directors, two university vice-chancellors, and senior wheat scientists from Pakistan's three main wheat-growing regions.

On Norm's side of the table were Hal Hanson; Oddvar Aresvik, a

Norwegian economist Hanson had embedded in the agriculture ministry; and Nacho Narvaez, who happened to be passing through to check on the local Wheat Apostles — a procedure instigated following Norm's disillusionments at Lyallpur and Cairo the previous year.

From the opening words the four foreigners knew they were about to be professionally prosecuted. Norm remembered the scene vividly:

> The vice-chancellor of the University of Sindh spoke first. He was a scientist of national distinction, but he began by waving Hal Hanson's report in the air and quoting my words then declaring: "Stop to think of what kind of foolishness this is."
>
> Coming in for special scorn was my claim that Pakistan could double its wheat output in eight years. "Anyone who predicts that the wheat crop will double in eight years," he said, "must be insane. There's been no such change in all our lifetimes!"
>
> Having finished dumping on my prose, he pronounced ten reasons why Mexican wheats would NEVER work in Pakistan.
>
> The first was that in Pakistan wheat had a yield ceiling. He read out the official numbers for every year from 1914 right through 1964. Each was around 800 pounds an acre, which I considered a disgrace. Then he declared: "These figures prove that Pakistan's wheat production will never rise!"
>
> He was especially scathing over the dwarf varieties; proclaiming they gave too little straw. Hell, he made such a to-do over that you'd think we planned to starve all the country's cows and water buffaloes!
>
> Then he declared that Mexican wheats were too delicate for Pakistan's harsh conditions; that they required too much water and fertilizer; and that their grains were the wrong color. Pakistanis," he crowed, "never ate red wheat!"

The Deputy Secretary chairing the session made no attempt to maintain order or balance. Sitting directly across the table, Narvaez pleaded repeatedly for a chance to speak. He was ignored. Finally he turned purple with frustration. Borlaug tried to calm him down:

> I kept saying in Spanish: "Nacho, control yourself; I'll deal with all this when the time comes."

Aresvik, the Ford Foundation economist, sat beside Narvaez. His ears were glowing with indignation and he was trying to get the chairman's attention by waving his arms. Borlaug hissed at Narvaez in Spanish: "Tell Oddvar to let the speaker have his say."

Only Hanson, an old hand at verbal contests, retained his composure, though his stone face only half hid a scowl.

For 45 minutes the Sindh professor spouted bile. Among his other claims: "You don't know Pakistan. Agricultural revolutions may happen in Mexico, but they *never happen in Pakistan*. Our farmers are illiterate; they are conservative and they are slow to change."

He charged that "Mexican wheats *require* fertilizer, which in Pakistan will merely make the weeds grow better."

He trotted out a rumor that was then panicking rural illiterates: Mexican wheats sterilized cows and buffaloes; they made Moslem men impotent and Moslem women incapable of bearing children. Diabolical infidels had sent them. Some said it was the CIA, others Israel.

Finally the professor wrapped up with the most damning of all indictments: Mexican wheats did not appear on the list of varieties officially approved for planting in Pakistan. Years of testing would be needed. Above all, the plants' disease susceptibility would have to be determined.

On that imperious note the prosecution ended its case. The chairman now turned to Borlaug, probably expecting fireworks. But Norm was forever proud of his self-control:

> I began by asking the professor a few quiet questions.
>
> "How much wheat is Pakistan producing?" He indicated indecision. So I told him that the previous year's production had been 4.3 million tons.
>
> "How much wheat is Pakistan importing?" The man had no answer. So I told him that in each of the previous five years it had received between a million and a million and a half tons and in 1964 was expecting two million tons.
>
> "Where do the imports come from?" Again he was stumped, so I enlightened him: "About one-fifth comes from Australia, slightly more from Canada, and the rest — 60 percent of the total — is from United States."
>
> "What's the color of the imported grain?" The professor said it was white. So I explained that only the Australian wheat was white. "Four-fifths of what's coming in," I said, "is red. Think about it. Have you seen red wheat lying around uneaten?"

Norm then explained that the red color is just the skin of the grain, the part that is milled away. The flour is white, regardless of seed color.

He also explained that fertilizer supplies nutrients to plants just as food supplies nutrients to people. And although fertilizer fosters weeds, the package of practices accompanying the Mexican seeds included weed controls.

Regarding the food for cows and buffaloes, he noted that dwarf wheats produce multiple stems so the amount of straw might not decrease.

As to disease susceptibility, he explained that the Mexican varieties had aced three years of testing in 50 countries (he was referring to Rodenheiser's seed distribution for stem-rust testing). "You couldn't expect better than that," he said.

Finally, he noted that waiting for official approval to release a high-yield variety while Pakistanis starved would be a crime.

In this manner, the bone-weary, jet-jangled volunteer, who was supposed to be training students in Mexico and who'd come at his own expense and against his will, refuted every criticism. And knew he'd failed:

> As we left the conference chamber, I was handed a note requesting we go to the secretary of agriculture's home.
> A driver was waiting outside, and soon the four of us were sitting on sofas in a large villa on the outskirts of Lahore.
> "I heard they treated you pretty rough," our host said as we sipped tea in that gorgeous room with tall ceilings and stone floors.
> I explained that whatever treatment I'd received didn't matter. Then I listed the ten charges and the facts disproving them.
> "Those facts," I said, "were all that mattered."

Clearly the very authorities empowered with pyramiding Pakistan's food production were committed to banning Mexican wheats.

They'd have succeeded too, were it not for that genial agriculture secretary. The non-scientist who may have seemed shallow and superficial now demonstrated mettle, not to say muscle.

In challenging his country's National Action Planning Committee, Malik Khuda Bakhsh noted that Borlaug had nothing to gain and had come halfway round the world through conviction. A scientist of his stature would never have done that, he said, *if the facts didn't warrant*.

He noted too that the Ford and Rockefeller Foundations had nothing to gain by introducing Mexican wheats, but were willing to fund the project in the interests of Pakistan. Those foundations, he said, *would never support technical projects not based in scientific reality*.

He pointed out that India was talking about using Mexican wheats. "Given that," he charged, "*shouldn't we keep the options open?*"

As to the red seed, the secretary declared that: "Until we can grow all we need, we'll plant whatever color wheat gives the biggest harvest."

Then a committee member piped up that Pakistanis wouldn't eat bread made from Mexican wheat. It tasted bad, he said. Several colleagues nodded assent.

So the agriculture secretary later had the ministry's chef bake bread from two local wheats and two Mexican wheats. Then the critics were made to don blindfolds. Truth be told, Borlaug's lines were still less than ideal breadmakers, yet no critic could distinguish them by taste.

Shortly thereafter the final decision was eased when Pakistan's president summoned Malik Khuda Bakhsh. Waving an Indian newspaper mentioning Borlaug's work Ayub Khan bellowed: "Why, has Pakistan not tried Mexican wheats?"

The secretary explained to the former field marshal that they were not only being tried, but "Norman Borlaug is here right now!"

In April, shortly after Norm had left Pakistan, the test results on the seed Pan Am had delivered became available. At three agricultural research institutes and several private farms across northern Pakistan Penjamo 62, and two varieties that would soon be named Sonora 64 and Lerma Rojo 64 topped 3 tons an acre. That far surpassed every local variety and utterly smashed the half-century average of 0.4 tons [800lb]. With them, Pakistan's 20 million-acre wheat crop could disgorge more than 40 million extra tons of food.

Shortly thereafter the agriculture minister called in Haldore Hanson and requested that the Ford Foundation fund a major program based on those Mexican seeds. Hanson in turn asked Norm to nominate a technical support leader. After a mini-minute's mental consultation, Borlaug blurted: "Ignacio Narvaez should do it. You couldn't find a better person."

Three months later, Narvaez again stopped off on his next inspection to ensure that the trainees would never again be squelched. This time he met Haldore Hanson, the agriculture secretary, and local wheat scientists. In their discussions and in a nicely documented report, the young Mexican outlined the possibilities for accelerating Pakistan's wheat production. The report circulated among the government leaders and generated heated discussion, much of it inflamed by the friction of mental resistance.

Despite the continuing local hostility the Ford Foundation awarded the grant and hired Narvaez as its technical advisor. The piano-playing former student would now move to Pakistan to promote Borlaug's vision in this part of the hungry world. He would take up his post in November 1965.

Regardless of the newspaper Pakistan's president had waved in the face of his ag secretary, Mexican wheats were languishing in India. No farmer had any. No official had endorsed them. National priorities still emphasized heavy industry, nuclear advancement and international eminence. In all the country there were only about 10 acres of Mexican wheats, and those were in the test plots Swaminathan had initiated.

Around this time Borlaug realized that the program in India needed a fulltime field commander – someone of character, calmness, confidence, and the courage to combat resistance. He could think of none better than Glenn Anderson. But was the kind-hearted Canadian available — and would he want to move to India?

> Glenn filled the bill perfectly. I called his home in Winnipeg only to find he'd come down with hepatitis. Despite feeling terrible, he was so interested that even before completely recovering he flew to New Delhi. Swaminathan took him on a brief tour of the northern plains and the valleys along the Himalayan foothills, where most of the wheat is grown. Then late in April Glenn flew straight to New York. After talking things over with George Harrar he called his wife and suggested she start packing.

In Mexico 1964 was the year wheat production surpassed demand: a half-million ton surplus was exported. Twenty years before, there'd been 40 pounds of locally grown wheat per Mexican. Now, after two decades of Borlaug, there were 81 pounds, even though there were 15 million more Mexicans. Put another way, while population had soared 78 percent wheat production had soared 200 percent.

Furthermore, that achievement was built on the weak-kneed plants that bent before the breezes. The 8156 dwarf wheats have yet to make their mark. Their debut is however imminent. By mid-year two of the four 8156 dwarfs had been named: Sonora 64 and Lerma Rojo 64.

Sonora 64 yielded 5580lb an acre. It had red seed, matured in four months, and was 3 inches less than a yardstick in height.

Lerma Rojo 64 could yield 6000lb an acre. It had red seed, matured in four and a half months, and was 3 inches taller than a yardstick.

The remaining pair were curvaceous twins with S-shaped stalks; one was a blond, the other a redhead. The white-seeded twin was named

Siete Cerros [see-ET-ee SAIR-os], after Sonora's capital of Hermosillo, which like Rome is a city of seven hills.

The redhead presented a unique baptismal dilemma because it had escaped CIANO under mysterious circumstances and begun appearing on a neighboring farm. The farm's owner happened to be notably solicitous of the scientists, each morning toting a tub of ice cubes to the lab where Eva Villegas was checking the bread-making qualities of every promising plant. Privately, the researchers believed that Juan ["Yaqui"] Vargas had one morning grabbed some seedheads or perhaps a seed sack, many of which lay around for days before being put into storage.

Whatever the cause, it would have meant nothing had not the Agriculture Ministry continued to oppose formally releasing these two varieties because of their susceptibility to a stem-rust strain found only in Mexico's more humid areas.

Yaqui Vargas, though, had no such concerns. He particularly loved the redhead and, began increasing the seed as fast as nature would allow. He also named it "Super X," which became its formal name, regardless of legality.

In India that summer the tests of the seed delivered by Pan Am caused controversy. In the experimental plots near New Delhi the Mexican wheats had grown so vigorously that at harvest in April 1964 it was found that they'd achieved ten times India's average per-acre yield. Seeing this, Swaminathan sensed he was on the threshold of a new food-production era. The Punjab Agricultural University test had turned up a similar result: Lerma Rojo 64 and Sonora 64 yielded over 4000 pounds an acre, or five times the national average.

On the basis of these two tests India's agriculture minister authorized the release of Mexican wheats for general planting. In so doing he brought down upon himself the wrath of the opponents of agricultural change, who soon uncovered the fact that the rest of the tests had found Mexican wheats inferior to the traditional varieties. To the critics, the twelve of the 14 tests that had failed could not be wrong. These foreign seeds would be disastrous for Mother India.

At this moment, only one man stood in the path of outright rejection. B. Sivaraman, the Ministry of Agriculture's Permanent Secretary, was a civil servant known for efficiency, honesty and management methods so creative they sent stodgy bureaucrats stark raving mad.

In his memoirs Sivaraman [seeva-RAH-man] tells how he learned of the bad test results. "D.P. Singh [a Planning Commission officer] came running to me with the figures . . . . If 12 of the 14 field trials showed the Mexican wheats to be bad, he demanded, why was the agriculture department pushing so hard to make the country use them?"

Unfortunately, in his panic, D.P. Singh had passed the news to his colleague Vijendra Kasturi Ranga Varadaraja Rao. One of the country's biggest wigs, Rao helped decide national policies. In fact, as the Planning Commission member dealing with agriculture he wielded veto powers over what could and couldn't be grown.

Sivaraman's memoir describes the outcome. "[Rao] thought this was an opportunity to put us in our place. He called a meeting of Dr. B.P. Pal, S.P. Kohli, and myself. At the meeting, he showed the results of the wheat trials and squarely accused Dr. Pal of releasing [Mexican] wheats for general planting by fudging the results. We were all aghast. Dr. B.P Pal was the doyen of the wheat researchers, a mild spoken man and a perfect gentleman. By no stretch of the imagination could he have perpetrated the crime accused of by Dr. V.K.R.V. Rao against the interest of wheat in the country. I was furious. I told Dr. Rao: 'Please put the accusation down in writing and send us the proceedings of this meeting.' But Dr. Rao did not have the courage to do that and face the resulting music."

Following this meeting Sivaraman sent for his assistant S.P. Kohli and Agricultural Production Commissioner, S.M. Sikka: "Please proceed at once to the 12 stations," he said, "and seize all the records of the trials. Check whether in each station the research worker in charge of each trial has carried it out according to the format laid out by the Wheat Coordinator [Swaminathan]. If the research worker has not carried out the trial according to the format I shall take drastic disciplinary action against all concerned."

In this way it was learned that on the 12 stations the researchers had ignored the explicit order to follow the protocol. The experiments had been manipulated to produce results adverse to the Mexican wheats.

The Anderson family reached New Delhi on August 15. The monsoon had just delivered almost a foot of rain, and the city streets were flooded. Yet the entire local Rockefeller Foundation staff turned out at the airport as a greeting committee. On the drive home the Rockefeller Foundation's field director for India gave Anderson his marching orders: "Borlaug hired you because you know your business," Ralph Cummings said. "India does not have enough to eat. You are to remedy that. How you achieve it is your decision!"

Soon thereafter America's agriculture secretary, Orville Freeman, visited Delhi, and found the backward farming so distressing that he urged that India modernize its agriculture, specifically by increasing the area under irrigation, increasing fertilizer production, and paying its farmers better.

Though neither Norm nor his former college buddy were aware of the other's activities, both knew that India had a remarkable agriculture minister. Norm sums up:

> In those fateful years we were fortunate that India's food supply was under the management of Chidambara Subramaniam. I got to know him well. He was a small man who stood very tall in my esteem.
>
> He was a joy to be with – his black hair slicked back and his face framed by thick glasses and usually split by a genuinely welcoming grin.
>
> He had the qualities needed to lead India out of its deadly condition. Both in mind and speech he exuded vigor and clarity. In outlook he was wise and progressive. By nature he was confident and courageous. And by manner he was caring and charismatic.

Subramaniam [soobra-MAN-ee-am] was new to the job. He'd been the Minister for Steel, Heavy Industry and Mines. But Prime Minister Shastri had cajoled him into switching to Agriculture because no cabinet member would accept that thankless portfolio. He thus became responsible for the food for almost half a billion souls at a time when farming was stalled and famine stalked the land.

Though neither farming nor food production were familiar to him, he knew how to lead. His first step involved countering the pessimism that pervaded the national view. "I gave an assurance to Parliament." He writes in his memoirs. "It was a somewhat rash statement . . . I declared that if any deaths should take place due to starvation I would resign from the ministership."

He also claimed that India would no longer import grain to keep its poor people from starvation.

Apart from a little flooding, that year's monsoon behaved perfectly, providing an optimal mix of water, warmth and sunshine. In 1964 India's wheat production reached 12 million tons, a million tons more than ever before. Pakistan achieved 4.5 million tons – half a million tons or 25 percent more than its previous best. These set the high point before Mexican wheats could make any mark.

Even so, a record harvest wasn't enough to feed everyone. Subramaniam had to pilgrimage to Washington, cap in hand. And this time he needed much more than ever before.

Agriculture secretary Orville Freeman was sympathetic. He and the pint-sized fireball with the power grin quickly concluded that for 1965 the U.S. should provide India 10 million tons of grain. Almost a million tons a month was a huge call.

The ultimate decision was up to the President. So Subramaniam trotted over to the White House. "I met [Lyndon Johnson] and we had a detailed discussion, and essentially he said: 'Ten million tons — of course we have that much, but can you deal with it? Can your ports handle that much? Can you disperse all that food into the villages so it reaches the hungry people?'"

To those questions there were no clear answers because this was two-and-a-half times what India had ever before absorbed. Subramaniam nonetheless replied boldly that if the President could deliver 10 million tons he would get all of it into the right mouths. Liking the little man's forthrightness, the President agreed.

Subramaniam proved a man of his word. Having formerly overseen India's heavy industries, he understood mass transport and got the 10 million tons of grain moving through the ports and out to the 50,000 Fair Price Shops. Trucks and trains carried a cargo vital to the survival of over 100 million people in the hungry hinterlands. Almost a million tons reached the needy reliably and rapidly *every month*.

Subramaniam also wanted India to modernize its agriculture. Knowing nothing about the topic, he called in specialists, and asked them to speak freely and frankly. "I uncovered," he writes, "a tale of woe."

Careerists in his own department were fearful. The scientific approach to agriculture, they said, was a fad that would fail. He quickly solved that problem by demanding their resignations and replacing them with competent technical specialists.

In a socialist nation this was heretical. The Cabinet was shocked. But Subramaniam explained that the country's agricultural development must be led by people with technical expertise.

Naturally, these radical actions were widely discussed, and after Ralph Cummings heard of them he called on the minister and informed him of the high yielding wheats in Mexico. During their meeting, the Rockefeller Foundation's local representative mentioned that small quantities of the new dwarf wheats were being tested for India's soils and climates and the results had been good.

To Subramaniam this came as a revelation. He was new to the post and was unaware of the Rockefeller Foundation, the dwarf wheats or Swaminathan. "Once I received this message," he wrote "I decided to proceed with the formulation of a strategy to utilize these new varieties."

When the local press heard that Subramaniam was considering focusing India's future on Mexican wheat, it poured torrents of hysteria into the public mind.

One prime reason for rejecting Mexican wheats was Norm himself:

> Because I was American-born and worked for the Rockefeller Foundation the communists claimed I was opening a back door to renewed foreign domination. Through my machinations, Mother India would become forever dependent on American fertilizer and pesticides.

Another reason was the scientists who swore that Mexican wheats were not as good as claimed. Such production might be possible in Mexico but in India nothing like it had ever been recorded. Moreover, Indian wheats had surpassed the Mexican ones in 12 tests out of 14.

Another reason newspapers highlighted was the belief that big farmers would benefit, leaving small farmers behind and create social tensions that would lead to rural riots:

> The idea that our work was unfair to the poor was hyped to incredible extremes. Sociologists howled that Mexican wheat would produce "irreversible social tensions" within rural areas. It would, they claimed, sunder India's "social harmony," causing riots to break out across the land. The new seeds, they said, must not be introduced until land reform [land giveaways to poor people] had been fully implemented. Even then, nothing should be done until the small farmers would use the new technologies as much as the big farmers. The people pushing this idea conceded that that would naturally delay the introduction of the new varieties on a large scale — but it was imperative that all farmers benefit equally.

Fortunately, Subramaniam could out-think the experts. He wrote in his memoirs: "The scientists expressed doubts as to the feasibility of the high yields that have been obtained by the new varieties. It is strange that these experts should admit that while such high yields are possible in other countries they are not possible in ours."

He also asked why the danger of social tension should be applied only to agricultural development. Should India stop developing industries, universities and medical schools solely on the basis that not everyone could benefit equally?

At that moment the agriculture minister had nowhere to turn for high-level support. Not a single Indian in any position of influence endorsed his proposed course. Now it proved fortunate that Cummings had put him in contact with Swaminathan and his peers. "The younger scientists," recalls Subramaniam, "took a more dynamic stand, saying I should make a bold decision and proceed to introduce the new varieties on a large scale."

Among New Delhi's government planners this sparked fierce opposition. The Planning Commission front man on agriculture was especially angry; V.K.R.V. Rao publicly declared that *he would not allow Mexican wheat into the country*.

The Cabinet was the one group that could have derailed everything. Thankfully, whereas each member expressed apprehension, none challenged their colleague. "With the Cabinet I could not afford to take risks," recalls Subramaniam. "I adopted the strategy of keeping its members fully informed by presenting a paper to them about what was being done, but I did not ask for a Cabinet decision. I asked only the Prime Minister for a decision to enable me to proceed at the time."

Prime Minister Shastri cautioned against, but did not reject, modernizing agriculture. The decision thus came down to Subramaniam alone. And he decided to go ahead: "The Agricultural Department members and senior scientists were all opposed. With the exception of a few young voices, they all said 'No, it's too dangerous.' But I heard those few voices, and that was all I needed."

As the year 1965 got underway, Pakistan's planners informed president Ayub Khan that even should the June monsoon again behave perfectly there'd still be not enough wheat to meet the national need. Unless he imported at least *a million tons*, Pakistanis were going to starve. And he'd better get used to it. This shortfall will be permanent and his country must live on the bread of charity *forever*.

Early in March Norm visited the presidential residence in Rawalpindi and met Ayub Khan beside a small plot that included both Mexican and local wheats. Squeezed between young orange trees, the planting looked odd but was very handy because Pakistan's leader passed by on his daily walk and could follow developments.

When asked what these few specimens signified, Norm responded with fervor:

> "Mr. President," I said, "in the next five years these can increase Pakistan's wheat production 50 percent.
> "In eight to ten years they can increase it 100 percent.
> "With these, Pakistan can meet all its wheat needs by 1970!"
> Ayub looked stunned, even disbelieving. I could see him thinking that five years was an impossibly short time to eliminate the huge shortfall he's just been told will be forever.
> I could see him also thinking: "This man must be as mad as people say."

As he left the residence Norm didn't know whether the forceful words had had the intended effect. He doubted it, but he thought he'd detected a gleam in the president's eye.

That June, the monsoon decided to go to the opposite extreme, and withhold the rains upon which a fifth of humanity depended. Both Pakistan and India were cruelly affected. Their wheat fields simulated sunburnt straw. Grain production tumbled, plunging two nations toward terrifying peril.

For the first time since the British had bailed out in 1947, an official famine was declared. The main hunger zone encompassed more than 20,000 square miles of northeast India, where almost 13 million people lived, most of them dependent on wheat for survival.

Mexican wheats now became South Asia's last best hope for a well-fed future. But therein lay a ghastly catch: neither Pakistan nor India possessed sufficient seed.

The amount of seed Borlaug had flown in on Pan Am could support tests and trials but producing the ton quantities needed to sow millions of acres would take four or five years of repeated plantings. The alternative was a new importation of unprecedented size.

Pakistan bucked the decision right to the top, and in mid-July President Ayub announced that his government would dip into its scarce foreign exchange and import *250 tons* of Penjamo 62 and Lerma Rojo 64 seed. He also pledged to provide enough free fertilizer to multiply that within two to three growing seasons into enough seed to sow Pakistan's entire 20 million acre wheat crop.

Also around this time, at a seminar in Ludhiana, just across the Punjab divide from Pakistan's Lahore, India's agriculture minister was shown the results from the test plantings based on the Pan Am delivery. The Mexican wheats produced so much more than any before that Subramaniam rapidly authorized the immediate purchase of *200 tons* of Lerma Rojo 64 and Sonora 64 seed from Mexico.

On the last day of July, Pakistan's order for 250 tons of seed reached the Rockefeller Foundation office in Mexico City. Norm happened to be acting office director, standing in for Ed Wellhausen, who was actually in India establishing a new arm of his corn research.

Soon thereafter, India's order for 200 tons of seed landed on Norm's desk in Viena 26. The combined 450 tons was more seed than had ever been shipped internationally *for any crop*. And Mexico had *never* exported seed. But what could possibly go wrong? Sonora's five farmer cooperatives already had more than enough seed on hand – clean, fumigated, quality tested, and waiting in warehouses, less than 500 hundred miles from the port of Los Angeles.

Borlaug quickly set about organizing the transfer. The seed had to make the last ship capable of delivering it before South Asia's planting deadline. He found that an American President Lines freighter, would leave Los Angeles August 12 and reach Bombay in early October and Karachi a week or two later. That would allow each country a month to move the seed to farming areas before the optimal mid-November planting date.

With so much riding on the outcome and with so little room for error, Norm planned to oversee every step in getting the seed to that ship in Los Angeles by the departure date. However, when news trickled out that he planned to oversee the seed export personally George Harrar intervened: "You stay right there," the voice from New York yelled down the phone line. "Your job is to manage the office until Ed gets back. Whatever happens, you're *not* to leave!"

At first Norm's absence from the frontlines meant nothing because things proceeded perfectly. Then suddenly the Mexican National Seed Corporation (PRONASE) barged in. Its director had quietly got the agriculture ministry to declare his agency the sole authority for exporting seed. And therein began a chain of misfortunes.

For starters, the governments of India and Pakistan were required to sign formal contracts with the government of Mexico. One particular sticking point had to do with Pakistan's insurance policy, which included the phrase "act of God." PRONASE objected, saying that God didn't do bad acts; the text must be amended to read "act of nature." The Pakistanis then took offense, "Legal precedent demands 'act of God.'" Sorting out semantics wasted precious time. Eventually the English version said "act of God;" the Spanish version, "acta de la naturaleza."

Next, PRONASE [pro-NAH-see] had trouble processing its seed. More time slipped by. Borlaug called and called until finally PRONASE decided to substitute older seed that was already clean, disinfected and waiting in a Mexicali warehouse. Thus, in the second week of August over 20,000 bags of Penjamo 62, Lerma Rojo 64 and Sonora 64 were removed from that warehouse close by the California border, carefully marked for delivery to India or Pakistan, piled into a fleet of 30 large trucks and dispatched northward. The delays had left no time to check the seed's germination.

Everything had been arranged for a quick and uneventful border crossing. Both the U.S. embassy and the Mexican ministry of commerce had assured Borlaug nothing could go wrong. Despite that, he sent Narvaez to supervise. This, Narvaez's final task before moving to Pakistan, would be quite simple: get a convoy of trucks into California and from there 200 miles up Highway 99, via the Imperial Valley to the port of Los Angeles at San Pedro. Although that should take no more than a day, Norm had hired the trucks and drivers *for three days*.

But in the outcome nothing proved simple. Narvaez spent two days battling Mexican officialdom in Mexicali and then he spent two more days a few yards away in Calexico battling American officialdom who didn't want Mexican trucks driving on California roads. Borlaug was on tenterhooks because demurrage charges had begun accruing on 30 trucks and 30 drivers.

More important, time was wasting. The ship was about to leave. Norm phoned the American President Lines president, George Killion, and persuaded him to hold the ship in port should the border problems continue.

At last, on Wednesday August 11 Narvaez got the trucks cleared through U.S. customs and called in the great news: they were about to head north with all due speed; he'd phone again from dockside.

A very thankful Borlaug called Killion again and advised that the delivery was back on schedule. He also arranged for a courier to carry the payment documents to PRONASE's office across town. One was a Rockefeller Foundation check for the Indian seed; the other a government letter of credit for the Pakistan seed. Norm was relieved:

> At that point there seemed nothing to do but sit back and wait for Nacho to tell me the seed was being loaded aboard ship. But no call came. I went to bed mystified, and about dawn the next morning hurried back to the office. Still nothing. All that Friday I sat by the phone. By Saturday morning I was getting really anxious. What could have happened? Why didn't Nacho call?

Late that morning PRONASE's director phoned, and declared in ominous tones: "The First National City Bank refuses to honor the letter of credit." Sr. Roldan explained that PRONASE's proper name [Productora Nacional de Semilla] had two misspellings. Until those are corrected he can't get paid.

Borlaug was now in pickle. Telecommunications then were tedious, not to say tenuous. Moreover though Pakistan might possibly reply the following day, the local bank was closed on Sundays. He spent hours trying to phone Lahore. He fired off more cablegrams. Finally, a reply arrived: "Give me time; a new letter of credit is forthcoming."

Meantime Narvaez faced greater frustrations. While he was on the road heading for Los Angeles a section of the city linking the freeway to the docks was engulfed by riot. The area generally known as "Watts" went up in flames and stayed alight for six days, leaving 34 dead and 856 injured.

Between seed and ship now stood burnt and burning buildings, trashed streets and California National Guard troopers clad in camouflage and wielding M-16s. No traffic, least of all 30 seed trucks, can get through. The officer doesn't care if someone might starve. He's got his problems; he's got his orders.

The ship's scheduled time of departure passed. Though prospects were now beyond hopeless, Borlaug called George Killion back and requested that the departure again be delayed. Now he's paying demurrage on 30 trucks, 30 drivers *and a ship*:

> On Sunday night the long-awaited call finally, came through. Nacho had gotten the trucks through the still smoking, looted and burned-out Watts. "Soon we'll be loading!" he said. "The ship will leave at two tomorrow morning."
>
> Those were some of the sweetest words I ever heard, but they raised a new dilemma: the new letter of credit hadn't arrived

from Pakistan. Should I let the seed be shipped when its owner, the government of Mexico, hasn't been paid? What if Pakistan changed its mind or merely refused to pay up?

Nacho needs instructions. Over the phone he's pleading for a decision: "Can we put the seed on the ship, yes or no?"

Among the many dilemmas Norm faced during a long and difficult career, this was perhaps the most momentous. Prudence required he order Pakistan's seed put back into storage until the financial details were regularized. But shipping it without delay could prevent a famine of unprecedented magnitude; no other ship could arrive in time for the planting season:

"Oh to hell with it," I barked down the phone line. "Put the seed on the ship, Nacho. I'll take the responsibility, and if something goes wrong, by God I'll personally pay it off myself . . . if it takes the rest of my life!"

Norm thus committed himself, his family and his future to what in today's terms would be a million dollar gamble that a civil servant half a world away would honor his word.

By now Borlaug surely deserved a break. But five times that Monday morning PRONASE's director called demanding the Pakistan money be transferred *immediately*!

From Sr. Roldan's tone, you'd think I was an embezzler trying to abscond with his letter of credit. But without the correctly spelled replacement there was nothing I could do.

Eventually, he went over my head and complained to the Rockefeller Foundation headquarters. They put John McKelvey on the case. John was an entomologist who'd worked with us in Mexico. Now he'd been instructed to "make Borlaug do the right thing by the host government." Every few hours that Monday he phoned, asking whether the Mexicans had been paid.

In the end I exploded: "What the hell! I didn't want this blasted job — Dutch [Harrar] ordered me to stay and run the office."

I hung up; sent yet another cable to Malik Khuda Bakhsh asking for action on the line of credit, and told my secretary I wouldn't talk to anyone from New York or Mexico.

Loyal Mrs Tayabas took the phone off the hook, and I went home to the apartment.

That was one of the few times he got home *before* dark. It was also the first time in weeks he got a sound sleep. His conscience was clear; the seed was on the high seas, a new letter of credit was on its way, nothing more could possibly cause a problem.

Sadly, he awoke to find he'd been mistaken. Turning on the radio on the morning of August 16, he learned that Pakistan and India were lobbing heavy artillery shells at each other. Their dispute over the enclave of Kashmir had escalated into open warfare. Indian tanks had crossed the border into Pakistan and advanced to within sight of Lahore.

He cabled Khuda Bakhsh, who was a mere 10 miles from that border, and miraculously got a quick reply. "DON'T WORRY ABOUT THE MONEY," the cable said. "WE'VE DEPOSITED IT STOP AND IF YOU THINK YOU'VE GOT PROBLEMS YOU SHOULD SEE MINE STOP ARTILLERY SHELLS ARE FALLING IN MY BACKYARD"

At this point there was not much Norm could do but pray things would work out. Then two days later he received a more worrisome telegram: the authorities in Lahore were convinced they'd never see their portion of seed. Once the freighter reached Bombay Indian officials would seize any cargo destined for the enemy. Borlaug must do something about that!

> Yet again I contacted the American President Lines, this time with absolutely no hope of success. But I was proven wrong. In Singapore, 12,000 sacks containing Pakistan's 250 tons of Penjamo 62 and Lerma Rojo 64 were removed from the hold and piled onto the dock. Two weeks later those sacks were placed in a second ship and delivered straight to Karachi port. They arrived October 22.

In the outcome the war was a waffly affair, and after 17 days Pakistan called for a ceasefire. Sporadic clashes of arms continued, however, and Norm guessed the seed was rotting on the docks. In reality, though, officials in both countries obtained rapid port clearance and rushed the precious cargo inland.

In Pakistan, all 12,000 sacks were unloaded, sorted, separated, labeled, placed into the proper trucks and railroad cars, and sped upcountry *in under 48 hours*. The first seed was in the ground near Hyderabad, over a hundred miles north, *within three days*. The last of the seed was planted on farms in Punjab and Northwest Frontier provinces at the top of the country *within ten days*; that is, by the beginning of December.

Most of Pakistan's plantings were designed as acre-sized display plots, which were established *on 2500 private farms*. The rest were 7500 acres of seed-increase fields established on 30 government farms.

The efficiency was amazing:

This huge and complex operation of seeding an area amounting to 12,000 acres scattered across the country would have been hard enough without a war going on. However, despite all the trans-shipments, only a few bags got broken and 99 percent of the seed got to the right place and was planted properly. The plantings were a month or six weeks past the optimal date, but still were in time to make a good crop.

Having seen the seed safely aboard ship, Narvaez put aside the fear of falling shells from Indian cannon, and headed for his new assignment. By the time he arrived in Lahore the seed he'd put on the ship in Los Angeles was being sown. Together with a Pakistani colleague, S. A. Qureshi, he inspected plantings from the rugged northwest frontier to Sindh in the south. The seed had been planted promptly and properly. And as President Ayub had promised, fertilizer was on hand and had been properly applied.

Two weeks later the pair retraced their steps expecting to find sturdy stands of greenery. Instead at their first stop in Northwest Frontier province they found mere scatterings of thin stalks amid expanses of brown dirt. Something was terribly wrong. Hastily they rushed south to Peshawar and put a phone call through to Haldore Hanson in Lahore.

Within an hour a cable was on its way to Borlaug in Mexico. "We have been struck a cruel blow," it began.

Stunned, he quickly repacked his suitcase:

When I got to Pakistan some of the large multiplication plantings were in the war zone near Lahore, and to check them out required a special pass. That night I heard the big guns firing and saw shells landing in the distance.

For the formal inspection we divided the country. I was to start in Sindh Province and move north; Nacho would start in Northwest Province and move south. We'd meet and compare notes in Multan.

Accordingly, I flew to Hyderabad. Only ten days had passed since the seeds had gone into the ground. I found germination was occurring but not enough. The stands were thin.

This made me very nervous. I interviewed the farmers and researchers; they'd done everything right. Something serious was wrong *with the seed*.

As I moved northward the picture stayed the same. After five days of scratching around in hundreds of fields I decided that only half the seeds were germinating; in some places, less.

When we met in Multan, Nacho and I came to the same conclusion: Penjamo 62 was bad; Lerma Rojo 64 was worse.

Neither was germinating properly.

At that point our whole endeavor seemed doomed. Pakistan had invested precious foreign exchange and we'd wasted it. After all the agony to deliver the seed, we'd let everyone down. And we had no clue what we'd done wrong.

The two of us were staying in a miserable — and I mean really miserable — hotel. We talked over the baffling situation most of the night. Then about four o'clock in the morning we decided we had to accept the situation and press on regardless.

Nacho had a bottle of whisky. We finished the last of it; then tried to sleep.

At first light Borlaug phoned the agriculture secretary and had to pass on his career's most agonizing message:

There's a serious problem! Poor germination! In each field still to be planted you've got to double the amount of seed. In fields already planted, double the fertilizer and double the number of irrigations that were scheduled.

Send telegrams to all the regions explaining these changes.

Then do a lot of praying.

With the war still unresolved Norm could not get the word to India. He had Hanson wire Mexico, telling Wellhausen to wire New Delhi and advise Glenn Anderson to double the quantity of seed, double the amount of nitrogen [fertilizer], and double the number of irrigations.

Then about the 10th of December Norm left Lahore in Pakistan and headed for New Delhi in India, a 300 mile flight that, thanks to the hostilities, demanded a 3000 mile detour via Dubai. On arrival he found that even before Wellhausen's telegram arrived Anderson had identified the germination problem and had taken action.

Years later Borlaug recalled his despair:

During the months of October and November, I experienced a thousand bad dreams as I shuttled back and forth between the two countries via Dubai. We were in a pickle. The entire future of the wheat revolution depended upon obtaining an adequate stand of seedlings. Both governments had backed the venture against the advice of their senior scientists. Both had invested precious foreign exchange in it. Now if the Mexican varieties didn't demonstrate their true potential we were sunk.

After Norm left Lahore, the genial agriculture secretary Malik Khuda Bakhsh followed through, and by mid-December the generous topdressing and the frequent soakings seemed to be paying off. Shoots were bursting out around each of the original stems. With the greenness spreading, a much relieved Borlaug headed home for Christmas:

We seemed to have had a narrow escape. The heavy fertilization and irrigations stimulated production of multiple stems but we still had no idea how things would work out. And we still had no idea what we'd done wrong.

S hortly after arriving in Pakistan, Narvaez mentioned the still-secret pair of Borlaug's fifth generation of wheats – the sisters with the curvaceous bodies and contrasting seed colors. He explained that those were superior to the types Pakistan had imported. Compared to Penjamo 62 and Lerma Rojo 64 they yielded more and one had the preferred white grain – the only white-seeded Borlaug variety.

In response, West Pakistan's governor, Malik Amir Mohammad Khan, had the central government formally request permission to buy 50 tons of Mexico's newest seed wheat.

The Mexican government summarily rejected the request. And for good reason: The white-seeded 8156 (Siete Cerros) had not been released and the red-seeded version (Super X) had altogether avoided government clutches.

Every possibility for getting Borlaug's best was thus closed. Every legal possibility, that is. Narvaez had also mentioned that a farmer whose land abutted CIANO had seed-increase fields of both Siete Cerros and Super X. The Pakistanis immediately demanded he approach the man.

That was of course Yaqui Vargas, the farmer who provided Eva's lab with the luxury of daily ice cubes. Narvaez asked Norm for help:

> Nacho called me to ask if I'd help him purchase some of the wheats this farmer was growing clandestinely. Obviously, I couldn't do that with a good conscience or within the law. Indeed, I told Nacho he was treading in dangerous waters; that if he continued trying to get illegal seed he'd be fired.
> Rather than take offence at that, he merely gave me some of my own medicine back. "I don't care if you fire me. Pakistan needs the best wheat. There's too much misery over here!"
> It made me wonder if I'd taught him too well!

On the other side of the bristling border the monsoon's misbehavior meant that in desiccated, crackle-dry, northeast India millions were living on rations that ensured survival but also malnutrition; hundreds of thousands were reduced to a diet rich in grass, leaves and bark. Norm witnessed the effects:

> In Bombay during those terrible days I saw miserable homeless kids clustered around hotels pleading not for money but for

scraps of bread. Each morning trucks circled the streets, picking up corpses.

That's when my patience ran out. India might not have new land for opening more farms but its existing land clearly could yield much more. Better varieties of wheat, for example, could do much to relieve this situation. Yet Indian wheat production, which had stood at 12 million tons in 1964, was worsening. The country needed between five and eight million tons more. I knew that was something we could achieve. I knew how to intensify every acre's production of wheat. And I knew there was no time to lose.

During these busy days Pakistan was moving ahead aggressively with Mexican wheats, and Indians were getting wind of it through newspapers smuggled across the border. Borlaug was constantly pressed to tell how the rival program was getting on.

Whenever I reached New Delhi the first question I was asked was: "How are the Mexican wheats doing in Pakistan?" And whenever I reached in Lahore the first question was: "How is India doing with the new varieties?"

To each I always answered the same. "They are doing very well, very well indeed. You are going to have to work as hard as you can just to keep up with them."

1966–1967
Opposition

n February, 1966 Ed Wellhausen informed the Mexican government that its seed had germinated so poorly that the plantings in Pakistan and India had nearly failed.

The agriculture minister dispatched an inspector to PRONASE's warehouse in Mexicali and seized the remaining samples. Tests showed that between one and two out of every three seeds refused to grow. In some sacks nine out of ten were dead. The inspector established the cause as "excessive fumigation with methyl bromide."

From this revelation Norm took no comfort:

> Probably, the ministry warehouse contained food grain along with seed grain. That's common, and if technicians applying fungicide make no allowance for the extra-tender nature of grain meant for planting they can wreck the germination.
>
> To me the last straw of this whole sorry episode occurred when PRONASE accused American President Lines of damaging the seed *aboard ship*. The company that had been so helpful had to go to considerable expense to fight this groundless charge.

Early in March Norm headed back to Asia. Thanks to the double dosages of water and fertilizer the feeble plantings had formed adequate stands. He guessed that come harvest time, they'd perhaps yield 80 percent of their natural potential. Indeed when the figures were tallied in April, even these grossly distressed stands had out-performed South Asia's best *by 70 percent*.

On this, his fourth March Mission, he found that after just six months on the job Narvaez was taking charge. With some of the 250 tons of Mexican dwarf seed he'd fashioned a national wheat test using acre-sized plots at 50 sites. Each contained 36 different new and old varieties laid out checkerboard style (to ensure each a fair share of sunshine, moisture and fertilizer).

Narvaez also had Mexican dwarfs growing on farms of high officials. There was even a plot at the presidential residence in Rawalpindi. On one of their personal briefings Narvaez spoke boldly: "Mr. President," he said, "this is the Mexican wheat, and over there is what Pakistan grows. Please tell me how the two compare."

The differences were of course dramatic, and Ayub Khan seemed delighted. Norm was too:

> Nacho proved very astute, and had already created confidence in our efforts among field scientists and the national leadership, from cabinet members right through to the president. This helped override the mid-level scientists and civil servants who were continually trying to block the program. Before Nacho arrived, they'd loudly denounced Mexican wheat, but after he'd made his connections [with the political leaders] they pretty much shut up.

During that trip Norm was invited to attend a political event in Rawalpindi, which the president would attend. It was the kind of event he hated, but it was one where he could make a personal point:

> We were returning to Rawalpindi after inspecting some of Nacho's field trials when the minister told me the president would be at this big gathering that afternoon and wanted to see me.
> "Well, can I go as I am?" I asked.
> "It's your decision," the minister replied, "but I think it would be better if you put on your tie and coat. I know that this is against your principles, but this gathering is not being held out in a farm field. It will be rather formal."
> Anyway, I went in clean khakis and open-necked sport shirt. There was a huge tent and thousands of people milling about. All the men were in white shirts and ties. To me that didn't matter; I was upholding the food producers' honor.

Across the border, India had a new leader; the Prime Minister was now Indira Gandhi. Agricultural modernization was then moving slowly, at least as viewed in national perspective. Subramaniam's push to import Mexican seed had so angered his opponents that they deliberately blocked his progress. In the raging debate the weight of opinion was firmly against the minister's push to update India's 5000 year old agriculture.

Opposition came from many quarters. Politicians used the issue for political leverage. Civil servants feared Subramaniam was undermining their authority. Journalists enjoyed frontpage headlines by panicking the public: The imported seeds, they wrote for all to read, would bring foreign pests and diseases and would ruin the already impoverished Indian farmer. The seeds had been developed by an American, and everyone knew Americans were no friends of India. Norm sums up:

> The situation was tailor-made for demagogues, fear-mongers, second-guessers and hate groups. We heard from them all. Many declared we were selling out the country. Some feared Mother India was being violated. We were foreign, and to some that was guilt enough.

During this 1966 March Mission he met Mrs Gandhi.

> I was amazed at how little she knew about the farming and food situation. During our session she said: "Doctor Borlaug, please tell me, is something happening out there in the farms or is it all propaganda? I ask this because when I go down to the Lok Sabha [parliament] I'm bewildered. A small group there says the new methods are going to revolutionize Indian food production. And a bigger group screams in loud voices that it's all faked – nothing's happening. What can I believe? Is it true?"
> "Give us one or two more years," I said, "and your question will be answered beyond any doubt. But I can tell you that at the moment things look extremely promising. You can count on India soon becoming self-sufficient in wheat."
> You should start preparing for that *right away*. Build godowns [warehouses] in the rural towns so all that grain can be safely protected from the monsoon rain."

One last ordeal awaited, and it awaited on what should have been friendly turf:

> On my way home to Mexico in early April I stopped by New York to check in with the main office. Ed Wellhausen happened to be also passing through. At about 10 that morning I was excitedly relating all I'd seen in Asia when George Harrar stalked in. "I want you and Ed to join me for lunch at noon," he barked, and stalked out.
> When noon came, we three went to the top floor. That was normal. But then George led us away from the foundation's lunchroom and into the Pan Am Restaurant. After we'd ordered, he raised the issue of my decision to ship the seed before Pakistan's payment arrived. "What the hell kind of a shop are you running, Norm?" he said, and I could almost feel the fire burning up his insides. "By God, if you pull any more of these stunts, you're going to get fired!"
> George had always been something of a father figure; now I felt I was being treated like a naughty boy. Being taken to the wood-

shed made me deeply angry.

"Dutch," I replied. "You're going to eat those words. Asia is about to produce the Rockefeller Foundation's biggest success.

"Sending that seed was the best decision I ever made!"

Shortly after Norm got back to Sonora in April an Indian official showed up. "I want to see what's going on here," V.K.R.V. Rao said with an abruptness that left no doubt he was to be believed *and obeyed*. Though very busy preparing for the harvest, Norm chose to accommodate the unexpected visitor:

> Who he was or why he was here I had no idea, but I figured he'd come on Subramaniam's behalf. Thus, despite the inconvenience, I dropped my prearranged plans and got my colleagues to drop theirs too. For us, Rao (he had so many initials we referred to him as "Alphabet" Rao) took priority.
>
> The first day we briefed him on the program and gave him the grand tour of the research operations.
>
> Next day we visited Yaqui Valley farmers who were testing the dwarf wheats. He spent hours with Roberto Maurer and Rafael Fierros and saw their fields' almost incredible productivity.
>
> The third day we took him to the government irrigation commission and to the farmers' seed cooperative and *patronato*.
>
> Finally, he inspected a large poultry operation, something he'd asked as a personal favor. Then he left.
>
> At the time I felt pretty good about all this. Alphabet Rao seemed truly impressed; I felt the three-day distraction to have been a good investment. I'd repeatedly pointed out that if India switched to the same varieties it could look just like this.
>
> I can't recall him challenging anything we said or even expressing any skepticism. No one witnessing the fantastic productivity and the prosperity so evident across the Yaqui Valley could fail to be convinced that financially strapped, famine-wracked India should try the same path. Its climate and conditions were almost identical. It just needed the seeds.
>
> I couldn't believe it when I heard that after Alphabet Rao returned home the Planning Commission sent the Cabinet a stiffly worded demand that *no more Mexican seed be imported!*

Previously such a demand would have been obeyed, and the Mexican wheat initiative would have died . . . along with millions of citizens. But during his 18 months in office Prime Minister Shastri had downgraded the Planning Commission and started moving India away from a strict socialist state.

Even so, overruling the country's highest advisory authority was so risky that Subramaniam's fellow Cabinet members urged him to concede. To that, he replied with fervor: "What's the risk? We're starving now; we cannot do worse. No, we're going to go ahead with the imports. In fact, we're going to buy far greater quantities than anyone has ever imagined."

It was during this interim filled with famine fears that Subramaniam addressed his Cabinet colleagues: "I want your collective opinion," he said. "We're considering importing *6000 tons* of Mexican wheat seed. What do you think?"

Hunger by then had gotten so dire that the cabinet's support was wholehearted. Even the communist finance minister pledged the precious dollars. Then Ralph Cummings tossed in enough Rockefeller Foundation dollars to buy 8000 tons more.

Everything now rode on this huge importation – bigger than any previously known. Instead of just mailing a check to Mexico, Subramaniam dispatched three experts.

That May, those three showed up in Obregón City to purchase *14,000 tons of Borlaug seed*. They insisted on inspecting the fields. But by then the Yaqui Valley harvest was almost over; only around the state capital were any fields unharvested.

The delegation flew to Hermosillo, where PRONASE welcomed them with an elaborate luncheon. But – remembering the poor germination of its last shipment – the visitors seemed unimpressed. After dining they announced they needed to sleep. Norm takes up the story:

> As soon as PRONASE's representatives had left the room, Dr. Sikka turned to me: "Tomorrow will you take us to a trustworthy cooperative?"
> The next morning, before dawn, we drove to the Hermosillo Farmers' Credit Union where in one hour the Indians arranged the purchase. Then we visited the farms from which the seed would come, and drove field to field until they'd identified enough acreage to ensure that the 14,000 tons of seed would come from top-quality plants.

S.P. Kohli later recalled the situation: "Dr. Borlaug helped us to arrange for the shipment of the seed, and all the seed was moved to the port. We supervised the cleaning of it. And before the seed was loaded, we experimented with the sack, testing its strength.

"We would throw each sack from a height to see whether it would burst! They all broke open and Dr. Sikka sent them all back."

Before the Indians were satisfied they'd twice demanded stronger sacks. And they'd ensured that the fumigation had been done with proper care to preserve the germination.

Though millions of tons of wheat had been shipped for eating, 14,000 tons was by far the biggest shipment of wheat for planting. It shattered the previous year's record of 450 tons.

Meanwhile, back in India that June the monsoon began a grim reenactment. For a second year in a row, the rains refused to drench the parched soils and bring the Ganges Valley to life.

This was monumental mistiming. The resulting devastation shook the nation to the core. India was already stretched to the limit. It had no food reserves to fall back on. And even with an abundant crop it would be short of food.

Once more the government reached out around the world. Once more millions of tons of wheat, corn and sorghum were hauled across the oceans, unloaded through crowded ports and rushed inland over hundreds of miles of congested roads and railways to serve millions of desperate Indians.

During the height of the crisis, ships docked at a rate of three a day. The ports dispersed the food on 7 trains a day, averaging 50 cars a train and 550 miles of travel. Through that year, 20 million tons of food grain got to the drought areas inland, where the number of fair price shops had been tripled to 150,000.

That July, Orville Freeman traveled to New Delhi bearing bad news: The United States had suffered a drought, he told Subramaniam, and might not be able to keep the food shipments coming.

Indeed, that August Freeman's staff suggested discontinuing the customary practice of authorizing food aid to India years in advance. It recommended, that Washington "agree to supply food aid to India through a series of short-run extensions of our present Public Law 480 agreement. It would be made crystal clear to the Indian government that agricultural performance would weigh heavily in determining the terms of future food assistance."

This began the "short tether" policy, by which Washington slowly dribbled food to India, never committing to anything beyond the upcoming shipments, and all the while pressuring India's government to produce more food for itself. Of this Norm had no inkling:

Thank goodness Orville didn't ask my opinion at the time. I'm far from sure what I would have said. Despite good intentions, he was stepping onto a very slippery slope. He was toying with people's lives. But what he was attempting was just what was needed.

Norm's insight would soon prove out. Lyndon Johnson soon seized upon this short-tether process for his own political purposes. Enraged by Mrs Gandhi's criticisms of the Vietnam War (which happened to be going badly) he insisted on retaining the short-tether policy even after the second successive monsoon failure. From here on, India must comply with the president's wishes before any food aid would be authorized.

Now things were getting personal, deadly personal. During the autumn months, when it became clear that further delays would lead to tragedy, even Johnson's supporters in Washington became alarmed. Executive branch officials as well as some congressmen advocated that food no longer be used for political leverage.

New Delhi began warning of catastrophe ahead. The pipeline had to be kept full and flowing steadily to the hungry millions, they said. The system was far too elaborate and too essential to be switched off and on at anyone's whim.

Johnson remained adamant. As he later said: "I stood almost alone, with only a few concurring advisors, in this fight to slow the pace of U.S. assistance . . . . This was one of the most difficult and lonely struggles of my Presidency."

In Pakistan a miracle was unfolding, though it was hard to detect behind the drought and despair over the monsoon. The vast irrigated areas still functioned fairly well with giant reservoirs on the Indus River and its tributaries doling out precious water for crops and people. But Pakistan is mostly arid, and when the new monsoon proved just as unkind and uncaring as the old, the future in this corner of the world promised to be bleak indeed.

On Pakistan's leadership the effect was electric. President Ayub decided to accelerate the Mexican wheat program to the point where his country would never again depend on another nation or the monsoon. Pakistan, he said, would grow all the food it needed and it would build reserve stocks for use during future famines.

That July, Ayub Khan committed his government to:

- Abandoning imported charity food;

- Implementing high-yield wheat production;
- Importing fertilizer and developing a domestic fertilizer industry;
- Providing credit so farmers could buy fertilizer and seed; and
- Paying farmers a fair price for their harvest.

To cap things off Ayub Khan announced that the government would pay farmers the international market price of 21 rupees per maund (a local measure amounting to about 80 pounds, or roughly a sackful of wheat). He went so far as to pledge that that price would remain *for the coming three years*. It was twice what the farmers had ever received, and rural Pakistan erupted in rapture.

Norm shared the thrill, but was also disconcerted:

> Ayub Khan's decision was a big call. Recent experience had shown that Pakistan could not feed itself with its traditional wheats alone, so he was essentially relying on my word.
>
> Abandoning the imports was to gamble with millions of lives. The president was relying on plants that were largely untested in Pakistan.
>
> Now the future sustenance for 100 million souls — rested on the 250 tons of Lerma Rojo and Penjamo we'd struggled so hard to deliver. To me, that was scary.

During this time Narvaez happened to visit the Lahore office of the U.S. Agency for International Development and casually mentioned the Sonora farmer who was growing Borlaug's most powerful wheats illegally behind the CIANO research station.

The director of USAID's agricultural office, Leon Hesser, wrote a proposal for a $25,000 grant to buy 50 tons of the seed and have it shipped to Pakistan. Hesser recalls the sequence: "I got the American Ambassador to sign off, and we called Staley Pitts, who was in the U.S. on home leave, and said, 'Get your ass down in Mexico and buy 50 tons of that white wheat and get it over here in time for fall planting.'"

Norm liked these guys a lot:

> In his freewheeling approach to problem solving, Staley Pitts was unlike any other USAID employee I've ever met. If something needed doing he'd have a go at it, no matter what barriers stood in the way. As a student, he'd played guard for the Kansas State Wildcats. I guess that's where he learned to be decisive, bold, courageous and able to break through an impenetrable defensive line.

Pitts was on a scheduled home leave enjoying a few weeks with his wife and 18-year-old son in the Los Angeles suburb of West Covina. On Sunday, September 4, he took his son Bob to a Los Angeles Rams pre-season game. Arriving home about midnight, he learned there'd been a call from Pakistan.

For the subsequent drama I'm beholden to the journalist Wayne Swegle who documented it soon thereafter in a Ford Foundation report that was never released, being judged too "hot to handle."

Pitts immediately returned the call and got his marching orders from Leon Hesser. Now all he had to do was withdraw the $25,000 from a local bank and get himself to Obregón City, Mexico and buy some of that Mexican wheat Narvaez had described.

Because of the Labor Day holiday nothing could be done until Tuesday, but then Pitts called the president of the American President Lines in San Francisco and said, "We've got people starving in Pakistan, you've go to help us." Despite his experience with Borlaug the year before, George Killion proved friendly and told him that a ship would sail from Los Angeles bound for Karachi on the 21st.

Getting a load of Siete Cerros on that freighter in a little over two weeks seemed quite impossible.

Pitts made it his mission. On Wednesday the 7th, he flew to Tucson, rode a bus to Nogales, crossed into Mexico, took a train to Obregón City, and telephoned Yaqui Vargas. "Do you have any of that special wheat Borlaug calls 8156 — the white one?" he asked. Vargas guardedly replied that he had 100 tons. Pitts said he'd like to talk about buying some.

During their meeting Yaqui Vargas said he'd sell only one ton. Pitts insisted that he wanted more. "I kept saying I needed a big order. The farmer kept saying no. And I kept waving $25,000 in front of his face."

Finally Vargas asked for a night to think about it. Next day, he returned to say he'd sell 50 tons of Siete Cerros, half his stash, and 50 tons of its red-seeded sister, the so-called Super X. Then came the inevitable bickering over price.

Even with the main issues settled, Pitts faced the impossible task of getting seed wheat out of Mexico. The varieties lacked government authorization. No one but PRONASE could legally export seed. The seed needed to be cleaned, carefully fumigated, and properly bagged. And to do all that he had 13 days.

Knowing nothing of the language and even less of Mexican brokers, truckers or customs agents, Pitts insisted that Vargas handle the details.

Finally, it was arranged that the load would be consigned to the Bank of America. Pitts would deposit the money and the bank would pay Vargas once the delivery was made.

After finishing that particular deal, Pitts walked out of the room and noticed Norm, who was staying at the Costa de Oro across the street

Norm remembers the scene:

> My first inkling of what was going on was when, on emerging from the motel, I heard a shout. It was Staley Pitts. "Dr. Borlaug," he yelled, waving his arms. "Come on over and tell me if this is the right seed."
>
> I went over, and he opened a sack. Inside was a sample of Siete Cerros – so badly contaminated it seemed to be half wild oats.
>
> "For heaven's sake," I said, "This variety hasn't been released yet. I don't know where the hell you got it, but it must be contraband."
>
> I was feeling quite nervous. "Listen," I said, "I'm standing out here in the main street and people are looking at us and wondering what mischief two damn gringos could be up to. If I'm caught with you and that wheat I'm going to be in deep trouble."
>
> This was a real concern. Technically, I was a guest in Mexico and could easily be deported. My relations with the authorities depended on trust. Any whiff of corruption would end everything.
>
> But at the same time I knew Pakistan's desperate situation, and in general heartily approved of Pitts's effort. In a food emergency, victims shouldn't have to die because some government official hasn't legalized seed of a staple food by enshrining it in some official ledger.
>
> "This is the right wheat all right," I said after a moment's thought, "but you can't ship it with all that wild oats in it."
>
> "Oh hell," he said, "We'll deal with that okay. I just want to be sure this is the right stuff."

Having verified the seeds' authenticity, Pitts returned to West Covina to enjoy the remainder of his home leave.

Although Vargas had promised to phone once the trucks crossed into the United States, by the 19th Pitts had heard nothing. The ship would sail in two days. Now he was frantic. After five hours trying to call Obregón City, he finally got through and learned that the trucks were at Nogales, but that unforeseen problems were blocking them from crossing the border. Vargas was sorry; he had no way to get the trucks out of Mexico.

"I was sunk," Pitts told Swegle. "I knew how Pakistan needed more food. But I seemed to be at the end of the line. Then my wife said, 'You'd better get down there; you won't be happy until you do.'"

So Staley Pitts forfeited more family time and headed back to Nogales by plane and bus. Crossing the border that bisects the town, he strolled around casually inquiring if anyone had seen a couple of trucks loaded with wheat. To his amazement, he was told they were at a checkpoint about two miles south. He found the place and traipsed from office to office, inquiring about how he could possibly get the wheat into Arizona. Eventually a man said he'd help, and had a pickup truck with Arizona license plates shuttle Pitts back into the U.S.

Swegle reported that apparently the seed-laden trucks were driven to Agua Prieta, 80 miles to the east, and driven across into Arizona after the customs officials went off duty at 5 pm. In the town of Douglas the bags were loaded into two American trucks and directed toward the port of Los Angeles at San Pedro, where they were put in bond to the Bank of America.

By then Pitts had returned to West Covina, but he was hardly happy. It was September 23. The seed had arrived two days late.

Fortunately, though, the ship had also been delayed. At seven the next morning — Saturday the 24th — Pitts went down to see the ship and what he recalls as: "Two of the most beautiful trucks in the world. Gee, I was sure happy to see them."

That happiness faded when the shipping office clerk refused to break the bond without a Bank of America agent present. Here was the ultimate frustration. Pitts had been assured Bank of America would send a representative, but no one had expected the delivery to occur two days late, and the man had taken the weekend off.

After all he'd done, Pitts was stymied. The ship was getting steam up. Then he had a brainwave and called George Killion at his home. As a result the President Line's president ordered his staff to break the bond and load the seed.

The following Tuesday Pitts met what he called "a very disconcerted Bank of America official." By then, though, the cargo was far out to sea. "This is all highly irregular," he was informed, but the transfer of funds was completed and Yaqui Vargas got paid.

Those first bulk samples of dwarf wheat arrived in Karachi Port on November 24. In America that was Thanksgiving Day. Of all Americans on that harvest-celebration day Pitts was the most thankful. Pakistan had Borlaug's best wheats before Mexico got them and (perhaps more to the point) before India got them. It now had 50 tons of Siete Cerros seed and 50 tons of Super X, the curvy sisters with the blond and red seed. And in Pakistan it was the winter-planting time.

Shortly thereafter Staley Pitts renamed the newly arrived super wheats Mexipak White and Mexipak Red. The names stuck and helped boost Mexican morale *and* Pakistani acceptance. And he later said: "This is the most illegal wheat in the world. The original seed was grown illegally, it was gotten out of Mexico illegally, it was placed on board ship illegally."

By November near-famine conditions pertained throughout the eastern end of the Ganges Valley. The drought struck northwest of Calcutta with particular ferocity. Instead of producing the normal 4.4 million tons of its main crop, rice, Bihar state produced only 1.2 million tons, or one-fourth of requirements for the nearly 30 million Biharis. For India as a whole, food grain production that year totaled 74.2 million tons, little more than the previous disastrous year and 15.2 million tons short of 1964 when the monsoon had been magnificent.

In the previous four years the U.S. had shipped food worth well over $1 billion. But President Johnson's short tether policy was causing concern. In late November Subramaniam forecast that without a prompt approval for India's latest 2-million-ton food aid request, the pipeline would run dry by mid-January 1967.

Even Orville Freeman advised the president not to delay the next 2-million-ton food-aid shipment, which he said was "the minimum necessary allocation to avoid breaking the pipeline."

The U.S. aid community soon took its concerns to the press, which produced a spate of editorials sharply critical of the president. On November 29 the New York Times denounced the short-tether policy as "a serious error." On December 11 the Washington Post commented: "There are good reasons for a firm American policy that, in the long run, will assist India in resolving its recurrent food difficulties. But people sometimes starve to death in the short run and India is on the brink of famine."

Lyndon Johnson recalled this period as one in which he weathered a "heavy propaganda barrage" waged by "Americans who considered themselves India's best friends . . . . In the press and at Washington cocktail parties I was pictured as a heartless man willing to let innocent people starve."

Johnson, however, would not be moved. He dispatched two separate study teams to India — one involving agricultural experts from the

Department of Agriculture, the other members of Congress.

These investigations were probably meant as nothing more than a way to push Mrs Gandhi past the breaking point. However, the USDA team reported that India's food needs had been, if anything, understated. And the congressional investigators recommended shipping at least 1.8 million tons of food to cover anticipated needs for the coming months of February, March and April 1967.

By mid-December Johnson felt he had to act, but he approved only half what the congressional study mission had recommended. India would get no more than enough to keep the pipeline from collapse. As Johnson explained later, "I kept the 'short tether' on. No one would starve because of our policies. India would receive the grain it needed, but on a month-by-month basis rather than a year-to-year basis."

Though delays in U.S. food-aid were of national concern, Prime Minister Gandhi refused to reduce her anti-Vietnam-War rhetoric.

Casting off its blinkers, New Delhi set out to review its overall attitude toward local food production. No Indian could deny the priority agriculture deserved. Given the country's peril, the food supply needed reorganizing "on a war footing."

Thanks to the hardhead in the White House on the far side of the globe India turned the critical corner in its approach to development. Subramaniam's way forward was finally cleared of bureaucratic obstacles. Opposition evaporated. And the lively agriculture minister publicly stated that India would no longer import grain to keep its poor people from starvation. India, he said, would feed itself. Like Ayub Khan in Pakistan, Subramaniam was now entrusting India's future to Borlaug policies and Borlaug seed. Most observers considered it foolish bluster.

The year 1967 began with an international panic. India's food situation had made the evening news. As northeast India's food supplies dwindled well-fed television viewers would get to watch 15 million people starve, most seeing it in living black and white during the dinner hour.

Next up, pundits jumped in with their pens and predictions and, as is their wont, described the future as a projection of the present. Seen thus, famine on a vast scale was preordained. Tables, graphs and scholarly reviews proved it.

Going beyond other prognosticators, William and Paul Paddock specified exactly when famine would strike. These learned brothers, primed with insights gained during long careers in foreign posts, posed the terse rhetorical question: "Something will turn up, or will it?" Then with persuasive, almost contagious, cynicism supplied the answer: agriculture could not possibly turn things around in time. They entitled their vivid and widely admired book *Famine 1975!*

Between its covers *Famine 1975!* presented published data certifying India as an incurable case. Its plight, moreover, was mere prelude to what would follow: "India . . . is the bellwether that shows the path which the others, like sheep going to the slaughter, are following," they wrote. "The hungry nation that today refuses to heed India's history will be condemned to relive it."

Having served notice of mass death to millions, the authors proceeded to assign the United States an eerie choice: which nations should be written off and which revived. Their book carried the subtitle: *America's Decision: Who Will Survive?*

Intellectuals the world around endorsed this genocide by deliberate neglect. Many learned, honorable, well-fed Westerners argued against sending more food aid. Garrett Hardin even came up with a handy guide for dealing with so disturbing a dilemma. Hungry countries, the ecologist said, were in a situation like that faced by survivors following a ship sinking. Letting more clamber aboard the already full lifeboat would be fatal to all. Better to let them perish. Either way, they were doomed.

Borlaug alone realized that the future would be quite unlike the present. At the very moment pessimism was powering the purists and pundits, South Asia was sowing his seeds. He tried his best to enlighten the doomsayers to the fact that the future would not be a continuation of the present:

> The critics ignored me. To them I was not to be trusted. I was just another of those "food-production boys."

On his fifth March Mission Norm started as usual in Pakistan. During the two week visit he got to see Ayub Khan. In this, their third meeting, Pakistan's president asked how things were going. Norm again spoke boldly:

> "Sir," I told him, "the wheat program is not only on target it's two years ahead of schedule!
> But to keep it on track you must back it up with supports:

"You must get more fertilizer through the port of Karachi and get it to the farming areas in good time for the planting season.

"You must provide the farmers with the credit to buy that fertilizer and improved seed.

"You must keep publicizing how much the government will pay at harvest time.

"And you must build enough godowns to store a huge harvest."

Norm also met the urbane Malik Khuda Bakhsh:

On my last evening Malik called Nacho and me to his office, and told us the government was preparing to make a major commitment to the two other Mexican dwarf wheats. He said he planned buying 40,000 tons, and it had to be the white seeded one!

That was a real shocker. The results were not yet in from Staley Pitts' 50 ton lots. Shipping 40,000 tons of seed was unprecedented. And that much Siete Cerros didn't exist.

Actually, I doubted *any* could be obtained. The variety had not been formally released, so the only possible source was Yaqui Vargas, who was bulking up the half he'd withheld from Staley Pitts.

"There's very little in Mexico," I explained, "Only one farmer has it, and he'll keep the seed for himself."

"What about the red one?" Malik said, referring to the Super X.

"There's going to be a lot of that," I explained. "But you don't need so much! Why not spend the money on fertilizer?"

"Well, how much will these yield?" he persisted, knowing the answer full well.

"Compared to Lerma Rojo or Penjamo, each acre will produce 400 to 800lb more, even in moderately fertile soils."

"If they produce half what you say Pakistan must have them!"

Norm brushed off Malik's completely ridiculous plan.

N ext, he spent two weeks touring India's wheat-growing areas with Swaminathan, Kohli and Glenn Anderson.

For the first time the new dwarf wheats were coming on line in farm country. Farmers were excited. Some were anticipating yields of 3 tons an acre. Previous harvests had typically been less than half a ton and even 1 ton had seemed quite unreachable.

Pessimism was dissipating like summer clouds. Even the critics were catching the wave. Norm himself was enthused:

During our tour in March of '67 we encountered farmers — both large and small — who were eager to be part of the new prosperity. I was reminded of the 1930s, when hybrid corn was first planted on the Borlaug farm.

This grass-roots enthusiasm was beginning at just the right

moment because much of the Indian government was still reluctant to commit to the widespread adoption of the package of seed and technology. In this, Pakistan was two years ahead. In India, Mrs Gandhi and minister Subramaniam were committed but government officials were still reluctant.

New Delhi's brassbound reluctance was exemplified by the government's approach to fertilizer production. The Planning Commission was at that moment half-heartedly negotiating contracts for construction or financing of fertilizer factories. In Socialist India letting private companies build factories was an anathema, and the commission dictated ruinous requirements and ridiculously low rates of return. Then out of the blue it issued an ultimatum: companies must submit their bids by midnight March 31st or forgo participation in the industry.

This was foolish but Norm knew the government would never relent. National elections were being held, and for the first time since Independence the vote was not predictable. For two decades the Congress Party had swept the polls; now, however, the masses were restive, and this election might prove a shocker.

Norm, however, was too buoyed up to worry about politics:

We had to report our findings to the Minister of Agriculture. I was looking forward to informing Subramaniam that everything he'd dreamed of was starting to come to pass.

Then, on March 29th, as we prepared to leave Ludhiana, a telegram arrived from Subramaniam himself. It said that we were invited to have lunch at the Escort Tractor Factory in the city of Meerut; we could stop off while en route to New Delhi. Poland had funded the factory and the luncheon would honor the Polish ambassador.

We arrived just before noon to find hundreds of farmers gathered for something like an agricultural fair. In the factory's forecourt small tractors stood in long gleaming lines. It sure looked impressive but one of my colleagues explained that there were two tractor companies and both were having difficulty selling their products; the accumulation of unsold inventory was causing concern. This day, the farmers didn't seem to be showing much interest either.

Presently we retired to a large and crowded room for the luncheon. I was placed near the president of the Escort Tractor Company, Mr. Nanda. A large number of journalists were on hand, as is common whenever a member of the diplomatic corps speaks.

Following the lunch Mr. Nanda rose and introduced the ambassador, who talked at length about the role of agricultural machinery in communist Poland.

Before closing the proceedings, Mr. Nanda introduced me and asked if I'd say a few words. Grabbing the microphone I described the outstanding success we'd seen everywhere during the past three weeks. I spoke of the enthusiasm of the farmers for the new wheats and the package of production technologies.

I closed with a special message to the journalists: "The grass roots are afire," I said, "and if the Government of India stimulates the adoption of this new technology, it will trigger a revolution in wheat production."

I indicated that government should provide the farmers:

- The right kind of fertilizer at reasonable prices;
- Credit for purchasing fertilizer and seed; And
- A fair price for the harvest.

That price, I said, should be roughly the international market price, or twice the present amount.

Then, again for the journalists' benefit, Norm appended a summary:

During the last two weeks I've seen the beginnings of a wheat revolution in your fields.

If the government gives full support, India can replace famine with plenty.

What India needs now is fertilizer, fertilizer, fertilizer; credit, credit, credit; and fair prices, fair prices, fair prices!

Those will give India more food.

If I were a member of your parliament, I would leap from my seat every 15 minutes and shout, "Fertilizers!"

No matter what the subject of debate, I would shout, "Fertilizers! Give the farmers fertilizers!"

This being Election Day he finished up by warning what would happen if these things were not done:

Unless there is more food, a volcano will erupt under this land's political leaders. The people will throw them out of office.

Around that vast and people-choked room a roar of laughter rose. Everybody seemed to be chuckling. The press loved it; Norm could see them scribbling as the applause rolled on and on.

But no official at the head table was clapping. This bumptious American had hijacked their meeting's purpose to honor Communist Poland's generosity.

Actually, Norm tended to sympathize. For years to come, his lack of tact bothered his mind. He'd not been attentive. He'd gone too far. He'd not said the right thing:

As I took my seat I noticed that the Polish ambassador seemed upset. It was only then that I realized that I hadn't even mentioned the importance of his government's tractors.

The next day they arrived in the capital to find New Delhi in ferment. Indians had voted out of office a third of the incumbents. The political elite whose domination had been almost unchallenged since India's founding, had suffered a deep wound.

Swaminathan and Norm went immediately to see the agriculture minister. Norm was bubbling:

> I made a dramatic entrance, pointing toward the window and asked Subramaniam: "Do you know what is going on out there? A revolution is starting. You must take action. Farmers are demanding more support. You must double and treble everything — fertilizer, water, credit."

Subramaniam held up a fistful of newspaper clippings from the morning papers and shouted: "Dr. Borlaug, you don't have to persuade me. I know what you said yesterday. I know what you are up to and I agree with you. But it is already too late for me. I've lost my seat in the Lok Sabha [parliament]. As of tomorrow night, I'm out of office, so I cannot help anymore!"

That news was so devastating Norm never got over it:

> We'd lost our leader. He'd focused so much on solving the food problem he hadn't gone home to campaign. It was not only tragic but ironic. Food shortages had terrified the voters. He'd done more than anyone to avert those shortages; he'd been the backbone that gave the effort strength. And he'd been too conscientious to tend to his career.
>
> Now there'd be a new minister of food and agriculture, and I feared the newcomer would bow before the critics' blandishments.
>
> Then suddenly the minister seemed distracted by a new thought: "Before you leave," he barked, "please go see Ashok Mehta. He is chairman of the Commission whose plans you are always criticizing. He is also in charge of fertilizer imports and fertilizer industry development."
>
> Then came another thought: "How long will you be in Delhi?"
>
> "I leave for Mexico tomorrow night at midnight."

With that, Subramaniam grabbed the phone on his desk and arranged for Borlaug and Swaminathan to meet the Deputy Prime Minister the following evening at six.

> As we left the minister's office I felt depressed and sad. Then he came to the door and yelled down the corridor: "Dr. Borlaug,

speak bluntly. Hit him hard, just as hard as you hit me. He needs to hear it straight from the shoulder!"

On the evening of the 31st of March, just as we were about to enter the Deputy Prime Minister's office, I said to Swaminathan, "I'm going to follow Subramaniam's suggestion. This meeting will likely be stormy, so you'd better keep a low profile. I could be banned from returning to India and, should that happen, you and Glenn [Anderson] will have to keep the program moving forward."

Ashok Mehta met us with polite greetings, and I explained what was happening in the wheat fields. I emphasized that untold thousands of farmers, small and large, had seen how the new wheat could increase production. "The grass roots are on fire" I said, "and you can expect an explosion because all those small farmers plan to plant Mexican wheats in November."

Their expectations, I stressed, could never become realities until the government discarded its current policies. Those, I said, were now obsolete. A new bold approach is needed. In particular the government must greatly expand the availability of fertilizer.

Ashok Mehta interjected to say that India did not have the foreign exchange to boost fertilizer imports, much less build large fertilizer factories.

I countered by saying that the development of a fertilizer industry was more important than any other sector, since fertilizer was essential for keeping crops fed and that was essential for keeping the populace fed.

"Ours is a socialistic government," he explained, "We cannot let companies build fertilizer plants."

"Mr. Deputy Prime Minister," I said, "in Mexico there is a socialistic government, and it allows companies to build fertilizer plants."

Then I raised the financial issues.

"You must greatly expand credit for farmers, so they can buy fertilizer and the best seed. Also you must discard the cheap food policy that subsidizes city folk at the farmer's expense. You must assure the farmers they'll get a fair price for their grain. You should double the payment to match the market price in the rest of the world.

Then I issued a blunt warning: "Unless the policy is changed soon, farmers will riot and social and political disorder will spread across the countryside. If this happens, you Mr. Minister will be ousted. Moreover, the Congress Party will go down to defeat and you personally will be to blame!"

My voice was rising. In all of India I was probably the only man who could have shouted down the deputy leader in his own office. Perhaps understandably, he reacted indignantly. For several minutes there was chaos with both of us yelling at each other until we both ran out of breath.

Finally, I brought the confrontation to a close. "Mr. Minister," I said, "I leave soon on a flight to Mexico. I must say these things that you do not like."

Leaning across the desk and looking into his astonished eyes, I commanded, "Tear up those five-year plans. Start again and multiply everything for farm support three or four times. Increase your fertilizer, increase your support prices, increase your loan funds. Then you will be closer to what is needed to keep India from starving.

"IMAGINE YOUR COUNTRY FREE OF FAMINE," I shouted. "IT IS WITHIN YOUR GRASP!"

Ten days later, following his return to Sonora, Norm received a series of articles clipped from India's major newspapers. They'd been forwarded by the Rockefeller Foundation and Ford Foundation offices in New Delhi. Dated April 1, 1967 they disclosed momentous news: "Last night at midnight the policies of the Government of India were changed." Ashok Mehta, they explained, was reopening negotiations with foreign chemical companies. Companies now had to at least until the end of the year, and perhaps beyond, to submit their contracts.

This was more revolutionary than it seems. India was not only abandoning socialism, it was abandoning its fixation with industrialization. Instead, it was lifting its sights to food production.

"The best hour of Dr. Borlaug's life," Subramaniam later reflected, "was that hour he spent with Ashok Mehta."

When the April harvest tallies were in, it became apparent that India's wheat production had soared. The previous year the national harvest had been 11 million tons. This year it was 16 million tons, or 4 million tons more than India had ever produced.

Norm had only just arrived in Sonora when telegrams from Pakistan began urging that he "get the Mexipak seed." This is when he learned that Malik Khuda Bakhsh had not after all given up his ridiculous notion.

Against his better judgment Norm visited Yaqui Vargas. Nothing he said could pry any loose.

Finally I was informed that Pakistan was sending its agriculture minister to buy *40,000 tons* of seed. There was but one catch: he'd buy nothing until he first got *2000 tons* of Mexipak White.

I couldn't believe it. Yaqui Vargas was the only source of Siete Cerros, and he probably didn't have 2000 tons. Even if he did, he'd *never sell his whole stash*.

That May, shortly after the Sonora harvest had been completed, a passel of Pakistani officials arrived in Sonora. It was led by the country's highest agriculture official, a Bengali from East Pakistan, which grew rice rather than wheat. Upon arrival he announced he'd come to buy 40,000 tons of seed wheat but absolutely, positively would not buy a single kernel until he had 2000 tons of the white-seeded version. Without that, he said, *he would buy nothing at all*.

The meeting was set for two o'clock the following afternoon at the Costa de Oro Motel. Norm went along to introduce the visitors:

The motel's small meeting room was packed with representatives from every farmer organization. Mexico's agriculture minister had sent Roberto Osoyo, to chair the session. The Pakistanis were there. Yaqui Vargas was there, seemingly somewhat unsteady. And I was there.

Speaking in Spanish, Sr. Osoyo welcomed everyone and explained the meeting's purpose was to bargain over the export of this extraordinary amount of wheat seed. Then he turned the microphone over to me. I introduced Pakistan's minister of agriculture and explained the background to his request, emphasizing how the new seed could offset his country's famine.

Then I proceeded to leave the room. The bargaining was something wholly between the Mexicans and Pakistanis and I neither needed nor wanted to be present. But as I stood up the Pakistani minister leaned over and grabbed my arm. "No, no," he said. "You are now my personal representative. I don't understand Spanish, and I want to know what I'm dealing with here. SIT DOWN!"

This arrangement was explained to the audience. Then the bargaining began. There was only one question to start with: Who would provide the 2000 tons of Siete Cerros? And of course there was only possible source, who'd made clear he wasn't going to give any up.

But soon everyone in the room was glaring at him, and after a while the tension started wearing him down. Grudgingly, he offered 200 kilos (500lb). It was pitiful. The glaring went on. The bargaining went on too. Rising by 200 kilo increments until, about an hour later, he'd conceded to sell a ton of Siete Cerros seed.

This was getting us nowhere. Pakistan's demand for 2000 tons seemed so far off that the other farmers were getting angry.

To me, Vargas' personal position was clear too: He was on the horns of a personal dilemma. If he grew his seed one more season, he could make a fortune selling it to farmers.

But the others didn't understand, and didn't care. It was agonizing to be in that room and feel the raw emotion flowing from all sides. Amid the Mexican agony the Pakistanis remained adamant. It was terrible. I could see the leaders of the credit unions, good business people, nearly frothing at the mouth in frustration. To them the golden prize of selling 40,000 tons of seed was being held hostage by one of their own number.

Finally, Yaqui Vargas got to 1500 tons. That was as far as anyone could push him. Probably it was all he had. I guess he decided that selling it was probably better than being forever ostracized. Mexicans were less individualistic than Americans; public opprobrium more powerful.

Then the Pakistanis agreed to regard 1500 tons as satisfactory. In less than five minutes they bought the other 40,000 tons. Contracts amounting to millions of dollars were agreed to in seconds. Most were for Super X, which had originally come from Yaqui Vargas too.

In this painful manner the Pakistan delegation succeeded in buying 1500 tons of Siete Cerros (Mexipak White to them), 40,000 tons of Super X (Mexipak Red), 200 tons of Sonora 64, and 20 tons of the very latest improvement: INIA 66, the first summer wheat capable of yielding 7000lb – 3.5 tons – per acre.

In August 1967, the giant cargo was loaded at the port of Guaymas. Last year's 14,000 ton world record had now been shattered. This one, almost three times larger, filled *four ships*.

> I drove the 80 miles [to Guaymas], and what a thrill it was to see those ships lined up along the dock, each being loaded with grain. This hive of activity made me think back to the moribund state of production in 1944 when local millers had shunned their own farmers and bought wheat in Canada and the U.S. These days, the world clamored for Mexican wheat.

Despite this being a Pakistani initiative, critics around the world damned Borlaug for "forcing" this unprecedented transfer of wheat seed upon an innocent Asian nation. The implication was that he'd made a fortune on the backs of poor people. He, of course, had neither profited from nor promoted the operation. Norm was amazed at how such falsehoods could make headlines the world around:

> In the United States and Europe a number of prominent academics insisted I was guilty of gross irresponsibility. I was, they proclaimed, "playing with the lives of millions of innocent people." They implied that I just didn't know what I was doing.
> Despite their distant viewpoint and lack of first-hand facts, they knew that sending wheat seeds halfway around the world was a despicable act, aimed at duping the innocent peasant farmers of

Asia who didn't know any better. My motivation, they implied, was either boosting my own ego or lining my own pocket.

The pressure for the seed was of course coming from the Pakistanis themselves – none more so than those innocent naïve farmers, who right now just couldn't get enough of the Mexipaks.

After the 40,000 tons of seed arrived, Pakistan's government sold it at an official price of 35 rupees a maund (about $200 a ton). But even at this steep rate there was insufficient to meet the demand. Seed began selling on the black market at prices up to three times higher.

That November, Pakistan planted Borlaug wheat on nearly 5 million acres, of which 3 million acres were sown to Mexipak Red. Narvaez estimated that the new varieties sown that November were, in order of importance, Mexipak Red [Super X], Penjamo 62, Lerma Rojo 64, Mexipak White [Siete Cerros] and Sonora 64.

During these days the Pakistani president and the Mexican scientist developed a surprising rapport. Hanson provides an example:

President Ayub Khan called Narvaez to Flagstaff House, the president's residence at Rawalpindi and asked for the results. Narvaez gave him the names of the landowners who achieved exceptional production, many of whom were the president's friends. The average yield from the Mexipaks was 2.5 to 3 tons, compared to Pakistan's old national average of 0.4 tons – the national standard between 1914 and 1964 that the Sindh professor had said would never change.

When Narvaez mentioned some failures, the president demanded names. Narvaez shuffled his feet, but the president insisted. Well, the young Mexican said, those men are well known to you.

The first was the secretary of agriculture [Malik Khuda Bakhsh].

Why?

Because, sir, he failed to instruct his farm manager about the new cultivation methods.

The president shook his head slowly. And the second failure?

That was the governor of West Pakistan [the Nawab of Kala Bagh].

Same reason.

And the third?

Narvaez looked steadily at the floor, then pointing a finger hesitantly at the president, he said: "The third, sir, was you. Same reason."

The president grimaced.

Although Pakistan's food problem was huge, it was of course dwarfed by the shortfall across the border. International observers concluded that millions of Indian boat people would soon flood the world searching for succor.

Now everything was up to the scientists. Anderson and Swaminathan co-opted the IARI and two of the new agricultural universities to multiply the seed. Glenn Anderson was the godfather of all this, supporting it with Rockefeller Foundation funds and guiding it with his collegial presence and his understanding of the wheat plant. He kept the whole focus forever on practical progress. Swaminathan led the technical side. They both shared the same spirit and proved unbeatable.

Uttar Pradesh Agricultural University planted 11,000 acres, most of it to a local selection from one of the 225 rejects Norm had flown in on Pan Am four years before. This Borlaug discard grew so well that the university offered discounted seed to any farmer who'd attend its field days. It set the price at 5 rupees a kilogram (about 30 cents a pound), and found itself besieged. Farmers not only came alone, they brought truckloads of friends, each of whom picked up a kilo. Some promptly sold their stash for 25 rupees.

Such scenes were typical across northern India's irrigated zone. Faculty members — including the university's vice chancellor — plowed up the lawns in the backyards of their bungalows and grew wheat. Some students were allotted five-acre plots to raise the new wheats and make their tuition money. Norm was impressed:

> The fact that they went in for seed multiplication with such enthusiasm and shared the seeds they produced with relatives and friends for further multiplication was a key factor in spreading the new high yielding varieties.
>
> During the craze, many people took advantage of the easy money to be made. But as with anything of value, crime soon showed its ugly head. As harvest time approached, the Indian Agricultural Research Institute had to post rifle-toting guards at its plots. Even so, one morning a guard was found tied to a tree, naked. He'd been stripped of his clothes.

On this March '67 trip Norm had brought Margaret. They'd been married 30 years already, and this was the honeymoon he'd always promised to give her. For the first time she was seeing the world – and his world too. Following their month in Pakistan and India they planned to proceed to Hong Kong and Hawaii for some happy time before heading home.

When they reached India the 18,000 tons of Mexican seed – imported and sown the previous November – was reaching maturity on over 700,000 acres. This brought on a great new controversy regarding the best strategy for fertilizing the plants. Norm found himself yet again the maverick fighting against the odds:

> Given India's worn-out soils, fertilizer would be a critical constituent in the operations for growing enough grain to feed the hungry. If Mexican seed was the catalyst for greater food production, fertilizer was the fuel feeding the engine that would feed the multitudes.
>
> Yet fertilizer use was vigorously opposed. Most vehement of all in this struggle were the academic and agricultural economists who marshaled "irrefutable" reasons why little or no fertilizer should be used. This was utter folly, given the hunger breaking out all round, and we ignored it.
>
> However, even within our own ranks a battle of wills arose because the country didn't have enough fertilizer for every farmer to employ the ideal amount. The immediate issue, therefore, was whether some farmers should get the ideal amount or whether all farmers should get some share.
>
> Glenn Anderson and I were for the first idea, and insisted that the maximum recommended amount — 120lb of nitrogen and 40lb of phosphorus per acre — be provided to farmers until the supplies were gone.
>
> On the other side was everyone else: the economists from the Ministry of Agriculture, the Planning Commission, and even most of my Rockefeller Foundation colleagues. They all insisted that the fertilizer recommendations should be scaled back to 40 pounds of nitrogen and 20 pounds of phosphorus per acre. That way, they said, three times more area and three times more families could benefit.

Norm felt that everything depended on getting this right. Yet he was losing the argument and decided that he had to stay in India and fight rather than see all his years of effort stymied at the last minute. Reluctantly, he told Margaret that she'd have to go on to Hong Kong and Hawaii alone.

In general conversation he never mentioned that part of the story, but he often spoke about the battle with his colleagues that got so heated they nearly came to blows:

> At first sight, [the opposing] view seemed logical and most equitable. But Glenn and I argued that this was the wrong moment because everyone would get only modest yield

improvements — maybe rising from 800 to 1000lb an acre. But with the whole program teetering on the verge of takeoff we needed a demonstration dramatic enough to sweep away all reluctance and resistance.

The strategic dilemma we were wrestling with had more to do with psychology than science. We knew from Mexico that traditional farmers readily accept practices that double or triple yield but reject practices that increase production only 10 or 20 percent.

"I want the differences in yield to be so big that everything the farmers have believed in comes down in shambles all around them," I said. "The object is to produce 5000 to 6000lb an acre or even more, and thereby create cultural shock. When the peasant farmer gets five or six times the income the new methods and practices will be adopted and the resistance and argumentation will disappear."

At one point, the debate became overly heated. Only with Ralph Cummings' quiet, measured diplomacy were we finally all calmed down. Glenn and I nonetheless stood our ground and eventually we prevailed. The higher fertilizer rate was applied, and fewer farmers got the benefit.

At that point everyone sat back to see if that shock therapy had been the right call.

Margaret never did get a proper honeymoon.

1968-1969

Problem Solved

By 1968 the earth was carrying 3 billion people, and food was being produced at maximum levels. Yet within half a century another 3 billion people were anticipated, and already some new arrivals were finding the pantry bare.

This year brought *The Population Bomb*, the bestseller in which author Paul Ehrlich declared: "The battle to feed humanity is over. In the 1970s, the world will undergo famine — hundreds of millions of people are going to starve to death in spite of any crash program embarked upon now."

This Stanford University insect specialist and equally plausible food-production experts dished out such unrelenting doses of a nerve-shattering negativity that the inevitability of global famine became accepted fact. None sought out Borlaug, none included his views, none referenced his work.

Borlaug, however, knew better. Descendants of his 8156th dwarf-wheat cross-pollination were spreading faster than any crop variety in history. Thanks to him and to the Wheat Apostles they were going global. That very year those high-yield food suppliers were planted on 6.7 million acres in India, 1.8 million acres in Pakistan, 1.3 million acres in Mexico, 420,000 acres in Turkey, 65,000 acres in Afghanistan, 61,000 acres in Nepal. And that's just the beginning. Acreage is starting to increase in Argentina, Brazil, Chile, U.S., Canada, South Africa, Morocco, Tunisia, Australia and more. The secret behind their success: dwarf wheats not only lift food output, they lift family income.

On his sixth March Mission he found South Asia transforming itself. Throughout the Ganges and Indus basins the food rush had begun. Thanks to the 40,000 ton Mexican wheat-seed importation, Pakistan has enough to plant 3 million acres. More than 30,000 demonstration plots, contrasting the old and the new, had been placed across the region.

When Norm reached India in March 1968 he, Swaminathan, Anderson and Kohli drove north from New Delhi and retraced the previous year's steps. Most farmers had now switched to Mexican wheats, and with the peak of the harvest just a few weeks ahead, a tremendous change was unfolding. The roof over food production was literally lifting skyward.

Culture shock was in evidence. Fertilizer was fueling the high production plants to the top of their performance range, typically around 3 tons an acre. The farmers with fertilizer couldn't believe their luck; the rest couldn't believe their eyes, and were committed to catching up next season.

Part of their tour was in the irrigated districts of Punjab but part was farther east in the area where, just two years before, famine had raged. Now it was a vast carpet of short, stiff-strawed, wheats, level as though freshly mowed, and hefting big heads loaded with plump grains. The 1967 monsoon had been magnificent and had revitalized the soils in time for the November planting. Now the results were plain to see.

The last stage of the 12 hour drive back to Delhi was a ride through a region in flux. People seemed buoyed by hope. Many were seizing the opportunity of their lives. The haunted hunger look, so recently dominant, had almost disappeared. Even the unflappable scientist was moved:

> The transformation seemed nothing less than miraculous even to we who were mentally prepared. All of us felt a sense of privilege at being able to witness the Punjab that March. The weather had been good; the heads on the wheats were heavy. We could see that the 1968 wheat harvest was going to be huge.
>
> When we got back to Delhi we met with the newly installed agriculture minister and tried to convey something of what we'd seen. It was hard to get across the magnitude and significance of the forthcoming harvest and of the farmers' euphoria to someone who had no notion of what had gone before and, in fact, had not the vaguest idea of scientific agriculture. He was from the northeastern state of Assam, which grew no wheat.
>
> In appearance, Jagjivan Ram was short and squat with a heavy frame and huge thick eyebrows. In manner, he was ponderous and pedantic and seemed a little lost. Now the whole plum of the food transformation fell right into his lap. He, not Subramaniam, got to reap the glory.

After seeing the new agriculture minister, Swaminathan and I went to pay our respects to Mrs Gandhi. We had tea with her and I described the enthusiasm of the farmers using the new varieties and methods. I informed her of the bountiful harvest that was about to begin. Then I bluntly repeated my routine recommendation: "Madam Prime Minister, the grass roots are on fire over all this and unless fertilizer, credit and fair prices are forthcoming, there will be trouble. Hundreds of thousands of farmers now know what can be achieved, and if the government provides the support millions more will participate. Then India's food supply will soar. The game is won if you do these things."

Mrs Gandhi made no particular comment, but asked a few thoughtful questions and I sensed she was putting the last of her doubts behind. Maybe even getting excited.

In New York that same April, the Rockefeller Foundation convened a "Strategy for the Conquest of Hunger" symposium. It asked Norm to stop by on his way home from India. Crossing the Atlantic he happened to be on the same Pan Am flight as Malik Khuda Bakhsh, and over lunch Pakistan's agriculture minister confessed: "My dear doctor, I can now tell you some things. After you left that crucial meeting in 1964, most of the senior scientists were vehemently opposed to you. In the whole action planning group *not one member supported going ahead with the Mexican wheats.*"

He was referring to the authorities charged with pyramiding Pakistan's food production, including the learned professor who'd declared that Pakistan's wheat production would never rise.

At the symposium the following day, Khuda Bakhsh announced to the world that the harvest then being gathered would make Pakistan self-sufficient in wheat production . . . two years before Borlaug's much-derided prediction of eight years. His country no longer needed to import food grain.

For his part, Borlaug told the symposium participants:

The most conservative man in traditional agriculture is the scientist, and sometimes I am not proud to be one of them. This is most discouraging. The scientist is a privileged person, the man who should lead us out of the wilderness of static, underproductive agriculture, and yet by his apathy and failure to exercise his unique vision, he keeps us in the swamp of despair.

The scientist fears change because he is in a relatively privileged position in his own society. If there is no breakthrough in yield, he will not be criticized. But if he makes a recommendation and something goes wrong, he may lose his job.

In many different countries there is no faith or understanding between the farmer and the scientist. Almost without exception the farmer says, "This man is a theorist. He is not a doer, and he can't help us." In the past; this complaint was all too often valid, but today the situation is rapidly changing.

O utside the capitals and confines of northern India and Pakistan Norm was not known. But the deluge of honors that would mark the rest of Borlaug's days began this month.

In April 1968 he was elected a Member of the prestigious U.S. National Academy of Sciences.

On May 17 Obregón City named a street in his honor. It was the same dusty main street he'd traversed on his first visit 24 years earlier. Now it was a wide boulevard that extended from the heart of a vibrant city out into the Yaqui Valley filled with square miles of his golden wheat. The tribute was popular: largely through his efforts the city, with its 170,000 people, was busy and booming. Farmers were providing the Northeast Agricultural Research Station (CIANO) $400,000 a year – five times more than the state and central governments provided.

By year's end a farsighted British television company, Associated Television, had produced a documentary on Norm. It called him The Prophet of Wheat and made him its Man of the Year for 1968.

These were his first recognitions and he was nonplussed. He couldn't understand why people would want to honor someone who'd merely done his job.

In India when the harvest had been completed in May the world had changed. Norm was then back in Sonora training the 1968 Wheat Apostles but even he was impressed:

> Despite my normal optimism, I'd underestimated how big the harvest would be. The better farmers in the Punjab routinely achieved 3000 to 3500lb an acre; some passed 5000. One was awarded a medal for attaining 7500lb an acre.
>
> I'd also underestimated the effects. Punjabi towns such as Ludhiana were literally buried in wheat. Town squares were filled with huge stacks of sacks.
>
> Nothing like that had been seen before and in the barely controlled chaos that resulted, everything was lacking except food. For one thing, there was a shortage of labor. It seemed as if every person was busy, yet many more were needed. Farm families were working from before dawn till after dark cutting the plants with sickles and stacking the sheaves by hand, and still

falling behind. No one had realized that it takes four times longer to cut and stack an acre of wheat when the yield is 5000 pounds than when it is 800 pounds.

No one had anticipated how much muscle power would be needed to haul all those heavy sheaves to the threshing floors. Nor had anyone prepared for the amount of time, effort, space and organization to thresh and winnow five times the normal amount. By tradition, threshing was accomplished by knocking the seeds off the cut stems by walking cows or buffalo over them. Winnowing involved tossing the resultant seeds into the air for the breeze to blow the husks away.

These methods could no longer cope. The harvest – which normally took three weeks – stretched beyond two months and became a major bottleneck. For one thing, there weren't enough threshing floors. For another, no one had foreseen what it would take to bag the threshed grain, load it on trucks and railroad cars, and move it out. There weren't enough bags to hold the grain, carts to haul the bags, bullocks to pull the carts, or trucks and trains to haul it away.

Worst of all, there were not enough storage warehouses. India had made no preparations for anything like this.

The culmination of the chaos came when the monsoon arrived in May 1968. It came three weeks early, and in many areas grain remained piled everywhere. Some was heaped up, unthreshed. Mountains of bagged grain stood by the railroad sidings, waiting for a train. When the monsoon rains began falling part of this was damaged or destroyed. In some areas local authorities closed the schools and packed sacks of grain into the classrooms. Kids could go outside, but not wheat.

When the dust had settled, the sweat had dried and the muscle-aches had faded, it became clear that 5 million extra tons of wheat had been added to India's national larder. This was a 60 percent increase over the bad years of 1965 and 1966 and a 42 percent increase over 1964, the best wheat year India had ever enjoyed before Borlaug.

None of the Planning Commission's five-year plans had conceived so magnificent a makeover. Norm's greatest satisfaction was to see that deluded dream works finally tear up its much-vaunted plans for heavy industries. Now it rushed to draw up plans for fertilizer imports, fertilizer factories, farmer credit, and for storing, transporting and marketing grain on a massive scale.

Only one thing remained bothersome:

I felt terrible that Subramaniam had missed out on the satisfaction and recognition. He'd been the architect of all that had transpired and in India the glory should have been his. He'd been proved right: His rash boast that not a single Indian would die of starvation had, in overall terms, been realized. So, too, had his claim that India would no longer import grain to keep its poor people from starvation.

In July, Indira Gandhi issued a postage stamp commemorating "India's Wheat Revolution 1968." It depicted three stylized heads of wheat and the library building of the Indian Agricultural Research Institute where in 1963 Norm had lunched with the dozen motivated visionaries and they had kicked everything off.

Although Mrs Gandhi formally issued the stamp, she probably wished she'd heeded Norm's plea two years earlier that she build more godowns in rural towns. Indeed, one of the secondary fall-outs from the massive piles of grain stacked up in the open was an abundance of rats. A cartoonist for one of the New Delhi newspapers ran a caricature of the stamp over the label "India's Rat Revolution 1968."

Another thing for which there was no shortage was moneylenders. With local markets flooded with grain, profiteers found opportunities to beat down the prices they paid farmers. Those middlemen could have reaped all the rewards, leaving the growers as poor as ever. However, the new agriculture minister began a vigorous program to build government godowns throughout the wheat lands. Jagjivan Ram also launched a giant procurement program, and by paying a good price he not only thwarted the profiteers, he ensured that the farmers got their profit and stabilized the market.

This was historic. It provided a buffer stock big enough to protect Indians against malign monsoons. And it allowed the government to dampen speculation. For example, when consumer grain prices began to soar later in 1968, it fed some of its buffer stock into the market, which offset hoarding and stabilized the supply as well as the price of bread.

By the time that happened, Norm was back in Mexico training more youths from seemingly every country but India. His mind was lost in that task. And he was glad to be free of Asia's hoopla.

With the coming of 1969 Borlaug's dwarf wheats were conquering the world by stealth and surprise. Across South Asia that January, farmers sowed them on more than half of

Pakistan's 15-million-acre wheat land and more than a third of India's 35-million-acre wheat zone. Just six years after a few grams of Borlaug seed first arrived, his wheats occupied 15 times more area on this side of the world than in Mexico.

During this 1969 March Mission Norm, together with Narvaez and two local agriculturists visited each of Pakistan's wheat-producing areas. The crop was advancing toward maturity, and wherever Mexipaks had been employed the fields shone with a goldening glow. In several places the seed was being multiplied on a massive scale. In others, both the white and red versions of the curvaceous sisters were in extensive production. The era of pint-sized plants had arrived.

Most impressive of all was the national mood swing. Famine was forgotten. Effervescent enthusiasm prevailed. Farmers were ecstatic over their good fortune. Extension workers eagerly promoted the new tools of their agronomy trade. Research scientists worked on future improvements. Formerly reluctant government officials eagerly lent support. Optimism had penetrated the national psyche:

> During the second half of February and the early days of March 1969 the crop was approaching maturity, and I accompanied Nacho, Qureshi and Z.A. Munshi to observe the outcome in each of the important production areas. What we found was astonishing. Wherever the Mexican seed was employed the fields looked beautiful. The new varieties had made a difference but so had Ayub Khan's 1966 decision to pay the international market price. The farmers had responded not only by planting more wheat but by managing their fields better. They were now striving to tease the utmost from their land. It was clear that within a month the harvest would be huge.

This has been called a rare example of a discovery delivering more than promised. And it had been accomplished while Borlaug spent most of his time 12,000 miles away engaged in formal duties in remote parts of Mexico. He'd been in Asia one month a year for seven years. On the back of those quick trips had come the present triumph. And he was the first to note that it was the plants and the other people who did the heavy lifting:

> Of course the real unsung heroes were the millions of farmers who'd had the vision and courage to dump the methods that had been in use for 5000 years. It was they who supplied the grassroots fire that pressured the planners and political leaders into action. The "skinny, unskilled, tradition-bound" Indian farmer

proved adventuresome, adaptable and even entrepreneurial when he could get five times more income from his labor. As in the Iowa of my youth, a high-yielding crop had transformed the standard of living of subsistence farmers, and given them a life.

As a sort of finale to the decade and its own involvement the Ford Foundation brought together in Pakistan most of the Wheat Apostles Borlaug had trained in Mexico. None would ever forget that celebratory occasion. There were by then more than 50. They came from 20, mostly hungry, countries. They felt a bond – a companionship of service in the fields of humankind. And they could see on all sides the worth of their efforts. Norm explains:

Those trainees were really the ones that brought about the changes in the food supplies in hungry nations. They were from many countries, other than India. New Delhi had at last relented and sent some students for training in Mexico, but it barred them from joining this reunion next door. I was sad that politics had interceded; everything we'd done prior to that had transcended politics, culture, language, and scientific background.

Stakman was there and the vice-president of the Ford Foundation, F.F. Hill was there. Frosty Hill was George Harrar's friend, which was why the Ford and Rockefeller foundations had collaborated so well. He'd previously been a professor of economics and vice president of Cornell University, but he was a down-to-earth character who'd grown up on the land and was steeped in practical farming knowledge.

We took the whole group from the Northwest Frontier Province to Punjab and on south all the way to Sindh. It was the run-up to the harvest. Everywhere, we saw beautiful fields of wheat. Everywhere, we saw the farmers' enthusiasm. Everywhere we examined the fields, visited farms and talked with public officials.

My constant concern was that a disease might unexpectedly show up. By now the Mexican dwarfs had spread to more than half the country's wheat acreage. That put a big responsibility on my shoulders. But everywhere the plants were healthy.

It was on this trip that Frosty Hill gave me a prediction: "Norm," he said, "enjoy this while you can. You'll never see it again. From now on things will just get worse. Bureaucrats will kill your whole darn program."

I didn't believe a word of it. After all, we had these wonderful plants. We had this wonderful cadre of Wheat Apostles. We had the ongoing training program and research operations in Mexico, Pakistan, India and six other nations. What could possibly go wrong?

After returning to Islamabad, Borlaug, Narvaez and Oddvar Aresvik (the Norwegian Hanson had embedded in Pakistan's agriculture ministry) called on the president:

> We went to inform Ayub Khan of the success that was shaping up. We told him that the early hopes of the wheat production campaign had become a reality. Pakistan's farmers were close to producing — or were even then producing — all the wheat Pakistan needed. Moreover, the country had the capacity to sustain a full food supply for the next 20 years if the research programs and the stimulatory economic policies were continued.
>
> We mentioned that there were 28 thoroughly trained Pakistani wheat scientists, who could maintain the program if provided proper political backing and financial support.
>
> Narvaez and Aresvik then informed President Ayub that the Ford Foundation considered their mission completed; within a few days they'd be transferred to Lebanon.
>
> President Ayub thanked us as well as the Ford and Rockefeller Foundations. As we were about to leave his office, he pinned to my jacket the Sitara-I-Imtiaz, a medal shaped like a half circle with moon and stars.
>
> Especially fitting was the manner in which the president said goodbye to Narvaez. At the close of our visit he walked to the car not with me, but with Nacho. As he pumped Nacho's hand for the last time he said: "Thank you, sir, for what you have done for Pakistan."Then the president mentioned in confidence that he'd had three heart attacks. Not even the Pakistani people knew. And the next day he'd be stepping down. The morning newspapers would explain that he was calling for new elections and turning responsibilities of government over to a caretaker president.

Next day, Ayub Khan did just that. His army chief of staff, Mohammad Yahya Khan, became the acting president. Considered the "Patton of Pakistan," this former general, so it was thought, would make a good interim leader.

The day that power changed hands happened to be Norm's 55th birthday – 25 March 1969 – and he spent it ensconced in the Ford Foundation staff house struggling to compose a readable account of all the wonders he'd seen.

That afternoon his train of thought was rudely interrupted by the shrill telephone; four economists wanted to come by the next day, would he see them? Borlaug agreed, but only reluctantly and only after they'd declared it urgent and *very* important.

When the economists arrived, three proved to be from a Harvard Group working under a World Bank grant; the other was from Pakistan's Agency of Procurement.

To Norm's amazement, they were perturbed that the harvest was going to be *too big*. Government, they avowed, could not keep its promise to pay farmers 21 rupees per maund. There weren't enough rupees. The harvest would bankrupt the nation.

The four financial-fortune-tellers had computed that the payment could not exceed 18 rupees, and were going to recommend that amount. They asked Borlaug to back them in this decision.

Norm instantly refused:

> "The government announced that price before the crop was planted," I told them. "You cannot renege on it now. The farmers made their plans and committed themselves to loans and obligations based on that pledge. If you reduce the price now, with elections for a new president coming up, you're going to create political chaos. I won't back you at all."

Four disgruntled economists left the staff house muttering about dumb scientists. But for Norm, fairness for farmers was paramount. Ten million peasants who'd soon be laboring to bring in the harvest had kept faith with their country. They'd made good their obligation and had produced a record harvest of over 8 million tons. By their efforts they'd kept every Pakistani fed. They should not be cheated.

Nacho Narvaez was by now revered in Pakistan. In less than three years he'd moved not only programs but people – even the nation. His final days were replete with testimonial dinners, state tributes, and parties arranged by friends, colleagues and team members.

The journalist Wayne Swegle documented the scene as colleagues showed their respect: "I listened in on some of the final visits he had with administrators, wheat botanists, and research workers. They discussed the future of wheat improvement programs which would be carried out after Narvaez left West Pakistan. But the talk kept slipping back to incidents of the past. They recalled with great feeling their days of trial, of triumph, of frustration, of building. I heard the voices of grown men — scientists — quaver with emotion as they recalled the past together and contemplated the future without their friend and advisor."

Anwar Hussain, the research director who'd once dismissed Mexican wheats in front of the press and the agriculture secretary, now said of Narvaez: "He will leave his shadow behind. And his shadow will remain with us for a long, long time. We will rely on his shadow."

A cross the nearby border, where just four years before, artillery shells had soared, the new harvest marked a turning point. India was a step behind Pakistan, but was operating on a far larger scale. There too problems of the past seemed over, and enthusiasm prevailed. Norm was amazed:

> India's rural regions, which before had been so apathetic, were embracing the new reality. Indeed, a kind of "wheat fever" was infecting everyone, including farmers both large and small, scientists, extension workers, professors, politicians and even the civil servants, whom everyone assumed to be immutable.

About the first of August, the most shocking telegram of all landed in Mexico. At the time, Norm was involved with the 1969 Wheat Apostles on the mountain plateau at Toluca:

> When I was working out of Mexico City in the summer of '69, I got probably the harshest communication I ever received. It was from Pakistan's new leader, and said in essence: "get your ass over here and explain this mess you've put me in."
>
> The language wasn't perhaps that crude but that's how I remember it. No national leader ever addressed me in terms so coarse, and I had no clue as to what I'd done wrong.
>
> Though Ayub was a gentleman – polished, smart, and a farmer to his soul – his successor was volatile and vulgar, given to cursing and indulgence. He was by far the crudest world leader I've met.
>
> At the time I knew nothing about Yahya Khan, and returned to Pakistan in all innocence and great puzzlement. In our first few minutes together he chewed me out with a level of abusiveness I'd never before experienced. In the same presidential palace where I'd been awarded the silver medal of distinction about four months earlier I now received a tongue lashing.
>
> "You wrote that damned report," Yahya screamed, "and you've destroyed me! In April we used your prediction to announce the country had achieved self-sufficiency in wheat. But you were way off the mark. There's not nearly enough to feed the country. I'm being forced to import 2 million tons more and that will ruin the country."
>
> "Look," I said, "There's something wrong here. I just can't believe that I overestimated the harvest by 2 million tons; I can't be that far off."
>
> "Well," he said, "You better damn well find out what's wrong, and fast!"
>
> "Give me a week," I said. "Don't do anything before that."

Norm was granted seven days to rescue his reputation and regain government support for the program. To make matters much worse he was coming down with pneumonia and felt terrible:

> Knowing there was no way I could complete the investigation in so short a time while alone and sick, I wired Narvaez in Lebanon and wrote Glenn Anderson in India and said "come on over right away; we've got big problems."

Then I got a Ford Foundation car and driver and visited a few big farmers whom we'd worked with in the Punjabi farming area around Lahore. These were relatively prosperous farmers with a few hundred acres and warehouses in which to store their harvest.

"How much did your wheat yield?" I asked the first one.

"Oh, the harvest was good."

"Well, how much was the yield?"

"I don't have the tonnage because I haven't sold any grain yet. It's all piled up in the godown over there." "Why is that?"

"The government cut the price just when the harvest was beginning."

Then I went to another big farmer, and a third. Same story.

Every farmer with storage was holding his harvest. Though partly a protest, this was mainly done to force the prices up.

By then my pneumonia was roaring, and I had to take to my bed at the Ford Foundation guesthouse.

When Nacho and Glenn arrived they came to my room and I croaked out what had happened. "The farmers are withholding their grain from the market," I said. "But before we tell the president we've got to get proper data. Our explanation must be fully confirmed and absolutely beyond question."

After that, the two of them scattered across the countryside; visiting government warehouses and interviewing farmers. Within five days they had the situation well documented.

Small farmers had sold at the lower price to pay back the moneylenders, but the big farmers were holding the country's food supply to ransom.

Moreover, the situation was getting more tense and more difficult by the day. Wheat stocks in the government warehouses were falling at twice the monthly rate of wheat consumption. That meant half of what was being bought was merely being hoarded.

All that had sent wheat and bread prices soaring. The masses were getting restive; the government was too, but it couldn't do much. Speculators had it over a barrel.

I was out of things by then; Glenn wrote most of brief report. The summary declared:

- Large quantities of grain are in the warehouses of large farmers;
- The original estimate of production was close to correct; and
- The government's reneging on the pre-sowing procurement price was largely responsible for large producers withholding their grain from the market, thereby resulting in playing into

the hands of grain traders and speculators to the detriment of consumers and the embarrassment of the government.

Finally, we went to the president's office to hand over the report and present our conclusions in person. It was not an easy meeting:

Yahya Khan was still boiling mad. He seemed on the sharp edge of a violent outburst, and our message didn't calm him one bit.

Glenn spoke first. He told the president: "We think that Borlaug was probably close to correct; Pakistan has produced enough wheat to be self-sufficient or close to it. There is no 2-million ton deficit."

Then I gave a brief summary and handed over the report. "Cutting the price of wheat," I said, "destroyed the farmers' confidence in your government and provoked the current crisis."

Then, remembering the hurtful, expletive-filled cablegram, I decided to speak up more boldly: "Mr. President, you were responsible. Your price cut was why the wheat didn't move into the market. The big farmers knew they had the government under the gun. If you put the price back up, all the missing grain will reappear."

I was now watching him closely, and saw his expression change by visible degrees. My words weren't going down well. Yahya then began swearing and slapping the report down on the edge of his desk. He did it over and over. Crash! Bang!

Glenn and Nacho were visibly shaken and probably feared I'd provoked a violent end for all of us. I certainly felt that was possible.

But then he looked straight at me and said something quite unexpected. "Five days after I took office a delegation of economists told me we'd grown so much wheat that the government couldn't buy it all at the official price. I asked them 'What should be done?' They replied, "Reduce the price to 18 rupees a maund."

When I heard those words, things suddenly made sense. I knew immediately it had to be the same group who in March had wanted me to share responsibility for slashing the promised price.

"I took their advice," Yahya continued, "and now you tell me this is what caused the shortages and the black-market prices."

He looked at me intently as if willing me to devise an answer. "Yes," I replied, "and the sooner you restore the procurement price to 21 rupees, the sooner the grain will flow into the market. That will reduce the hoarding as well as the black market. It will bring down the price of bread."

Yahya remained violently angry and clearly distraught, but I paid no heed. "If there isn't enough money to pay for it," I said, "you should print more because the country's political stability is at stake. There's now a lack of confidence in the government that wasn't there before. Better to print more money than to have a political explosion. The countryside is quiet and peaceful even though three political parties are campaigning for the election. If you mix in food-price rises and bread shortages, political chaos will again erupt across Pakistan."

This was bitter medicine for a politically weak caretaker president. However, he quickly restored the originally promised floor price, and the whole harvest came flooding onto the market. Then the price of bread returned to normal. The crisis passed.

Three months later, when all the political and economic dust had settled, the harvest was officially estimated to have been 6.618 million tons. Borlaug had been right on target. Pakistan was out of danger from famine. It no longer needed other countries' wheat. There was bread aplenty. The price was right. And Pakistani peasant farmers earned their promised share.

Norm's efforts had thus reached fruition.

I heard all kinds of yield estimates — mostly ranging from 7 million to 8 million tons. The government routinely underestimates by about 20 percent, and several authorities think actual production was nearer 9 million tons. Out of the crop harvested in the spring of 1969 about 1 million tons proved surplus to local needs. Overnight [West] Pakistan became a wheat exporter. By May 1969, it was shipping about 100,000 tons to East Pakistan per month.

When you traveled in the countryside in 1969, South Asia looked very different. The Mexican wheats had smashed through the yield ceiling and lifted farm income. Indian and Pakistani farmers who previously earned $15 an acre now earned $66 an acre. The extra buying power stimulated rural industry by increasing demand for fertilizers, pumps, machinery and other materials and services. Among the greatest life changes was a huge reduction in drudgery. By 1969 five Indian factories were annually churning out 18,000 tractors a year, 35,000 more were imported, and the demand had soared so much that prospective purchasers had to make written application and wait a year or two for delivery.

Personal spending also increased. People invested mostly in their homes. They built new houses, added new rooms, made major repairs, and installed electricity, running water, and improved latrines.

Home life improved too. Brick houses replaced the mud-walled huts.

Electricity lighted the nights. Sewing machines were popular. Transistor radios brought entertainment, education, new visions and advice into remote villages. Demand for consumer goods soared. Clothing ranked high, not just as a necessity but as a means for boosting self-respect and adding brightness to life.

Moreover, the increase in rural wealth forced the governments to provide public services. Starting in 1969, villagers demanded better roads, better public transportation and better schools; and began getting them. Soon bicycles, motor scooters and motorcycles could be seen in the most distant villages, and truck and bus service became routine so farm folk could for the first time enjoy the freedom of travel.

Sadly, this transformation failed to seize a place in the general histories of the decade or the century. It's never been properly understood or appreciated. However, certain writers have provided a few hints:

Swaminathan, who'd led the local research that supported the events in India and deserves much of the credit for the outcome, addressed the legacy the farmers were building for themselves in the May 11, 1969 issue of the *Illustrated Weekly of India*: "Brimming with enthusiasm, hard-working, skilled and determined, the Punjab farmer has been the backbone of the wheat revolution. Revolutions are usually associated with the young, but in this revolution, age has been no obstacle to participation. Farmers, young and old, educated and uneducated, have easily taken to the new agronomy. It has been heart-warming to see young college graduates, retired officials, ex-army men, illiterate peasants and small farmers queuing to get the new seeds. At least in the Punjab, the divorce between intellect and labor, which has been the bane of our agriculture, is vanishing."

Don Paarlberg, farmer, author, professor of agricultural economics, and coordinator of the program that had shipped millions of tons of American grain to South Asia later wrote that: "[Borlaug's work] was a breakthrough, a quantum leap, an event unusual in agriculture, where advances typically are gradual. And the breakthrough in genetics touched off revolutionary changes elsewhere. As it became clear that the new wheat would make fertilizer pay fabulous returns, fertilizer use trebled in a single year."

"There were several things about this breakthrough that make it special and gave it particular significance. It came in a hungry part of the world, not in those countries already surfeited with agricultural output. It came in the tropics, which had long been in agricultural torpor, not in the temperate climates, where change was already occurring at a pace more rapid than could readily be assimilated. It produced new knowledge and technology that could be used by farmers on small tracts of land, rather than being, like many technological changes, useful only on large farms. It was a breakthrough that came voluntarily, up from the grass roots, rather than being imposed arbitrarily from above."

B ut to Norm the memory that stayed most firmly had nothing to do with fields so vast they vanished into the sunlight on the horizon. The incident occurred during the 1969 trip in Pakistan with all the Wheat Apostles he had trained:

> About dusk we arrived at Lahore where we were to spend the night. We were dusty, tired and hungry, so I was less than pleased to be greeted with the message from a local farmer: "My wheat is sick. The Doctor must come." Directions for getting to the farm, which was a few miles out of town, followed.
>
> Fearful that there was a serious problem I climbed back into our van with a few others, including Lowell Hardin from the Ford Foundation. It was almost dark when the young Pakistani farmer who had left the message directed us to his 10 acre wheat field. Gently waving in the lengthening shadows was a magnificent crop of Mexipak. It was still deep green in color and so dense, uniform and sturdy that one could toss his hat onto the flat surface of the plump heads and there it would stay. To me, it looked like a 100 bushel per acre crop in a country where traditional varieties had averaged less than 10.
>
> Our farmer host walked us along the irrigation ditch to the far corner of the field. "Where is the sick wheat?" I demanded.
>
> "There," he responded, pointing to a few plants showing obvious signs of high salinity. But that was just a matter of getting the soil to drain better. So by then we all knew that the crop was well and thriving.
>
> Somewhat grudgingly we reversed our tracks and walked back toward the van at the corner of the field. There a transformation had taken place. Carpets now covered the bare ground. Lanterns had been hung. Chairs had appeared. The neighbors had gathered.
>
> "Dr. Borlaug," said our host, "we apologize for bringing you here under false pretenses. But we wanted somehow to thank you for changing our lives. This new wheat will make it possible for me to get married to that beautiful young woman there. We will build a

house where we now stand. We knew not how to show our appreciation. So we asked the women. They went to work and made this."

He turned and two of the ladies held up a beautiful quilt. Each square had been made by a different family. Collectively the women had pieced the squares together.

"Take this home to Mrs Borlaug please," our host requested. "Keep it as a reminder that without the new wheat the better life we see ahead would not have been possible."

As the moon came out and a tear rolled down a dusty cheek, I concluded that yes, successful development does have a human face.

AUTHOR'S NOTE

The subsequent years of Norman Borlaug's life were no less challenging. Within months of the incidents the last chapter describes, he was invited to Norway to lecture at the University of Oslo. Over dinner that evening, his hosts challenged his work. They charged that he'd made India's food production dependent on modern methods, including agricultural chemicals; that he'd forced traditional wheats into extinction, leaving India vulnerable to crop collapse; and that farm mechanization had thrown millions of impoverished Indians out of work.

Norm answered all these falsities with facts. Later, having learned that his hosts had been the Nobel Peace Prize Committee, he was relieved that they'd been suckered into believing the myths then circulating in the Western press. That way, he'd not have to wrestle with fame and could continue working in the research fields. His answers, however, must have been convincing because that October he learned he'd been awarded the 1970 Nobel Prize for Peace.

This was perhaps the most deserved Nobel Prize. During the 1970s his dwarf-wheat seeds spread to wheat lands worldwide. Many were carried home by the Wheat Apostles. Some were spread by the Canadian and American researchers who went to Sonora to harvest the plots he'd sown for them as a contribution to the conquest of stem rust. Worldwide, wheat shrank from the old shoulder-high plants that bent before the wind to waist- or knee-high dwarfs that stayed erect and held up huge loads of grain.

The Hope and Kenya resistances Norm and Enciso combined when they'd worked as if the weight of the world rested on their shoulders would prove vital too. Back then in 1948 he thought he was double-charging the chromosomes as a contingency; he couldn't know he was actually freeing the world's wheat crop of stem rust *for half a century*. Not until 1999 did the wily fungus find a way to take down the Hope and Kenya resistance combo. Norm was alarmed to hear of stem rust's return (in Uganda), and at age 85 he stimulated a worldwide effort to find new sources of resistance, a project (now funded by the Bill and Melinda Gates Foundation) that is starting to show some success.

After his development of dwarf summer wheat, breeders of other cereals reduced the size of rice, corn, sorghum, barley and more; Norm himself incorporated the dwarfing gene into pasta wheat and triticale. Crops the world over shrank to half their age-old height. No longer as high as an elephant's eye, modern corn, for instance, is barely taller than the fences surrounding it. Norm's work (along with Orville Vogel's in Pullman, Washington) thereby broke the mindset that the bigger the crop plant, the better. In the upshot cereal staples became more efficient and capable of providing food to billions more people.

The fact that Marroqui genes cut weeks off the growing time meant that farmers in places such as India and China could grow two crops a year *in the same ground*. Indeed, dwarf wheat and dwarf rice could be grown sequentially, making it possible to annually produce 2 tons of wheat and 3 tons of rice on an acre of land that previously had barely produced half a ton of either. The most progressive farmers could even slip in a third crop: mung bean or potato, for instance. Food production and rural employment thus soared, while the farmland area stayed within bounds.

All of this was of global significance. During the 1960s – the era of this book's final five chapters – there were 3 billion humans; today there are more than 7 billion. Despite periodic localized famines caused by weather or woeful government, humans have stayed fed while our numbers have doubled.

Since his day, no critic or innovator has come up with better alternatives to his approach. He always wished they would; his only desire was that people be fed – the more ways the better. Norm would be the biggest fan of any system that could produce yields like his – 3 tons-, 4 tons-, 5 tons (of *dry* food) per acre.

Before Borlaug's seeds arrived, the area encompassing today's India, Pakistan, Bangladesh and China was synonymous with famine. Since then, those nations have fed themselves. India and China have actually risen to become great powers on the world stage. Neither could have achieved that if recurrent starvation still threatened their people and economies.

Although Borlaug strove to feed the hungry, his efforts nowadays also benefit Americans, Canadians, Brazilians, Turks, Australians, Europeans and more. Their breads, cookies, crackers, cakes, pastries, pancakes, doughnuts, rolls, bagels and breakfast cereals come from dwarf wheats containing gene combos produced by cross-pollinations Borlaug and the bird boys made in Mexico in the 1950s and 1960s.

Africa is serial-starvation's last holdout. Partly that's because wheat will not grow in that continent's hungry zone. Partly, too, it's because of poor governance, poor policies and poor infrastructure, which not even he could overcome.

In 1977 the White House honored Norm with the Presidential Medal of Freedom. In 2007 the U.S. House of Representatives bestowed on him the Congressional Gold Medal. Only four others had been considered worthy of those and the Nobel Peace Prize: Martin Luther King, Jr., Nelson Mandela, Mother Teresa and Elie Wiesel. Insiders who know his accomplishments agree that he quite properly stands with them in the great pantheon of humanitarian heroes.

During his last five years of life Norm suffered from a rare form of leukemia. He died on September 12, 2009. He was then 95, and had remained alert and involved until the final few days.

In the weeks that followed, Hundreds of encomiums, condolences, and memories came in from colleagues, national leaders around the world, secretaries of agriculture, the Secretary of Defense (Robert Gates), the Secretary of State (Hillary Clinton), students and more. Three states – Iowa, Minnesota and Texas – declared days of mourning and flew flags at half-mast. The Iowa State legislature has since authorized a statue to be placed in the U.S. Capitol in Washington D.C.

I hope this book serves to keep Norm's story in the public mind. For the future peace and prosperity of humankind there's hardly a more important role model than Norm Borlaug.

PICTURE CREDITS

The image of the Norman Borlaug statue in the frontispiece and the line art on the cover were provided by Jen Deutsch, Benjamin Victor Studios, Northern State University, Aberdeen, South Dakota.

Joanne Lane, plates 1 and 3

Tom Spindler, plate 2

Jeanie Borlaug Laube, plates 4, 5, 6, 7, 9, 10

Ruben Heermann, plate 8

Rockefeller Archive Center, plates 12, 13, 15, 16, 17, 18, 24, 28, 29

CIMMYT, plates 14 and 19

Corbis, plates 20 and 21 [Ted Streshinsky photos]

World Food Prize Foundation, plate 25

Marc and Evelyne Bernheim, plates 26, 27

Rollie Henkes, plate 30

Les Wollam, plate 31.

The dust-jacket cover photo is thanks to Shirley Streshinsky, whose husband Ted visited Sonora in 1983 to photograph Norm for *Science Year, The World Book Science Annual 1984*.

The author photo is by Robert Vietmeyer.

The maps were created by Cirrus Cartography.

PRONUNCIATION GUIDE

PEOPLE

Ayub Khan	*EYE-oob karn*
Borlaug	*BOR-LOG*
Calles	*KY-es*
Campoy	*cam-POY*
Enciso	*en-SEE-soh*
Eva [Villegas]	*EH-vah*
Harrar	*ha-RAH*
Hope [Pablo]	*HOO-PAY*
Jorge	*HOR-HAY*
Narvaez	*nar-VY-es*
Obregón	*oh-breg-ON*
Patrón	*pa-TRONE*
Pepe	*PEP-ee*
Sivaraman	*seeva-RAH-man*
Stakman	*STAKE-man*
Stak	*STAKE*
Subramaniam	*soobra-MAN-ee-am*
Swaminathan	*swah-mee-NAH-than*
Villegas [Eva]	*vee-AY-gas*
Yahya Khan	*YAH-YAH karn*

ORGANIZATIONS

CIANO	*see-AH-no*
Ejidal	*eh-HEE-dal*
Geneve [Hotel]	*HEN-eh-vah*
PRONASE	*pro-NAH-see*

PLACES

Bajío	*bah-HEE-oh*
Cajeme	*cah-HEM-ee*
Calle	*ky-YEH*
Chapingo	*cha-PING-oh*
Ciudad (city)	*see-oo-DAHD*
Coahuila	*coh-ah-WEE-la*
[La] Piedad	*pee-eh-DAHD*
Puebla	*PWEB-lah*
Saltillo	*sol-TEE-oh*
Tehuacan	*TEE-wah-kahn*
Toluca	*tol-OO-kah*
Torreón	*tor-ee-OHN*
Yaqui	*YAH-kee*
Valle [valley]	*VY-YEH*
Hermosillo	*ermo-SEE-oh*
Punjab	*puhn-JARB*
Uttar Pradesh	*oo-tah prah-DESH*

PLANTS

Lerma Rojo	*LEHR-mah ROH-hoh*
Kentana	*ken-TAH-na*
Marroqui	*marrow-KEE*
Nazas	*NAH-zas*
Pitic	*PIT-EEK*
Penjamo	*pen-HAH-moe*
Siete Cerros	*see-ET-ee SAIR-os*

GLOSSARY OF NAMES

Following is a selection of individuals whose names may cause confusion:

Oddvar Aresvik. Norwegian economist Hanson embedded in Pakistan's agriculture ministry to foster the introduction of Mexican wheats.

Rodolfo Calles. Son of a president and former Sonora governor, he initially resisted Borlaug but eventually became his biggest backer.

Ralph Cummings. Directed the Rockefeller Foundation's New Delhi office; told India's agriculture minister about Mexican wheats; funded seed imports.

Haldore Hanson. The Ford Foundation's Pakistan program director, he supported Borlaug's efforts and helped introduce Mexican wheats.

George Harrar. Directed the Mexican Agricultural Program and later the Rockefeller Foundation itself. He and Borlaug had a rocky but respectful relationship, and he made possible the great uplift in wheat, rice, and more.

Ayub Khan. Pakistan's president; a gentleman farmer and former general, he backed Borlaug and his seeds in face of local opposition.

Yahya Khan. Pakistan's interim president.

Malik Khuda Bakhsh Bucha. Pakistan's Agriculture Secretary (later Agriculture Minister). Saw the correctness of Borlaug's plans and overrode his advisors.

Ignacio Narvaez. Met Borlaug by accident; later became his successor in Mexico and oversaw Pakistan's wheat program.

John Niederhauser. Introduced Little League to Mexico with Norm; Awarded the World Food Prize for overcoming the potato's main disease, Late Blight.

B. Sivaraman. Agriculture administrator who uncovered the fact that 12 of his countrymen's tests of Borlaug's seeds had been falsified.

E.C. Stakman. Norm's mentor at the University of Minnesota; father figure behind the conquest of stem rust and much of Borlaug's success.

C. Subramaniam. India's Minister of Agriculture; supported Borlaug's seeds and the scientists developing them despite almost universal condemnation.

M.S. Swaminathan. Led the scientific and technical support behind India's agricultural modernization; later awarded the World Food Prize.

Eva Villegas. Rose from assistant librarian to play crucial role in improving dwarf wheat's bread-making quality; later awarded the World Food Prize.

INDEX

Contributed by Paul Vasold

The *Borlaug* trilogy previously published by Bracing Books is a worthy companion to *Our Daily Bread*. Those three volumes are also built around Norman Borlaug's recollections. They include photographs of the major players. They incorporate sidebars and historical context that add meaning and perspective. And they have Afterword sections written by Norman Borlaug himself. They are:

Borlaug; Volume 1, Right off the Farm. 1914 – 1944. This book covers Part I of *Our Daily Bread,* the section dealing with the Home Side/U.S.A. It has 278 pages, 60 photographs and 5 maps.

Borlaug; Volume 2, Wheat Whisperer. 1944 – 1959. This book covers Part II of *Our Daily Bread,* the section dealing with the Near Side/Mexico. It has 302 pages, 64 photographs and 2 maps.

Borlaug; Volume 3, Bread Winner. 1960 – 1969. This book covers Part III of *Our Daily Bread,* the section dealing with the Far Side/Asia. It has 242 pages, 42 photographs and 1 map.

These as well as *Our Daily Bread* and other books authored by Noel Vietmeyer are available from:

- Bracing Books, 5921 River Drive, Lorton, VA 22079
- www.bracingbooks.com
- Amazon.com
- The author at noelvi@cox.net